# Engineering, Science, Technology, and Social Science

# *Editorial Advisory Board*



## *The Career Information Center includes:*

- Agribusiness, Environment, and Natural Resources / 1
- Communications and the Arts / 2
- Computers, Business, and Office / 3
- Construction / 4
- Consumer, Homemaking, and Personal Services / 5
- Engineering, Science, Technology, and Social Science / 6
- Health / 7
- Hospitality and Recreation / 8
- Manufacturing / 9
- Marketing and Distribution / 10
- Public and Community Services / 11
- Transportation / 12
- Employment Trends and Master Index / 13

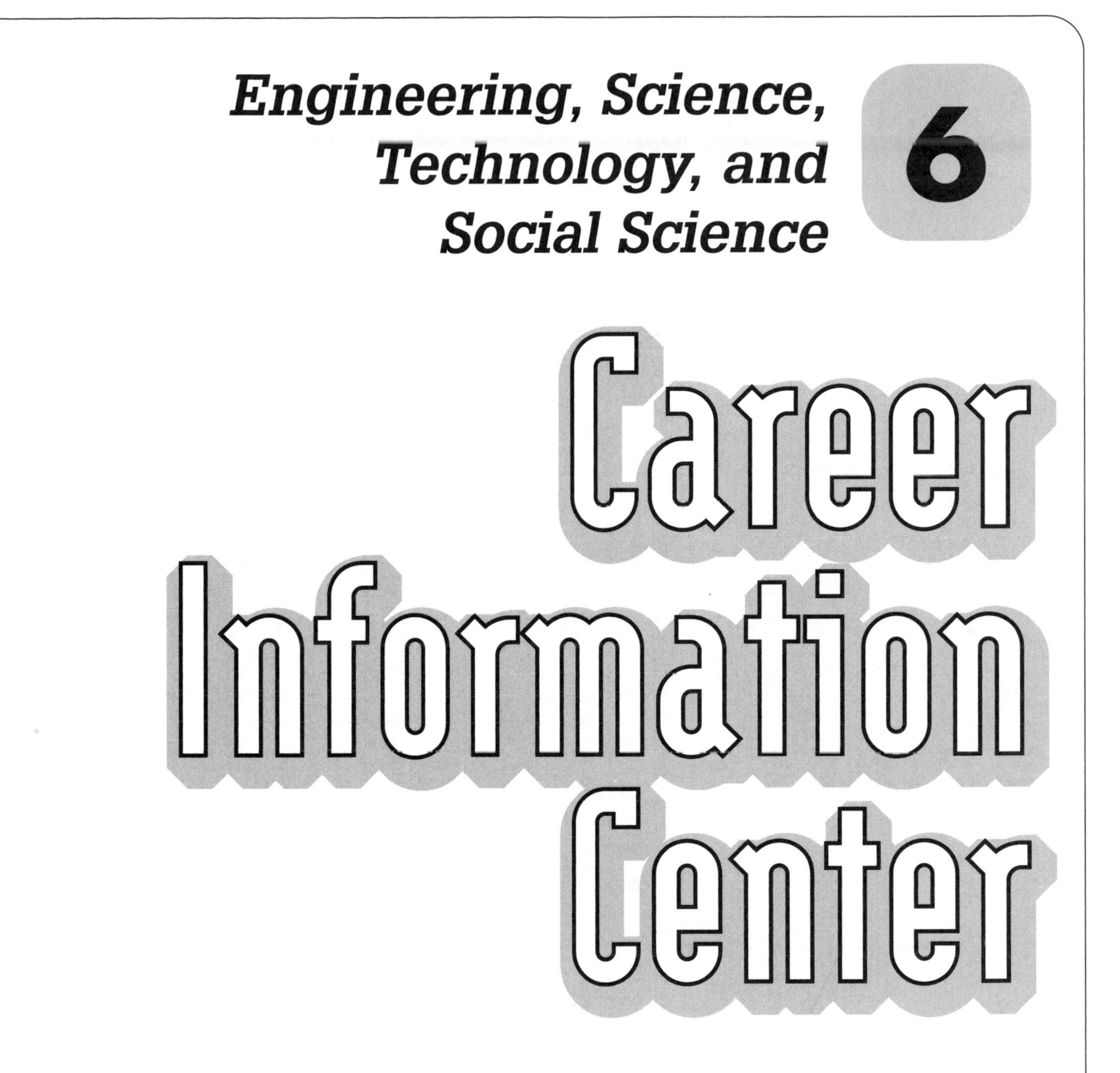


## Ninth Edition

MACMILLAN REFERENCE USA

*An imprint of Thomson Gale, a part of The Thomson Corporation*

Detroit • New York • San Francisco • New Haven, Conn. • Waterville, Maine • London

THOMSON
GALE

**Career Information Center, Ninth Edition**

Paula Kepos, Series Editor

**Project Editor**
Mary Rose Bonk

**Editorial**
Jennifer Greve

**Imaging**
Lezlie Light, Daniel Newell, Christine O'Bryan

**Permissions**
Kelly A. Quin, Tim Sisler, Andrew Specht

**Manufacturing**
Rhonda Dover



*For more information, contact*
Macmillan Reference USA
An imprint of Thomson Gale
27500 Drake Rd.
Farmington, Hills, MI 48331-3535
Or you can visit our Internet site at
http://www.gale.com



ISBN 0-02-866047-1 (set)
ISBN 0-02-866048-X (v.1)
ISBN 0-02-866049-8 (v.2)
ISBN 0-02-866050-1 (v.3)
ISBN 0-02-866051-X (v.4)
ISBN 0-02-866052-8 (v.5)
ISBN 0-02-866053-6 (v.6)
ISBN 0-02-866054-4 (v.7)
ISBN 0-02-866055-2 (v.8)
ISBN 0-02-866056-0 (v.9)
ISBN 0-02-866057-9 (v.10)
ISBN 0-02-866058-7 (v.11)
ISBN 0-02-866059-5 (v.12)
ISBN 0-02-866060-9 (v.13)
ISSN 1082-703X

This title is also available as an e-book.
ISBN 0-02-866099-4
Contact your Thomson Gale representative for ordering information.

Printed in the United States of America
10 9 8 7 6 5 4 3 2 1

# Contents

# Job Summary Chart

| Job | Salary | Education/ Training | Employment Outlook | Page |
|---|---|---|---|---|
| **Job Profiles—No Specialized Training** | | | | |
| **Aerospace Engineering and Operations Technician** | Median—$52,250 per year | High school plus training | Good | 31 |
| **Alternative Fuels Vehicle Technician** | Median—$38,000 per year | High school plus training | Very good | 33 |
| **Cable Television and Telecommunications Technician** | Median—$17.36 per hour | High school plus training | Poor | 35 |
| **Chemical Technician** | Median—$18.35 per hour | High school plus training | Fair | 37 |
| ★ **Electrical and Electronics Engineering Technician** | Median—$46,310 per year | High school plus training | Good | 39 |
| **Electrical and Electronics Installer and Repairer** | $15.54 to $25.86 per hour | High school plus training | Fair to Good | 42 |
| **Electromechanical Engineering Technician** | Median—$41,440 per year | High school plus training | Good | 44 |
| **Electronic Home Entertainment Equipment Installer and Repairer** | Median—$13.44 per hour | High school | Poor | 46 |
| **Hydraulic and Pneumatic Technician** | $20,000 to $50,000 per year | High school plus training | Good | 48 |
| ★ **Mechanical Engineering Technician** | Median—$43,400 per year | High school plus training | Good | 50 |
| **Metallurgical Technician** | Median—$43,400 per year | High school plus training | Fair | 53 |
| **Nuclear Technician** | Median—$28.46 per hour | High school plus training | Fair | 55 |
| **Pharmaceutical Technician** | $15.97 to $18.35 per hour | High school plus training | Very good | 57 |
| **Photonics Technician** | Median—$55,000 per year | High school plus training | Excellent | 59 |
| **Precision Instrument and Equipment Repairer** | $13.47 to $21.25 per hour | High school plus training | Fair to Good | 62 |
| **Robotics Technician** | $30,400 to $50,500 per year | High school plus training | Excellent | 64 |
| **Semiconductor Processor** | Median—$13.85 per hour | High school plus training | Poor | 66 |
| **Telecommunications Central Office Technician** | Median—$23.96 per hour | Varies—see profile | Poor | 68 |
| **Telephone Service Technician** | Median—$23.96 per hour | Varies—see profile | Poor | 70 |
| **Wireless Communications Technician** | Average—$45,000 per year | High school plus training | Good | 72 |
| **Job Profiles—Some Specialized Training/Experience** | | | | |
| **Biological Technician** | Median—$15.97 per hour | 2- or 4-year college | Good | 75 |
| **Genetic Engineering Research Assistant** | Median—$15.97 per hour | College | Good | 77 |

★ **High-growth job**

★ **High-growth job**

| Job | Salary | Education/ Training | Employment Outlook | Page |
|---|---|---|---|---|
| **Photonics Engineer** | Varies—see profile | College or advanced degree | Excellent | 155 |
| **Physicist** | Median—$87,450 per year | Advanced degree | Fair | 158 |
| **Political Scientist** | Median—$86,750 per year | Advanced degree | Fair | 160 |
| **Robotics Engineer** | $50,000 to $60,000 | Advanced degree | Very Good | 162 |
| **Safety Engineer** | Median—$63,730 per year | College | Good | 164 |
| **Sociologist** | Median—$57,870 per year | Advanced degree | Fair | 167 |
| **Systems Engineer** | Mean—$74,140 per year | College or advanced degree | Good | 169 |
| **Telecommunications Consultant** | Median—$65,130 per year | College | Excellent | 172 |
| **Telecommunications Design Engineer** | Median—$50,846 per year | Varies—see profile | Fair | 173 |
| **Zoologist** | Median—$50,330 per year | Advanced degree | Good | 175 |

★ **High-growth job**

# Foreword

The ninth edition of the *Career Information Center* mirrors the ongoing changes in the job market caused by new technological and economic developments. These developments continue to change what Americans do in the workplace and how they do it. People have a critical need for up-to-date information to help them make career decisions.

The *Career Information Center* is an individualized resource for people of all ages and at all stages of career development. It has been recognized as an excellent reference for librarians, counselors, educators, and other providers of job information. It is ideally suited for use in libraries, career resource centers, and guidance offices, as well as in adult education centers and other facilities where people seek information about job opportunities, careers, and their own potential in the workforce.

This ninth edition updates many of the features that made the earlier editions so useful.

- A Job Summary Chart, a quick reference guide, appears in the front section of each volume to help readers get the basic facts and compare the jobs described in the volume. High-growth jobs are highlighted and identified with a star.
- Each volume of the *Career Information Center* begins with an overview of the job market in that field. These "Looking Into..." sections have been completely revised and updated. They also include new graphs, charts, and boxes providing information such as industry snapshots and the fastest-growing and top-dollar jobs in the field. The "Global View" feature tells how the new global economy is affecting jobs in the field.
- Each volume has a section called "Getting Into...," which contains useful information on entering the particular field. It offers self-evaluation tips and decision-making help, and it relates possible job choices to individual interests, abilities, and work characteristics. There is also practical information on job hunting, using the Internet and classified ads, preparing resumes, and handling interviews. "Getting Into..." also includes a section on employee rights.
- Each volume has a listing of all job profiles in the series and the volumes in which they appear, making access to profiles in other volumes easy.
- *Career Information Center* contains 694 job profiles. Each profile describes work characteristics, education and training requirements, getting the job, advancement and employment outlook, working conditions, and earnings and benefits.
- Job summaries, provided for each job profile, highlight the education or training required, salary range, and employment outlook.
- Volume 13 has been revised to reflect career concerns of the new century and employment trends through the year 2014. This volume includes updated articles on benefits, employment law, health in the workplace, job search strategies, job training, job opportunities at home, and identifying opportunities for retraining.
- More than 530 photographs provide a visual glimpse of life on the job. Photos have been selected to give the reader a sense of what it feels like to be in a specific field or job.
- Updated bibliographies in each volume include recommended readings and Web sites in specific job areas. Additional titles for the vocational counselor are included in Volume 13.
- Each volume also contains a comprehensive directory of accredited occupational education and vocational training facilities listed by occupational area and grouped by state. Directory materials are generated from the IPEDS (Integrated Postsecondary Education Data System) database of the U.S. Department of Education.

The *Career Information Center* recognizes the importance not only of job selection, but also of job holding, coping, and applying life skills. No other career information publication deals with work attitudes so comprehensively.

# Using the Career Information Center

The *Career Information Center* is designed to meet the needs of many people—students, people just entering or reentering the job market, those dissatisfied with present jobs, those without jobs—anyone of any age who is not sure what to do for a living. The *Career Information Center* is for people who want help in making career choices. It combines the comprehensiveness of an encyclopedia with the format and readability of a magazine. Many professionals, including counselors, librarians, and teachers, will find it a useful guidance and reference tool.

The *Career Information Center* is organized by occupational interest area rather than in alphabetical order. Jobs that have something in common are grouped together. In that way people who do not know exactly what job they want can read about a number of related jobs. The *Career Information Center* classifies jobs that have something in common into clusters. The classification system is adapted from the cluster organization used by the U.S. Department of Labor. Each of the first twelve volumes of the *Career Information Center* explores one of twelve occupational clusters.

To use the *Career Information Center*, first select the volume that treats the occupational area that interests you most. Because there are many ways to group occupations, you may not find a particular job in the volume in which you look for it. In that case, check the central listing of all the profiles, which is located in the front of Volumes 1 through 12. This listing provides the names of all profiles and the volume number in which they appear. Volume 13 also includes a comprehensive index of all the jobs covered in the first twelve volumes.

After selecting a volume or volumes, investigate the sections that you feel would be most helpful. It isn't necessary to read these volumes from cover to cover. They are arranged so that you can go directly to the specific information you want. Here is a description of the sections included in each volume.

- **Job Summary Chart**—This chart presents in tabular form the basic data from all profiles in the volume: salary, education and training, employment outlook, and the page on which you can find the job profile. Jobs with a high growth potential are highlighted and starred.

- **Looking Into...**—This overview of the occupational cluster describes the opportunities, characteristics, and trends in that particular field.

- **Getting Into...**—This how-to guide can help you decide what jobs may be most satisfying to you and what strategies you can use to get the right job. You will learn, for example, how to write an effective resume, how to complete an application form, what to expect in an interview, how to use networking, and what to do if someone has discriminated against you.

- **Job Summary**—These summaries, located at the beginning of each profile, highlight the most important facts about the job: education and training, salary, and employment outlook.

*Education and Training* indicates whether the job requires no education, high school, college, advanced degree, vocational/technical school, license, or training.

*Salary Range* provides median or average salaries that may vary significantly from region to region.

*Employment Outlook* is based on several factors, including the Bureau of Labor Statistics' projections through the year 2014. The ratings are defined as follows: *poor* means there is a projected employment decrease of any amount; *fair* means there is a projected employment increase of 0 to 8 percent; *good* means there is a projected employment increase of 9 to 17 percent; *very good* means there is a projected employment increase of 18 to 26 percent; and *excellent* means there is a projected employment increase of 27 percent or more. The outlook is then determined by looking at the ratings and other employment factors. For example, a job with excellent projected employment growth in which many more people are entering the field than there are jobs available will have an outlook that is good rather than excellent.

For all categories, the phrase *Varies—see profile* means the reader must consult the profile for the information, which is too extensive to include in the Job Summary.

- **Job Profiles**—The job profiles are divided into three categories based on the level of training required to get the job. Each profile explores the following topics: description of the job being profiled, the education and training requirements, ways to get the job, advancement possibilities and employment outlook, the working conditions, the earnings and benefits, and places to go for more information.

*Job Profiles—No Specialized Training* includes jobs that require no education or previous work experience beyond high school.

*Job Profiles—Some Specialized Training/Experience* includes jobs that require one, two, or three years of vocational training or college, or work experience beyond high school.

*Job Profiles—Advanced Training/Experience* includes jobs that require a bachelor's degree or advanced degree from a college or university and/or equivalent work experience in that field.

- **Resources—General Career Information** includes a selected bibliography of the most recent books and Web sites on general career information, including how-to books on such topics as resume writing and preparing for tests. In addition, there is a special guide to readings for the career counselor in Volume 13.
- **Resources—**Each volume also contains a bibliography of books and Web sites for specific fields covered in that volume.
- **Directory of Institutions Offering Career Training—**This listing, organized first by career area, then by state, includes the schools that offer occupational training beyond high school. For jobs requiring a bachelor's degree or an advanced degree, check a library for college catalogs and appropriate directories.
- **Index—**This index, which is located at the end of each volume, lists every job mentioned in that volume. It serves not only to cross-reference all the jobs in the volume but also to show related jobs in the field. For example, under the entry OCEANOGRAPHER, you will find chemical oceanographer, marine biologist, and marine geophysicist.
- **Volume 13, Employment Trends and Master Index—**This volume includes several features that will help both the job seeker and the career counselor. A useful guide provides the *DOT (Dictionary of Occupational Titles)* number of most of the job profiles in the *Career Information Center*. There is also a special section on career information for Canada. The updated and revised "Employment Trends" section contains articles on health in the workplace; search strategies for finding your first job; employment trends for women, minorities, immigrants, older workers, and the physically challenged; employment demographics; benefit programs; training; employment opportunities at home; employment law; and identifying opportunities for retraining. The articles provide job seekers and career professionals with an overview of current employment issues, career opportunities, and outlooks. Finally, there is a master index to all the jobs included in all 13 volumes.

The *Career Information Center* is exactly what it says it is—a center of the most useful and pertinent information you need to explore and choose from the wide range of job and career possibilities. The *Career Information Center* provides you with a solid foundation of information for getting a satisfying job or rewarding career.

# Comprehensive Job Profile List

The following list includes job profiles and corresponding volume numbers.

# Looking Into Engineering, Science, Technology, and Social Science

The twentieth century was defined by technology. A short list of life-changing technological innovations from the 1900s includes cars, jets, space satellites, radio, television, photocopiers, pacemakers, the Internet, refrigerators, washing machines, cell phones, and digital computers. Imagine working in a field that regularly produces things that most people, once having used them, would not want to live without. These tools, devices, and machines that we take for granted all owe their existence to the privileged practitioners of engineering, science, technology, and social science.

The differences among them are not always obvious, and these terms are not easy to define. Although these three fields overlap, important distinctions do exist. *Science* is a discipline that focuses on understanding the natural world, such as understanding how energy is transformed from one state to another. *Engineering* is a process that applies scientific knowledge and scientific methods to the development of tools, machines, materials, and processes that have practical applications and solve human problems. For example, an engineer would use knowledge of how energy can be changed from one form to another to develop a solar heating system for a home. *Technology* has many definitions, but one is the tools, machines, materials, and processes that have practical applications and help solve human problems. In this case, the solar heating system would be the technology that solved the problem of generating heat in a home.

Scientists use scientific methods to understand the natural world. For example, the fact that the earth revolves around the sun is taken for granted today, but that fact was not always known or accepted. How, then, did this fact become universally accepted? It happened as a result of the work of scientists like Galileo who observed the heavens, amassing data and developing hypotheses, or explanations, that helped guide inquiry and make sense of observations. Galileo had invented a telescope that enabled him to chart the phases of Venus. These observations did not support the idea—dominant at the time—that the earth was the center of the universe. It was only when scientists put the sun at the center of their model solar system—as Copernicus had first suggested—that their observations made sense.

This simple example is essentially representative of the way much of science is done. Scientists make observations about nature and then develop hypotheses to explain these observations. The hypotheses are then tested, and new data may confirm or disconfirm them. Hypotheses that are tested over and over again, and those that are repeatedly confirmed are powerful concepts that help scientists make predictions about the world and explain particular phenomena. These powerful explanatory concepts are called scientific theories, which are much different from everyday theories, hunches, and guesses. One example is the cell theory, which states that all living things are made up of one or more cells, the smallest living units of structure and

Scientists, such as these biochemists, study the chemical structure and changes in living things in order to create new products or solve practical problems. *(USDA-ARS.)*

function of all organisms. In addition, the cell theory states that all cells arise from preexisting cells.

Engineers are the vital links between science and technology. An engineer implements the discoveries of science by creating and designing products that can serve society. Training for this career includes a solid education in the scientific discipline in which the engineer plans to work. Engineers apply this scientific understanding to the development of products that can be useful to human beings. An electrical engineer may apply knowledge about electricity to solve a problem with integrated circuits; a chemical engineer may apply knowledge about the chemistry of carbon to develop a new type of paper. None of the services we use daily—electrical power, phones, even running water—would be available in the safe, sanitary, and convenient forms we experience today if they were not under the supervision of engineers.

## THE NATURAL SCIENCES

The traditional disciplines of the natural sciences are physics, chemistry, and biology. (Astronomy, also a traditional field of science, is sometimes considered a subfield of physics.) These disciplines overlap to a certain extent. For example, it is impossible to understand the biology of a living cell without understanding the physics and chemistry of the molecules that make up that cell. A biologist is generally knowledgeable about basic principles of chemistry and physics, and chemists and physicists who work on living systems are generally familiar with basic principles of biology.

Because the amount of knowledge of each scientific discipline is vast, scientists generally specialize. For example, a physicist who is an expert on thermodynamics is not likely to be an expert on astrophysics as well. Similarly, a biologist who is an

## Global View: Engineering, Science, Technology, and Social Science

Engineering in the United States has long been a profession geared toward the domestic market. At one time, almost every automobile and household appliance in the United States was designed and built in this country. Since the 1970s, however, foreign engineering firms have made serious inroads into the U.S. market for everything from the designing of power tools to services such as environmental cleanup. The rise of free-trade agreements such as NAFTA and GATT has accelerated this process by opening up markets worldwide. Increased competition from foreign firms presents several challenges and opportunities for U.S. engineering.

One of the main challenges is holding on to business in the face of foreign competitors who operate at a lower cost. A growing number of domestic firms are building plants in countries where wages, even for highly trained engineers, are considerably lower than wages in the United States. For example, skilled engineers in Mexico and Poland earn less than half of what U.S. engineers earn. As more production moves to overseas facilities, engineers in the United States will be faced with a shrinking job market.

Another challenge is capturing more of the world market for goods engineered in the United States. One reason Japanese auto and appliance manufacturers have fared so well in the United States is that they have been more responsive to the needs of American consumers. By contrast, American companies often fail to win new customers by offering the same products to every market. Engineers will need to become more aware of the importance of cultural differences as well as practical ones in global markets, such as differing electrical currents or driving on the left-hand side of the road.

One great opportunity presented by globalism is the opening up of developing countries to U.S. engineering expertise. The expansion of economies in Asia, Latin America, and Eastern Europe is accompanied by a demand for projects at which American engineers excel, including the designing and building of ports, airports, telecommunications systems, and power grids. The increasing demand for cleaner and "greener" development means that there will be a growth of environmental engineering projects. Some experts believe that Western Europe and the Pacific Rim present great opportunities for environmental engineering firms.

expert on evolution is not likely to also be an expert on neuroscience. However, all of these experts would probably be somewhat knowledgeable about many subjects within their major discipline. It takes many years of focused study to attain a level of expertise in a given specialized area of the natural sciences—a level of expertise that is required if one hopes to advance in that field.

Natural scientists investigate every aspect of our world, from the inanimate to the animate. At this very moment, physicists are busy investigating the farthest reaches of the known universe for clues as to how it started; biologists are studying agents of infection to understand complexities of the processes that allow them to cause disease; and chemists are the studying chemical processes hypothesized to have started early life on this planet billions of years ago.

## Physics

Physicists study the structure of matter, the nature of energy, and the interactions between them. Physics can be broken down into many important specialties. For example, astronomers and astrophysicists are concerned with the structure of the universe and with the formation of planets, stars, solar systems, and galaxies. Nuclear physicists are interested in the physics of the atom and its particles. Quantum physicists study the behavior of the electrons that circle the nucleus of the atom and try to understand the forces that determine this behavior. Cosmologists investigate the origin of the universe and in doing so develop theories about its ultimate fate. Physicists are typically trained to do research in either theoretical or experimental physics. Theoretical physicists construct theories about nature, and experimental physicists design and implement experiments to test these theories. Physicists (including astronomers) held about sixteen thousand jobs in the United States in 2004.

## Chemistry

Chemists and materials scientists search for and use new knowledge about chemicals. Like physicists, chemists specialize in one area and pursue research in either theoretical or experimental chemistry. Analytical chemists determine the nature of substances by identifying the molecules of which they are composed. Organic chemists study molecules that contain carbon, which are primarily found in living organisms. Inorganic and physical chemists study the molecules found predominantly in nonliving systems and the complex interactions of these molecules under the influence of different physical states and conditions. Biochemistry is a subdiscipline of both chemistry and biology. Biochemists, like molecular biologists, study the chemical composition of living things. Materials scientists study the structures and chemical properties of various materials to develop new products or enhance existing ones. Chemists and materials scientists held about ninety thousand jobs in the United States in 2004.

## Biology

Biologists study the living world. Just as chemists and physicists concentrate on specific subdisciplines, so do biologists. Microbiologists study microbes such as bacteria and viruses. Some of their work focuses primarily on pathogens to devise new methods of dealing with the illnesses they cause in humans and animals. Evolutionary biologists study the process of evolution, the descent with modification, of different lineages from common ancestors. Geneticists study genes, the basic units of heredity, and their variations. Ecologists study living environments, such as tropical rain forests or coral reefs, to learn how the living organisms within such an environment interact with it and with each other. Biological scientists held about seventy-seven thousand jobs in the United States in 2004.

## Qualifications

To pursue a career as a research scientist or as a teacher at the university level, an advanced degree is required. A doctoral degree (PhD) is usually necessary for these positions. Furthermore, individuals who choose such a career path must continue to study the scientific literature and refine their experimental abilities to keep pace with advances in their discipline.

Not all scientific careers require a doctoral degree, however. For example, a master's degree is sometimes sufficient to teach at junior colleges and technical colleges, and is sufficient to teach in secondary schools. In addition, the nation's high schools, middle and junior high schools, and elementary schools are having trouble recruiting enough people qualified to teach the sciences. In many scientific fields today, a tremendous shortage of qualified scientists exists at the intermediate levels of the educational system, whereas an oversupply of qualified scientists exists at the higher levels. The importance of quality science teachers at intermediate levels cannot be overemphasized.

Skills that are important if one is to excel in a scientific field include a keen interest in the natural world and an ability to reason clearly. An individual who is planning to pursue a career as a research scientist should have a strong background in mathematics and computers. It is also important to be familiar with how research work is conducted in the laboratory setting.

## THE FIELD OF ENGINEERING

Engineers apply the theories and principles of science and mathematics to developing solutions to the practical problems of living. For example, engineers devise better ways to extract energy from various natural sources. They also design and develop vehicles such as supersonic aircraft and sophisticated automobiles that allow us to travel quickly and safely. Engineers have developed all the technologies that we take for granted in the modern age, such as television, computers, and sophisticated equipment that physicians use to diagnose disease. The almost routine use of technological innovations such as cellular telephones, fax machines, and fiber optics is the result of creative applications of scientific theory by talented engineers.

Engineers are currently involved in a wide variety of challenging problems that require their technical skills and broad knowledge. For example, engineers are being called on to devise new ways of generating energy for our planet, which is rapidly being depleted of its fossil fuels. In addition, engineers play a critical role in developing new technologies to increase food production in an already overburdened world that must feed an additional 100 million new people each year. Engineers also devise technologies to clean up the pollution that is threatening the earth.

### Where Engineers Work

Like scientists, engineers typically specialize. For example, a chemical engineer might work for a chemical manufacturer. An electrical engineer might work for a utility company, a computer chip manufacturer, or an automobile manufacturer. An engineer who specializes in aerospace engineering might work for the National Aeronautics and Space Administration (NASA) or for one of the large corporations that design and manufacture weapons used by the armed forces. Engineers also teach in colleges and universities around the world, training the next generation of engineers. In addition, engineers are involved in research that will lead to new developments in their field.

In 2004 engineers held 1.4 million jobs in the United States. About 40 percent of these jobs were in manufacturing, and about 27 percent were in the professional, scientific, and technical services sector. Nearly 14 percent held local, state or federal government jobs. Only 3 percent of engineers were self-employed, usually as consultants.

### Types of Engineering Specialties

Engineers can specialize in many fields, only a few of which are mentioned here. When we think about traditional engineering, the work of civil engineers generally comes to mind. Civil engineers plan, design, and oversee the construction of highways, bridges, and buildings. Without their work, crossing a bridge or visiting the top floor of a skyscraper would not be safe. In 2004, 237,000 jobs were held by civil engineers, the greatest number of any single engineering specialty.

Taken together, however, electrical and electronics engineers hold more jobs than civil engineers: nearly 300,000 in 2004. If computer hardware engineers are included in this category, the number of jobs held in 2004 rises to about 376,000. Electrical, electronics, and computer hardware engineers manage the production of electrical energy and design electrical systems and equipment that can be used for many applications. For example, electrical and electronics engineers have developed products used as control systems in such advanced technologies as airplanes, automobiles, and computers. Computer hardware engineers develop new hardware for computers and computer networks; their work affects everything from manufacturing to communications and the arts. (The work of computer software developers, who may have the job title of "computer software engineer" or some other, is not usually considered a specialty of engineering—it's part of a professional field often called computer science.)

Mechanical engineers design, test, and manage the operation of all kinds of machines, including engines, heating and cooling equipment, and household appliances such as refrigerators and dryers. Their work makes the things we often take for granted, such as a safe car or a cold refrigerator, possible. In 2004 mechanical engineers held 226,000 jobs in the United States.

Chemical engineers apply the principles of chemistry to solve problems with the production or use of chemicals and biochemicals. For example, chemical engineers might develop a process used by a manufacturer to make a certain drug or a synthetic material such as plastic. Chemical engineers also develop treatments that minimize industrial pollution. In 2004 chemical engineers held thirty-one thousand jobs in the United States.

Aerospace engineers plan and design the manufacturing of airplanes and spaceships. They understand how a plane needs to be designed to minimize its resistance to the air, and they are responsible for designing planes that are safe. In 2004 aerospace engineers held seventy-six thousand jobs in the United States.

Nuclear engineers design and maintain nuclear power plants and nuclear submarines. They also design equipment that involves radioactive materials, such as that used to diagnose and treat medical problems. This group held seventeen thousand jobs in the United States in 2004.

Before a building is completed, a team of mechanical engineers determines the needs of the workers and supervises production. *(© Martha Tabor/Working Images Photographs. Reproduced by permission.)*

## Qualifications

To become an engineer, a person must complete a four- or five-year program in engineering at an accredited college or university. Nearly all colleges and universities in the United States offer bachelor's degrees in engineering. Most offer programs in electrical, computer, mechanical, or civil engineering. An engineering student must have an analytical mind, an ability to innovate and solve problems, and excellent mathematical abilities. Good English and writing skills are a big plus.

After graduating from college, new engineers usually take entry-level jobs under the supervision of experienced engineers. As they gain experience, they move on to more complicated tasks. Like scientists, engineers must be knowledgeable about computers because most engineering work is now done on computers. Computer-aided drafting and design (CADD) systems now perform much of the drafting and design work that engineers once did by hand.

Engineering students prepare themselves to use and improve existing technology and to anticipate future trends in technology. Major areas of growth in the coming decades include miniaturization and microelectronics, in which ever smaller computer chips are used to increase the power of computers; robotics, in which more advanced machines are made to function in place of humans; digitalization, in which even more aspects of technology are affected by computers; and communication, in which the spread of innovations such as fiber-optics and wireless communications systems are used to improve global communication.

# TECHNOLOGISTS AND TECHNICIANS

Technologists and technicians are the skilled personnel who assist scientists and engineers in their work. Technologists and technicians might be called on to operate a machine, perform a laboratory experiment, or test a new piece of equipment. The titles "technologist" and "technician" are often used interchangeably, but they may designate distinct functions. In some workplaces, technologists assist scientists and engineers in developing and testing new products, conducting experiments, and monitoring the quality of manufacturing processes. In the laboratory, however, this type of person is generally called a laboratory technician. In other fields, technicians are generally individuals who have been trained to operate equipment or machinery.

Technologists and technicians are employed by manufacturers, consultants, government agencies, construction firms, research laboratories, utilities, and service companies. Many work in the biomedical, energy, and environmental industries. Some technical fields are growing rapidly, and the demand for skilled technologists and technicians is growing along with them. The computer, health, and engineering industries are expected to create the largest number of technical jobs in the early twenty-first century.

## Qualifications

Technologists and technicians are not required to complete as much formal education as scientists and engineers. Some people obtain jobs in technical specialties after graduating from high school, but

Technicians often work with engineers to conduct experiments and develop new technologies. *(© Take 2 Productions/ Ken Kaminesky/Corbis.)*

most employers require that job applicants complete at least a two-year technical course at a vocational school or community college. In the sciences, a bachelor's degree is generally necessary for the job of technician or technologist. Students interested in technical careers should take mathematics, science, and possibly shop courses in high school.

Many people become interested in a technical career after being trained in some technical specialty in the armed forces. For example, a person might learn about electronics by working as a radar operator in the Air Force. However, before people with military experience can qualify for a civilian job, they usually need one or two years of additional training.

## SOCIAL SCIENTISTS

Social scientists study society, including events, achievements, behavior, and relationships. Their research provides insight into human problems and often suggests possible solutions. Social scientists specialize in various fields, such as economics, history, political science, archaeology, anthropology, geography, and sociology.

In the United States in 2004, social scientists held about eighteen thousand jobs. About half are employed as economists. Economists analyze how human and natural resources are allocated to produce goods and services. Many economists work for the U.S. Department of Commerce and other government agencies. They monitor the economy and suggest ways to improve it.

Historians research, analyze, and interpret the past. They work for universities, museums, historical societies, and government agencies, preserving historic sites, records, and artifacts. Archaeologists study past cultures by examining buildings and artifacts. Cultural anthropologists study variation among human cultures, both past and present, while physical anthropologists study human evolution, physical variation, and classification. Geographers analyze physical and cultural information on local, regional, and global scales; increasingly they are using geographic information system (GIS) technology to create computerized maps that track such things as population growth, environmental hazards, and natural resources. Political scientists study governments and political organizations. Sociologists analyze how people interact with one another and how they behave in groups.

Many social scientists teach in universities and colleges. Others work for private industry and business consulting firms, where they are involved in financial operations, in personnel or human resources development, or in the design and marketing of products and services. Many social scientists conduct experiments for research organizations, and thousands are employed by federal, state, and local governments.

## SPECIALIZED AREAS ON THE CUTTING EDGE

Medicine, communications, and transportation have changed greatly in the past few decades. The work of scientists, engineers, and technicians has completely changed the way doctors diagnose and treat diseases, the means by which people exchange information, and the way people and goods move from one place to another.

### Medicine

Perhaps in no other area of human endeavor have the contributions of scientists, engineers, and technologists been combined to such great effect as in

## Industry Snapshots

### ENGINEERING

The outlook for all types of engineering jobs will be good during the next decade, although growth in employment opportunities varies across specialties. A decline in job growth is expected for petroleum engineers, and for mining and geological engineers. Slower than average job growth is expected for aerospace engineers, marine engineers and naval architects, and nuclear engineers. Faster than average job growth is expected for environmental engineers and biomedical engineers. Starting salaries of engineers are higher than those of college graduates in other fields.

### SCIENCE

Science teachers at the elementary and high school levels will be in demand in the decade ahead. Competition will be keen, however, for positions at the college or university level. The demand for scientists in the field of biotechnology will remain strong.

### TECHNICIANS AND TECHNOLOGISTS

Overall, employment opportunities for engineering technicians and science technicians will increase about as fast as average through 2014. Opportunities for technicians and technologists will be enhanced by the growth of technological industries such as robotics, fiber optics, superconductors, and microelectronics.

the field of human health. These professionals have produced spectacular new drugs, equipment, and procedures useful in the battle against illness. Furthermore, scientists are refining their focus on the causes of many different illnesses, which may soon bring advances that can lead to cures. Diagnostic machines, such as those for CAT (computerized axial tomography) scans and MRIs (magnetic resonance imaging), have allowed physicians to effectively diagnose many illnesses that were previously difficult to recognize. Surgeons now often perform delicate, lifesaving operations with the use of lasers instead of scalpels.

Some of the more exciting advances sweeping through the medical field have come about as a result of biotechnology, which is the use of scientific and engineering principles to manipulate organisms. Researchers are trying to develop vaccines to prevent and treat AIDS, malaria, genital herpes, and certain kinds of cancer. Molecular biologists and biochemists are gaining insight into the genetic components of certain illnesses, including cystic fibrosis, many types of cancer, and sickle cell anemia. Genetic engineers have also made breakthroughs in cloning mammals, which will likely have a profound impact on organ transplants, infertility treatments, and other medical procedures.

## Communications

Communications refers to transmitting information and involves a spectrum of technologies. The work of scientists and engineers in these areas can be found all around us. People in New York can see and talk to people in Moscow by way of satellite hookups; television viewers can choose from hundreds of channels, thanks to cable hookups and satellite dishes; fax machines can send duplicates of documents between offices thousands of miles apart; computer users can log on to the Internet from any place that is wired, and, with wireless technology, from some places that are not; and people

Physical anthropologists are social scientists who study fossils to trace the evolution of human beings. *(© Martha Tabor/ Working Images Photographs. Reproduced by permission.)*

## Top-Dollar Jobs in Engineering, Science, Technology, and Social Science

These are high-paying jobs described in this volume. The figures represent typical salaries or earnings for experienced workers.

| | |
|---|---|
| **$80,000 and up** | • Astronomer<br>• Fire Protection Engineer<br>• Mathematician<br>• Nuclear Engineer<br>• Physicist<br>• Political Scientist |
| **$70,000–$70,999** | • Aerospace Engineer<br>• Artificial Intelligence Specialist<br>• Chemical Engineer<br>• Economist<br>• Electrical and Electronics Engineer<br>• Microwave Engineer<br>• Quality Control Manager<br>• Systems Engineer |
| **$60,000–$60,999** | • Air Conditioning Engineer<br>• Anatomist<br>• Biochemist<br>• Biologist<br>• Biomedical Engineer<br>• Botanist<br>• Ceramic Engineer<br>• Ergonomist<br>• Forensic Scientist<br>• Genetic Engineering Research Scientist<br>• Industrial Hygienist<br>• Mechanical Engineer<br>• Metallurgical Engineer<br>• Photonics Engineer<br>• Safety Engineer |

can talk to each other with cell phones from almost anywhere. Using a Global Positioning System (GPS) receiver, which utilizes satellite navigation, even a solitary sailor in the middle of the Pacific Ocean can precisely locate her position.

The computer revolution has brought the average consumer a personal computer that is exponentially more powerful than the much larger, more expensive computers of a generation ago. Computer technology has revolutionized communications, allowing telecommuting workers to work at home while remaining in contact with their employers via e-mail and wide area computer networks (WANs). The rapid expansion of the Internet created a new mass medium in less than a decade, and computer communications will continue to evolve in ways that are impossible to predict. It's the nature of computer technology to change at a very fast pace.

### Transportation

Scientists, engineers, and technicians play key roles in the design and production of products that move people and things from place to place. Researchers are constantly looking for ways to design transport vehicles that are faster, stronger, and safer. One example is the Japanese (Shinkansen) and French (TGV) high-speed "bullet" trains, which travel at speeds of up to 277 miles per hour.

## NEW DEVELOPMENTS IN THE FIELD

New developments in science and technology are so abundant and so constantly changing that it is difficult to single out only a few of them for discussion. At every turn, one encounters the direct results of technical innovation.

### The Digital Revolution

Computers were originally developed to perform mathematical calculations quickly and accurately. Few could have predicted how well computers would do this—well enough for an IBM computer named Deep Blue to soundly defeat world chess champion Garry Kasparov by 1997. The dependence of modern financial transactions on computers is so great that as the year 2000 approached, people feared—unnecessarily, as it turned out—that existing software would be unable to process new dates and banking would come to a halt. But mathematical applications are far from the only ones that now depend on computers; the processing and transmission of text and images is of greater significance in most people's daily lives. Computer technology has made possible a social and economic revolution in which digital technology affects society on every level, from manufacturing to communications to arts and entertainment.

To demonstrate how the digital revolution has fundamentally altered technology, we can turn to artificial intelligence (AI) as one example. AI systems allow computers to perform complex analytical tasks requiring the ability to predict future possibilities. Many companies now use "expert systems," an example of artificial intelligence, to diagnose and solve manufacturing and transportation problems before they arise. Some railroads, for example, use expert systems to simplify the routing and scheduling of trains. In this way digital technology has touched even railroading, the epitome of a nineteenth-century "smokestack" industry.

Although it is impossible to predict future developments in computer technology, the general trend is clear: Computer chips will continue to be smaller and more powerful, allowing computers and computer networks to perform even more quickly and efficiently. Changes in computer science will spur developments in electronics, communications, software, and other technology-related industries. The changing nature of the computer industry and its ancillary industries will produce a changing job market, offering great opportunities to scientists and engineers willing and able to cope with change.

### Robotics

In science fiction, robots are often portrayed as antagonists to human beings. In reality, robots are simply computers with a limited ability to duplicate human movements, and they can serve many useful functions. Most of the robots used today were built to perform only one or two specific functions. One robot may tighten screws on a washing machine chassis, while another may spot-weld fenders onto cars. More sophisticated robots have optical components that allow them to "see" objects, or arm-and-hand mechanisms that allow them to detect the characteristics of an object, such as its position, size, texture, and temperature.

Robots in the United States today are used most often in manufacturing, primarily in the automobile, nuclear, mining, aerospace, metals, and textile industries. Japan currently makes greater use of robots in industry than does the United States; however, it is likely that in the future American industry will rely increasingly on robots to perform tasks that have historically been performed by low-skilled workers. Robots may even be developed for use in homes; a simple robot vacuum cleaner is already on the market.

## Fiber Optics and Lasers

The communications industry is undergoing a technological revolution. There are now so many ways to transmit information that the major focus has become how to send voice, data, and video signals most efficiently. *Fiber optics*—the use of light signals to transmit information through transparent fibers—may be the ultimate solution to this problem because fiber optic cables can transmit all three signals mentioned above over the same network. Many types of workers, including physicists, chemists, and electrical, chemical, and mechanical engineers, are employed to research and develop fiber optic products.

Lasers (light amplification by stimulated emission of radiation) are concentrated beams of light employed in many devices to accomplish tasks in science, industry, medicine, and communications. Most households today have compact disc players and DVD players, which use laser technology to reproduce digitally recorded sound and pictures. Laser technology is also important in fiber optic communication systems. Dentists use lasers to bond protective coatings to teeth, eye surgeons use them to remove cataracts, and computers use them to store and read data. The military has developed sophisticated lasers that are used in weapons and navigation systems, and scientists hope to use lasers to stimulate the fusion of hydrogen nuclei to produce a virtually unlimited source of energy.

## Ceramics and Superconductors

Superconductors are materials that can transmit electrical impulses over long distances without losing power. Considerable research is under way to develop superconductors that can operate effectively at the high temperatures encountered in many electrical devices, including computers. Researchers have discovered that certain ceramic materials enable superconductors to work at higher temperatures.

Scientists are experimenting with ceramics not only to improve superconductors but also to develop materials to replace metals as the primary material used by many manufacturers. New possibilities include the use of ceramics in the construction of space stations and rockets and in the development of artificial body parts to replace those damaged by injury or disease.

A laser is a new development in technology that has a variety of useful purposes in fields such as telecommunications, medicine, construction, and defense. *(© Roger Ressmeyer/Corbis.)*

## Environmental Technology

The growing realization that humans must protect the earth's air, water, and soil in order to survive is fostering technological developments that can clean up and prevent pollution in the natural environment. The chemical industry, in particular, has been developing new manufacturing methods that reduce toxic waste. The chemical industry has also been developing methods to recycle waste products.

Scientists and engineers are searching for better ways to clean up oil spills, reduce toxic emissions from factories, find clean sources of drinking water, and dispose of solid waste. This research will likely continue in the future, requiring more environmental scientists and engineers.

## Biotechnology

As mentioned previously, biotechnology is the use of scientific and engineering principles to manipulate organisms. Recombinant DNA technology is a biotechnological breakthrough that allows scientists to manipulate the hereditary molecule, deoxyribonucleic acid (DNA), in various ways, including inserting pieces of DNA from one species into another species. This technology has many practical applications. For example, the human gene (DNA sequence) responsible for the production of insulin can be inserted into bacteria to enable a population of bacteria to generate human insulin, thus greatly reducing the cost of treatment for diabetics and reducing the possibility of reaction to insulin derived from non-human sources.

Another biotechnological breakthrough, the polymerase chain reaction (PCR), allows scientists to replicate exponentially pieces of DNA molecules. This important advance has many applications. For example, it allows scientists to sequence minute traces of DNA from crime scenes that previously were not useable as evidence.

DNA is at the forefront of another ongoing research project. The Human Genome Project, launched in 1990 by the U.S. Department of Energy and the National Institutes of Health to map the approximately 25,000 genes in human DNA, was completed in 2003. This detailed DNA information will be key to a deep understanding of the structure, organization, and function of DNA. One hope is that this information will lead to new treatments of disease.

# EMPLOYMENT OPPORTUNITIES

The Bureau of Labor Statistics expects overall engineering employment to increase about as fast as the average for all occupations between 2004 and 2014. The fast-growing service industries should generate most of the employment growth for engineers.

Analysts expect the years ahead to bring a sharp increase in the demand for qualified science teachers at the primary and secondary levels. The competition will be keen, however, for scientists and engineers looking for teaching positions at the college or university levels. Many qualified people apply for very few openings at colleges and universities across the country.

In the social sciences, overall employment is expected to grow more slowly than average for all occupations through 2014. However, the job growth outlook for anthropologists and archaeologists is better than for other social scientists; they will experience average employment growth.

## Looking Into the Future

Several trends will affect the availability of jobs in the engineering, scientific, and technical fields. The end of the Cold War was expected to bring decreases in defense expenditures that translated into a decreased demand for specialists such as physicists

Engineers, such as this ceramic engineer, are often involved in the research and development of new, more effective materials to use in industry. *(© Martha Tabor/Working Images Photographs. Reproduced by permission.)*

and engineers. However, the administration of President George W. Bush substantially increased the defense budget in the early years of the twenty-first century. The "War on Terror," the reconstruction of Iraq, and potential trouble spots elsewhere signal higher defense budgets ahead. Should defense spending level off again, it is possible that funds previously used for maintenance of the armed forces could be reallocated to basic and applied research, thus generating an increased demand for these specialists.

Another important trend is the rapid emergence of a truly global economy. The U.S. economy has changed substantially as a result of this global economic network, and many of the labor-intensive industries that were once the backbone of the U.S. economy are now obsolete. Low-skill, low-technology industries are now found primarily in developing nations. The United States has the best higher education system in the world for science and engineering, and it also invests more money in basic research than does any other nation. Because of this advantage, the U.S. economy has technologically advanced, information-driven industries such as telecommunications, aerospace engineering, computers, and pharmaceuticals. The current trends suggest that the American economy of the future will be even more dependent on these high-technology industries.

These complex and sophisticated industries will require a highly skilled, technically knowledgeable workforce. For this reason, workers with scientific knowledge, engineering skills, and technical skills will continue to be in great demand. However, because of the rapid pace of change, it is likely that the workers most suited to play a critical role in the future will be adaptable and have a broad range of skills and abilities.

# Getting Into Engineering, Science, Technology, and Social Science

Good jobs do not magically appear. Anyone who has been in the job market knows that landing the right job takes planning, preparation, perseverance, and patience. This is true whether you are looking for your first job, reentering the job market, trying to get a new job, or planning a mid-career change. This essay is designed to guide you through the process of finding a job, from helping you define your career objectives to suggesting ways to prepare yourself for interviews. Use the advice and checklists below to help identify the kind of work that fits your personality, skills, and interests. Then learn how to locate job openings that match your criteria. Finally, use these tips to help you create a resume and prepare for the interview that helps you land the job that's right for you.

## PLANNING YOUR CAREER

What are your unique skills? What kind of workplace appeals to you? What do you find most rewarding in your daily life? Answering these questions can help you identify a career path that will enrich your life, financially and otherwise. Most people enjoy doing a job well. There is an inner satisfaction that comes from taking on a challenge and accomplishing something worthwhile. Whether you are just starting out in the working world or you are at the midpoint of a career, it is worth taking some time to consider whether or not you are in the right kind of work—or looking for the right kind of job. If you are unhappy or dissatisfied in your daily work and are just trying to do enough to get by, you may not be in the right job or the right field. The following ideas can help you match your skills and interests with the kind of work you will find most rewarding.

### Evaluate Yourself

Before you make any career decisions, think about subjects or topics that interest you and tasks you do well. This can help you pinpoint the kind of work you would be happy doing. One way to go about this is to compile a self-inventory chart. Such a chart will be helpful as you decide which jobs you want to consider. Including details about your work history and educational background will also make the chart useful to you as you compile your resume, write cover letters, complete job application forms, and prepare for job interviews.

Begin your self-inventory chart by listing all the jobs you have ever had, including summer employment, part-time jobs, volunteer work, and any freelance or short-term assignments you have done. Include the dates of employment, the names and addresses of supervisors, and the amount of money you earned. Then compile a similar list of your hobbies and other activities, including any special experiences you have had, such as travel. Next, do the same for your educational history, listing schools attended, major courses of study, grades, special honors or awards, courses you particularly enjoyed, and extracurricular activities.

At this point, you may see a career pattern emerging: perhaps your list is already suggesting a direction for your career search. If the picture still lacks detail or focus, expand your self-inventory chart by compiling a list of standard workplace aptitudes, and rate yourself *above average*, *average*, or *below average* for each one. Some skill categories to include in your list are administrative, analytic, athletic, clerical, language, leadership, managerial, manual, mathematical, mechanical, sales, and verbal abilities. Also rate your willingness to accept responsibility and your ability to get along with people. In combination with your educational background, work history, and list of personal interests, this information should help you understand why some kinds of work appeal to you and others do not.

### Evaluate Workplace Characteristics

Another tool to help you find a rewarding job is the "Work Characteristics Checklist" below. Some of these characteristics will be attractive to you. Some will not. Perhaps you will discover that having a workplace with flexible hours, for example, is more important to you than being able to work outdoors. Or maybe you will find that these are both very significant issues in your quality of life.

This checklist can be useful as a guide as you compile your own list of what is important to you in a job or workplace. Do not expect a job to meet all your requirements, however. Focusing on the job characteristics that are most important to you will help you identify the type of work you would find

## Work Characteristics Checklist

*Do you want a job in which you can*

- work outdoors?
- be physically active?
- work with your hands?
- be challenged mentally?
- work with machines?
- work independently?
- work on a team?
- follow clear instructions?
- earn a lot of money?
- have a chance for rapid advancement?
- have good benefits?
- travel in your work?
- work close to home?
- work regular hours?
- have a flexible schedule?
- have a variety of tasks?
- have supervisory responsibilities?
- express your own ideas?
- be a decision maker?

most rewarding. It will also be helpful when it is time to decide whether or not to apply for jobs you discover during the search process.

### Evaluate Career Options

Now that you've evaluated your personal skills, aptitudes, interests, and experience, and you've identified the kinds of workplace characteristics that are important to you, do you feel confident that you know what kinds of jobs you'd be good at? If not, you may wish to consult an experienced career counselor or take advantage of online resources that can help you find a good career field match.

Most high schools, vocational schools, and colleges provide vocational testing and career counseling guidance for students and alumni. Some local offices of the state employment services affiliated with the federal employment service offer free counseling. Commercial career centers also offer guidance services.

There are many tools available to test your interests and aptitudes for the purpose of career counseling. The personal profile that emerges from a skills inventory can be matched with potential career fields to show you what kinds of jobs might be good matches for your interests. These assessment tools will also show you what kind of training is necessary to qualify for jobs in these career fields. You may find programs like this online that you can try for yourself. For a more comprehensive approach, you may prefer to look into aptitude tests that are administered and interpreted by a career counselor.

Most major cities have professional career consultants and career counseling firms. You should make sure to check their reputations before paying for their services. A list of counseling services in your area is available from the American Counseling Association in Alexandria, Virginia (http://www.counseling.org).

You can also search the Internet for many services that career counselors provide. Some sites have online counselors who can help you with a variety of tasks, such as obtaining information on jobs, careers, and training. They may be able to provide information on available services, including housing assistance, day care facilities, and transportation. A list of career planning resources, including Web sites, is available at the end of this volume.

## EVALUATE SPECIFIC JOBS

After you have considered what you do well and what you enjoy doing, and identified some career options that provide a good match with your interests and abilities, you're ready to focus on the specific types of jobs that may be available to you. First, make a note of all the jobs in this volume that interest you. Then examine the education and training required for these jobs. Decide whether you qualify or would be able to gain the qualifications.

If possible, talk with people who have the kinds of jobs you are considering. Firsthand information can be invaluable. Also look through the appropriate trade and professional journals listed at the end of this essay and check the section at the end of the volume called "Resources" for books and Web sites that contain more detailed information about the jobs. In addition, counselors usually are helpful. For more detailed information, you can contact the trade and professional associations listed at the end of each occupational profile.

Once you have found out all you can about a particular type of job, compare the features of the job with your work characteristics checklist. See how many characteristics of the job match your work preferences. By completing these steps for all the jobs that appeal to you, you should be able to come up with a list of jobs that match your interests and abilities.

## FINDING JOB OPPORTUNITIES

Once you've decided what kind of job suits you, the next step is to look for available positions. Obviously, the more openings you can find, the better your chance of landing a job. People usually apply for many job openings before they find the right employment match.

## Job Finder's Checklist

The following list of job-hunting tips may seem obvious, but getting all the bits and pieces in order beforehand helps when you're looking for a job.

***Resume*** Find out whether you will need a resume. If so, bring your resume up to date or prepare a new one. Assemble a supply of neatly printed copies and have an electronic version ready to e-mail to prospective employers.

***References*** Line up your references. Ask permission of the people whose names you would like to use. Write down their addresses, phone numbers, and job titles.

***Contacts*** Put the word out to everyone you know that you are looking for a job.

***Job market*** Find out where the jobs are. Make a list of possible employers in your field of interest.

***Research*** Do a little homework ahead of time—it can make a big difference in the long run. Find out as much as you can about a job, the field, and the company before you apply. A knowledgeable job applicant makes a good impression.

***Organization*** Keep a file on your job-hunting campaign with names and dates of employers contacted, ads answered, results, and follow-up.

***Appearance*** Make sure that the clothes you plan to wear to an interview are neat and clean. You may need to dress more formally than you would on the job, particularly if you are visiting a personnel office or meeting with a manager. Keep in mind that people will form an opinion of you based on their first impressions.

There are many ways to find out about or apply for job openings. Some of these job-hunting techniques are explained on the pages that follow, along with information about how to follow up on job leads.

### Applying in Person

For some jobs, especially part-time or entry-level jobs, you may be able to find employment by visiting the company or companies for which you would like to work. This works best when a company is expanding or jobs are plentiful for other reasons, or when a "help wanted" sign is posted at the company. Applying in person can sharpen your interviewing techniques and give you a chance to see a variety of workplaces. This direct approach is best for hourly labor or service jobs; when applying for other types of work, it is not the method to use unless you are directed to do so. Applicants for professional or supervisory jobs should always send a letter and resume to the company.

### Phone and Letter Campaigns

To conduct a phone campaign, use the business listings of your telephone directory to build a list of companies for which you might like to work. Call their personnel departments and find out whether they have any openings. This technique is not useful in all situations, and it has its drawbacks: you may not be able to make a strong impression by phone, and you will not have a written record of your contacts.

Letter writing campaigns can be very effective if the letters are well thought out and carefully prepared. Your letters should always be typed. Handwritten letters and photocopied letters convey a lack of interest or motivation.

You may be able to compile a good list of company addresses in your field of interest by reading the trade and professional publications listed at the end of this essay. Many of the periodicals publish directories or directory issues. Other sources you can use to compile lists of companies are the trade unions and professional organizations listed at the end of each job profile in this volume. The reference librarian at your local library can also help you find appropriate directories.

You can also e-mail letters to human resource departments of many companies. Be sure to follow all the same guidelines as you would for traditional letter correspondence.

Whether they are paper or electronic, your letters should be addressed to the personnel or human resources department of the organization. If possible, send the letter to a specific person. If you don't know who the correct person is, try to find the name of the personnel director through the directories in the library. You can also call on the phone and say, "I'm writing to ask about employment at your company. To whom should I address my letter?" If you can't find a name, use a standard salutation. It's a good idea to enclose a resume (described later in this essay) with the letter to give the employer a brief description of your educational and work experience.

Keep a list of all the people you write to, along with the date each letter was mailed, or keep a photocopy of each letter. Then you can follow up by writing a brief note or calling people who do not reply within about three weeks.

## Job Databases Online

The World Wide Web can be an excellent resource for job hunters. The Internet currently has thousands of career-related sites where you can read about job openings or post your resume in a database for a possible match with available jobs. Some sites, such as The Monster Board (http://www.monster.com), help you build a resume and post it online as well as allow you to search through a massive database of help-wanted listings. Others employ a search engine to find jobs that match your background, then post your resume online for employers. The Web site called CareerBuilder (http://www.careerbuilder.com) uses an interactive personal search program that lets you select job criteria such as location, title, and salary; you are then notified by e-mail when a matching position is posted in the database.

Many companies post job openings in their human resource Web pages. You can usually access these lists by visiting the Web site of a company and clicking on a link called "jobs," "careers," or "employment opportunities." If you find a job that interests you during your online search, whether it's posted at a company's own Web site or on a general listing of jobs, follow the directions given for applying for the position. Some online ads will provide the contact information you need to send your resume and cover letter directly to the employer, either by e-mail or by traditional mail, but other ads

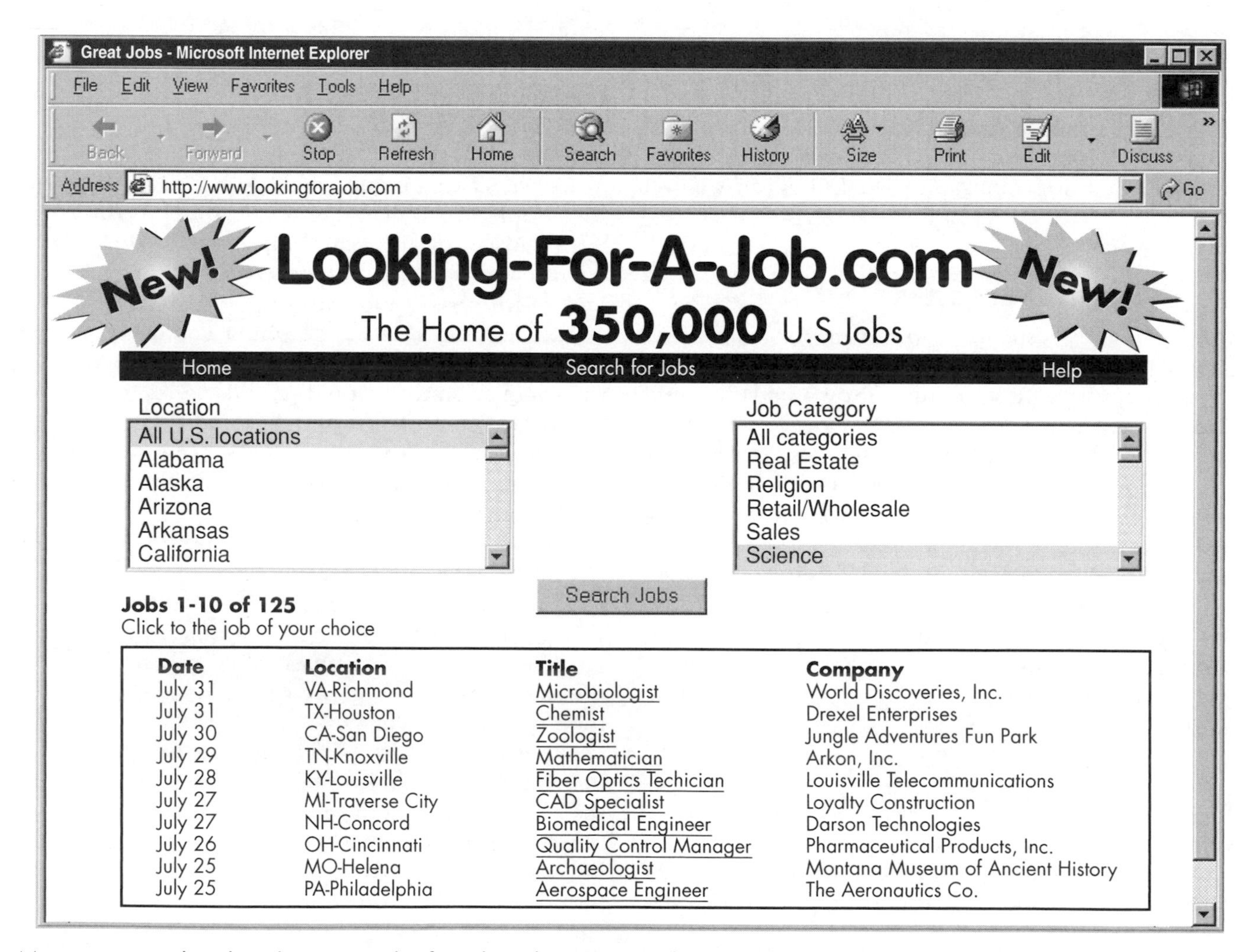


| Date | Location | Title | Company |
|---|---|---|---|
| July 31 | VA-Richmond | Microbiologist | World Discoveries, Inc. |
| July 31 | TX-Houston | Chemist | Drexel Enterprises |
| July 30 | CA-San Diego | Zoologist | Jungle Adventures Fun Park |
| July 29 | TN-Knoxville | Mathematician | Arkon, Inc. |
| July 28 | KY-Louisville | Fiber Optics Techician | Louisville Telecommunications |
| July 27 | MI-Traverse City | CAD Specialist | Loyalty Construction |
| July 27 | NH-Concord | Biomedical Engineer | Darson Technologies |
| July 26 | OH-Cincinnati | Quality Control Manager | Pharmaceutical Products, Inc. |
| July 25 | MO-Helena | Archaeologist | Montana Museum of Ancient History |
| July 25 | PA-Philadelphia | Aerospace Engineer | The Aeronautics Co. |

Many career-related Web sites can be found on the Internet. This hypothetical site (for illustration purposes only) allows job-seekers to search for a position by location and by job description.

direct job hunters to apply directly through a link at the job description.

Job hunters can often find job listings through the Web sites of the professional associations in their career fields. State government Web sites may also provide links to job listings—or to non-government sites that list available jobs.

## Help-Wanted Ads

Many people find out about job openings by reading the "help-wanted" sections of newspapers, trade journals, and professional magazines. Employers and employment agencies often, though not always, use these classified ad sections to publicize available jobs.

Classified ads use unique terms to convey basic information. You will find some common abbreviations in the chart in this essay titled "Reading the Classifieds." You can usually decode the abbreviations by using common sense, but if something puzzles you, call the newspaper and ask for a translation. Classified ads usually list the qualifications that are required for a particular job and explain how to contact the employer.

As you find openings that interest you, answer each ad using the method requested. Record the date of your contact, and if you don't hear from the employer within two or three weeks, place another call or send a polite note asking whether the job is still open. Don't forget to include your phone number and address in your initial contact.

Some help-wanted ads are "blind ads." These ads give contact information for replying but provide no name, phone number, or address that would identify the company. Employers and employment agencies may place these ads to avoid having to reply to all of the job applicants or being contacted directly by job-seekers.

## Situation-Wanted Ads

Another way to get the attention of potential employers is with a situation-wanted ad. You can place one of these in the classified section of your local newspaper or of a trade journal in your field of interest. Many personnel offices and employment agencies scan these columns when they're looking for new employees. The situation-wanted ad is usually most effective for people who have advanced education, training, or experience, or who are in fields where their unique skills are in great demand.

### Reading the Classifieds

#### HELP WANTED

**BIOCHEM. RESEARCH**—B.S./M.S./Ph.D., f/p Radioimmunoassays. Carter Agency, 84 West Street, 000-0000.

**BIOLOGICAL TECHNICIAN**
Prfr. someone working toward B.S. Unique position w/importer of tropical birds and reptiles. Related exp. helpful. Responsible for proper care & handling. Sal. commensurate w/educ. & exp. Send resume to Box 3470, Times.

**CHEMICAL ENGINEER**—Process/Project min. 8 yrs. petrochemical exp. f/p. Grant Engineering Agency 000-0000.

**DESIGNER/DRAFTER**—Electronics firm seeks individual w/min. 3 yrs. exp. in pc board layout & mechanical design. Good salary, benefits. 000-0000.

**Economist, Ph.D.**
Write proposals for international developmental economics research projects. Excellent salary, benefits. Extensive travel required. Interviewing June5–9, Central Plaza Hotel. Logamatica. Call (000) 000-0000 for appt.

**ELECTRONICS ENGINEERS**—Semiconductors. Diodes, filters, hybrid circuits. Resume, salary history in confidence to Box 8464 Examiner.

**ENGR./CHEMICAL**—Excel. sal. Min. 3 yrs. exp. in pharmaceutical quality control. Must know equip. & process. X1919 Post-Dispatch.

**LAB-MGR.** technical services, fee neg., Clinical Chemistry. Action Agency, 27 Delaware Avenue, 000-0000.

**MECHANICAL ENGINEER**
Experienced machine design, plant layout & methods. Montgomery County. Send resume & salary requirements to Box 483, Evening News. Equal Opportunity Employer.

METALLURGICAL TECHNICIAN
Excellent oppty. for person w/R&D background in heat treating. Send resume to Box 983, Chronicle.

#### CLASSIFIED ABBREVIATIONS

|  |  |
|---|---|
| avail. immed. | available immediately |
| biochem. | biochemical |
| chem. | chemical, chemistry |
| col. | college |
| corp. | corporation |
| div. | division |
| educ. | education |
| engr. | engineer |
| equip. | equipment |
| exp., expd. | experience, experienced |
| fee neg. | fee negotiable (fee can be worked out with employer) |
| figs. | figures |
| f/p., f/pd. | fee paid (agency fee paid by employer) |
| f/t | full time |
| K | thousand |
| knowl. | knowledge |
| M | thousand |
| mech., mechs. | mechanic, mechanical, mechanics |
| mfg. | manufacturing |
| mfr. | manufacturer |
| mgr. | manager |
| min. | minimum |
| oppty. | opportunity |
| pc | personal computer |
| pfd., prfr. | preferred, prefer |
| p/t | part time |
| sal. | salary |
| T.A. | teaching associate |
| techs. | technicians |
| temp. | temporary |

#### SITUATION WANTED

**ANTHRO**
Cultural Anthropologist w/3 yrs. field experience in Central America seeks appointment in American Southwest to pursue comparative studies. Publications in major journals, book in progress. Two years undergraduate teaching experience. Box X6061 Bugle.

**CERAMIC ENGINEER**—6 yrs. exp electronic ceramics. Avail. Feb. f/t. Box 483 Daily News.

**CHEMICAL ENGINEER**—8 yrs. plastics exp. Seeks job in design. Box 1256 Sentinel.

**CHEMIST**
Cosmetics & toiletries exp. Wishes to relocate West Coast. Z4728 Chronicle.

**DRAFTER**
Experienced mechanical, electrical, instrumentation, structural. Highly competent with ink & plastic on mylar. CAD training a plus. Samples of lettering & line work available. P.O. Box 2321, or call 000-0000.

**ELECTRONICS TECHNICIAN** with 2-way radio equip. exp. 000-0000 after 6 p.m.

**ENGINEERING COLLEGE STUDENT**
seeks on-the-job practical training in biomedical field. Gary (000) 000-0000.

**HISTORIAN/WRITER**
2 years exp. as T.A.; Ph.D. in history; edited book on local history and written journal articles. Desire position editing, writing, doing research. Call evenings 000-0000.

**LAB ASSISTANT**
Recent graduate, honors student. Seeks position as assistant in mammalian behavioral research lab. Desires opportunity to continue study. Sandra Irrizarry, 000-0000.

A situation-wanted ad should be brief, clear, and to the point. Its main purpose is to interest the employer enough so you are contacted for an interview. It should tell exactly what kind of job you want, why you qualify, and whether you are available for full-time or part-time work. Use the same abbreviations that employers use in classified ads.

If you are already employed and do not want it known that you are looking for a new position, you can run a blind ad. A blind ad protects your privacy by listing a box number at the publication to which all replies can be sent. They are then forwarded to you. You do not need to give your name, address, or phone number in the ad.

### Networking

A very important source of information about job openings is networking. This means talking with friends and acquaintances about your area of interest. If any of them have friends or relatives in the field, ask if they would be willing to speak with you. There's nothing wrong with telling anyone who will listen that you are looking for a job—family, friends, counselors, and former employers. This will multiply your sources of information many times over.

You can use the Internet to make contacts, too. You can meet people with similar interests in news groups, which are organized by topic. Then you can correspond individually via e-mail. Many fields have professional organizations that maintain Web sites. These can help you keep current on news affecting your field, including employment opportunities.

Sometimes a contact knows about a job vacancy before it is advertised. You may have an advantage, then, when you get in touch with the employer. Don't, however, use the contact's name without permission. Don't assume that a contact will go out on a limb by recommending you, either. Once you have received the inside information, rely on your own ability to get the job.

## Notes on Networking

***Let people know you're looking.*** Tell friends, acquaintances, teachers, business associates, former employers—anyone who might know of job openings in your field.

***Read newspapers and professional and trade journals.*** Look for news of developments in your field and for names of people and companies you might contact.

***Use the World Wide Web.*** Make contacts through news groups, or find information on Web sites for professional organizations in your field.

***Join professional or trade associations.*** Contacts you make at meetings could provide valuable job leads. Association newsletters generally carry useful information about people and developments in the field.

***Attend classes or seminars.*** You will meet other people in your field at job-training classes and professional development seminars.

***Participate in local support groups.*** You can gain information about people and places to contact through support groups such as those listed by *The Riley Guide,* available online at http://www.rileyguide.com/support.html, as well as through alumni associations.

***Be on the lookout.*** Always be prepared to make the most of any opportunity that comes along. Talk with anyone who can provide useful information about your field.

### Placement Services

Most vocational schools, high schools, and colleges have a placement or career service that maintains a list of job openings and schedules visits from companies. If you are a student or recent graduate, you should check there for job leads. Many employers look first in technical or trade schools and colleges for qualified applicants for certain jobs. Recruiters often visit colleges to look for people to fill technical and scientific positions. These recruiters usually represent large companies. Visit your placement office regularly to check the job listings, and watch for scheduled visits by company recruiters.

### State Employment Services

Another source of information about job openings is the local office of the state employment service. Many employers automatically list job openings at the local office. Whether you're looking for a job in private industry or with the state, these offices, which are affiliated with the federal employment service, are worth visiting, online or in person, if there are offices locally.

State employment service offices are public agencies that do not charge for their services. They can direct you to special programs run by the government in conjunction with private industry. These programs, such as the Work Incentive Program for families on welfare, are designed to meet special needs. Some, but not all, of these offices offer vocational aptitude and interest tests and can refer interested people to vocational training centers. The state employment service can be a valuable first stop in your search for work, especially if there are special circumstances in your background. For example, if you did not finish high school, if you have had any difficulties with the law, or if you are living in a difficult home environment, your state employment service office is equipped to help you.

### Private Employment Agencies

State employment services, though free, are usually very busy. If you are looking for more personal service and want a qualified employment counselor to help you find a job, you might want to approach a private employment agency.

Private employment agencies will help you get a job if they think they can place you. Most of them get paid only if they're successful in finding you a job, so you need to show them that you are a good prospect. These agencies will help you prepare a resume if you need one, and they will contact employers they think might be interested in you.

Private employment agencies are in the business of bringing together people who are looking for jobs and companies that are looking for workers. For some positions, usually mid- and higher-level jobs, the employment agency's fee is paid by the employer. In such cases, the job seeker pays no fee. In other cases, you may be required to pay the fee, which is usually a percentage of your annual salary. Paying a fee can be a worthwhile investment if it leads to a rewarding career.

Some agencies may also ask for a small registration fee whether or not you get a job through them. Some agencies may demand that you pay even if you find one of the jobs they are trying to fill through your other contacts. Be sure to read and understand the fine print of any contract you're expected to sign, and ask for a copy to take home. Since the quality of these agencies varies, check to see if an agency is a certified member of a state or national association.

Some employment agencies, called staffing services, operate in a different way. They are usually paid by employers to screen and refer good candidates for job openings. They earn money when they refer a candidate who is hired by the employer. The employee pays no fee. Staffing firms, however, only spend time on candidates they think they may be able to place.

Private employment agencies are usually helping many people at one time. They may not have the time to contact you every time they find a job opening. Therefore, you may need to phone them at reasonable intervals after you have registered.

### Civil Service

In your search for work, don't forget that the civil service—federal, state, and local—may have many jobs in your field. You may contact the state employment office or apply directly to the appropriate state or federal agency. The armed services also train and employ civilians in many fields. Don't neglect these avenues for finding jobs. Civil service positions usually require you to take a civil service examination. Books are available to help you prepare for these exams, and your local civil service office can also provide information.

### Unions

In certain fields, unions can be useful sources of information. If you are a member of a union in your field of interest, you may be able to find out about jobs in the union periodical or through people at the union local. If you do not belong to a union, you may contact a union in the field you are interested in for information about available employment services. You will find addresses for some unions in the job profiles in this book.

### Temporary Employment

A good way to get a feel for the job market—what's available and what certain jobs are like—is to work in a temporary job. There are both private and state agencies that can help place people in short-term jobs. Some jobs are seasonal, and extra workers may be needed in the summer or at another busy time.

Temporary employment can increase your job skills, your knowledge of a particular field, and your chances of hearing of permanent positions. In today's tight labor market, many companies are using the services of temporary workers in increasing numbers. In fact, temporary agencies may sign multimillion-dollar contracts to provide businesses with a range of temporary workers. In some cases, temporary workers are in such demand that they may receive benefits, bonuses, and the same hourly wages as equivalent permanent employees. Some temporary agencies are even joining with companies to create long-term career paths for their temporary workers.

## MARKETING YOURSELF

An employer's first impression of you is likely to be based on the way you present yourself on print. Whether it is in an application form or on a resume, you will want to make a good impression so that employers will be interested in giving you a personal interview. A potential employer is likely to equate a neat, well-written presentation with good work habits, and a sloppy, poorly written one with bad work habits.

## Writing an Effective Resume

When you write to a company to follow up a lead or to ask about job openings, you should send information about yourself. The accepted way of doing this is to send a resume with a cover letter.

The work resume is derived from the French word résumer, meaning "to summarize." A resume does just that—it briefly outlines your education, work experience, and special abilities and skills. A resume may also be called a curriculum vitae, a personal profile, or a personal data sheet. This summary acts as your introduction by mail or e-mail, as your calling card if you apply in person, and as a convenient reference for you to use when filling out an application form or when being interviewed.

## DO YOU KNOW YOUR RIGHTS?

### JOB DISCRIMINATION—WHAT IT IS

#### Federal and State Law

An employer cannot discriminate against you for any reason other than your ability to do the job. By federal law, an employer cannot discriminate against you because of your race, color, religion, sex, or national origin. The law applies to decisions about hiring, promotion, working conditions, and firing. The law specifically protects workers who are over the age of forty from discrimination on the basis of age.

The law also protects workers with disabilities. Employers must make their workplaces accessible to individuals with disabilities—for example, by making them accessible to wheelchairs or by hiring readers or interpreters for blind or deaf employees.

Federal law offers additional protection to employees who work for the federal government or for employers who contract with the federal government. State law can also provide protection, for example by prohibiting discrimination on the basis of marital status, arrest record, political affiliations, or sexual orientation.

#### Affirmative Action

Affirmative action programs are set up by businesses that want to make a special effort to hire women and members of minority groups. Federal employers and many businesses that have contracts with the federal government are required by law to set up affirmative action programs. Employers with a history of discriminatory practices may also be required to establish affirmative action programs.

#### Discrimination against Job Applicants

A job application form or interviewer may ask for information that can be used to discriminate against you illegally. The law prohibits such questions. If you are asked such questions and are turned down for the job, you may be a victim of discrimination. However, under federal law, employers must require you to prove that you are an American citizen or that you have a valid work permit.

#### Discrimination on the Job

Discrimination on the job is illegal. Being denied a promotion for which you are qualified or being paid less than coworkers are paid for the same job may be forms of illegal discrimination.

Sexual, racial, and religious harassment are forms of discrimination and are prohibited in the workplace. On-the-job harassment includes sexual, racial, or religious jokes or comments. Sexual harassment includes not only requests or demands for sexual favors but also verbal or physical conduct of a sexual nature.

### JOB DISCRIMINATION—WHAT YOU CAN DO

#### Contact Federal or State Commissions

If you believe that your employer practices discrimination, you can complain to the state civil rights commission or the federal Equal Employment Opportunity Commission (EEOC). If, after investigating your complaint, the commission finds that there has been discrimination, it will take action against the employer. You may be entitled to the job or promotion you were denied or to reinstatement if you were fired. You may also receive back pay or other financial compensation.

#### Contact a Private Organization

There are many private organizations that can help you fight job discrimination. For example, the American Civil Liberties Union (ACLU) works to protect all people from infringement on their civil rights. The National Association for the Advancement of Colored People (NAACP), National Organization

A resume is a useful tool in applying for almost any job, even if you use it only to keep a record of where you have worked, for whom, and the dates of employment. A resume is required if you are being considered for professional or executive jobs. Prepare it carefully. It's well worth the effort.

The goal of a resume is to capture the interest of potential employers so they will call you for a personal interview. Since employers are busy people, the resume should be as brief and as neat as possible. You should, however, include as much relevant information about yourself as you can. This is usually presented under at least two headings: "Education" and "Experience." The latter is sometimes called "Employment History." Some people add a third section titled "Related Skills," "Professional Qualifications," or "Related Qualifications."

If you prepare a self-inventory such as the one described earlier, it will be a useful tool in preparing a resume. Go through your inventory, and select the items that show your ability to do the job or jobs in which you are interested. Plan to highlight these

for Women (NOW), and Native American Rights Fund may negotiate with your employer, sue on your behalf, or start a class action suit—a lawsuit brought on behalf of all individuals in your situation.

## WHAT TO DO IF YOU LOSE YOUR JOB

### Being Fired and Being Laid Off

In most cases, an employer can fire you only if there is good cause, such as your inability to do the job, violation of safety rules, dishonesty, or chronic absenteeism.

Firing an employee because of that employee's race, color, religion, sex, national origin, or age (if the employee is over forty) is illegal. Firing an employee for joining a union or for reporting an employer's violation (called whistle-blowing) is also prohibited. If you believe you have been wrongfully discharged, you should contact the EEOC or the state civil rights commission.

At times, employers may need to let a number of employees go to reduce costs. This reduction in staff is called a layoff. Laying off an employee has nothing to do with the employee's job performance. Federal law requires employers who lay off large numbers of employees to give these employees at least two months' notice of the cutback.

### Unemployment Compensation

Unemployment insurance is a state-run fund that provides payments to people who lose their jobs through no fault of their own. Not everyone is entitled to unemployment compensation. Those who quit their jobs or who worked only a few months before losing their jobs may not be eligible.

The amount of money you receive depends on how much you earned at your last job. You may receive unemployment payments for only a limited period of time and only so long as you can prove that you are actively looking for a new position.

Each claim for unemployment compensation is investigated before the state makes any payments. If the state unemployment agency decides to deny you compensation, you may ask the agency for instructions on how to appeal that decision.

## OTHER PROTECTIONS FOR EMPLOYEES

### Honesty and Drug Testing

Many employers ask job applicants or employees to submit to lie detector tests or drug tests. Lie detector tests are permitted in the hiring of people for high security positions, such as police officers. Some states prohibit or restrict the testing of applicants or employees for drug use. Aptitude and personality tests are generally permitted.

### Other Federal Laws

The Fair Labor Standards Act prescribes certain minimum wages and rules about working hours and overtime payments. Workers' compensation laws provide payment for injuries that occur in the workplace and wages lost as a result of those injuries.

The Occupational Safety and Health Act sets minimum requirements for workplace safety. Any employee who discovers a workplace hazard should report it to the Occupational Safety and Health Administration (OSHA). The administration will investigate the claim and may require the employer to correct the problem or pay a fine.

### Rights Guaranteed by Contract

Not every employee has a written contract. If you do, however, that contract may grant you additional rights, such as the right to severance pay in the event you are laid off. In addition, employees who are members of a union may have certain rights guaranteed through their union contract.

Before you sign any contract, make sure you understand every part of it. Read it thoroughly and ask the employer questions. Checking the details of a contract before signing it may prevent misunderstanding later.

**Reena Singh**
48-10 River Run Drive
Boston, MA 54321
(707) 321-4567
rsingh@email.com

▸ **EMPLOYMENT OBJECTIVE:** Managerial position in engineering.

▸ **EXPERIENCE:**

1995 to 2000 — *Supervisory Mechanical Engineer*
Peterson Supply Company, Boston, MA.
Responsible for full-scale proposals for custom-built industrial equipment to satisfy client requirements. Supervised design, production, testing, and installation of projects. Devised company production procedures manual and designed production floor layout for new plant facility. Promoted from Assistant Supervisory Engineer in 1996.

1992 to 1994 — *Mechanical Engineer*
Springfield Electronics Company, Newton, MA.
Designed structural parts for manufacturing radios, televisions, recording equipment, and personal computers. Introduced changes in design to improve speed of assembly and achieve cost savings.

▸ **TEACHING EXPERIENCE:**

2001 to 2003 — *Teaching Assistant*
Business Communications Course, Glendale University, Boston, MA.

1995 to 1996 — *Mathematics Teacher*
Montgomery High School, Newton, MA.

▸ **EDUCATION:**

2003 — *Master of Business Administration*, Glendale University, Boston, MA.
1996 — *Teaching Certification Program*, Harrison Community College, Boston, MA.
1993 — *Bachelor of Science in Mechanical Engineering*, Winchester College, Philadelphia, PA.

▸ **PROFESSIONAL QUALIFICATIONS:**
Licensed Professional Engineer, State of Massachu
Member, American Society of Mechanical Engine
Teaching certification in mathematics, secondary

▸ **REFERENCES:** Available upon request.

- State your name, address, telephone number, and email first.
- State job objective or general career goal in a few words.
- List education and work experience in reverse chronological order, with most recent item first.

**Alex Morton**
112 Hamilton Road
San Francisco, CA 12345
(505) 123-4567
ajmorton@email.com

***Employment Objective:***
Laboratory technician in biological sciences.

***Experience:***

***Research Assistant***
Southern California State University, Los Angeles, CA.
Assisted with research project on genetically transmitted diseases. Project was conducted under direction of university faculty member and funded by state and private foundation support. Publication in preparation. 2000–2004, part-time.

***Laboratory Assistant***
Welltree Pharmaceutical Corporation, San Francisco, CA.
Responsible for conducting routine toxicity tests on production samples. Maintained laboratory log book and test results and produced reports. One report resulted in improvements in factory technique. 2001 summer.

***Field Assistant***
Biology Section, State Department of Fish and Wildlife, San Francisco, CA.
Assisted with research on several species of fish and game animals. Prepared biological specimens for state natural history collection. Participated in population census for two endangered species. 2000 summer.

***Education:***

***Bachelor of Science, 2002***
Southern California State University, Los Angeles, CA.
Major in biology, minor in anthropology.
Coordinator, Topics in Anthropology discussion group.
Member, Student Wildlife Federation.

***References***
*Available upon request.*

- List your work experience first if it is more important than your educational background.
- Keep descriptions of your education and work experience brief.
- List special skills and qualifications if they are relevant to the job.

items on your resume. Select only those facts that point out your relevant skills and experience.

Once you have chosen the special points to include, prepare the resume. At the top, put your name, address, and phone number. After that, decide which items will be most relevant to the employer you plan to contact.

***State Your Objective*** Some employment counselors advise that you state a job objective or describe briefly the type of position for which you are applying. The job objective usually follows your name and address. Don't be too specific if you plan to use the same resume a number of times. It's better to give a general career goal. Then, in a cover letter, you can be more specific about the position in which you are interested.

***Describe What You've Done*** Every interested employer will check your educational background and employment history carefully. It is best to present these sections in order of importance. For instance, if you've held many relevant jobs, you should list your work experience first, followed by your educational background. On the other hand, if you are just out of school with little or no work experience, it's probably best to list your educational background first and then, under employment history, to mention any part-time and summer jobs you've held or volunteer work you've done.

Under educational background, list the schools you have attended in reverse chronological order, starting with your most recent training and ending with the least recent. Employers want to know at a glance your highest qualifications. For each educational experience, include years attended, name and location of the school, and degree or certificate earned, if any. If you have advanced degrees (college and beyond), it isn't necessary to include high school and elementary school education. Don't forget to highlight any special courses you took or awards you won, if they are relevant to the kind of job you are seeking.

***Chronological and Functional Resumes*** Information about your employment history can be presented in two ways. The most common format is the chronological resume. In a chronological resume, you summarize your work experience year by year. Begin with your current or most recent employment and then work backward. For each job, list the name and location of the company for which you worked, the years you were employed, and the position or positions you held. The order in which you present these facts will depend on what you are trying to emphasize. If you want to call attention to the type or level of job you held, for example, you should put the job title first. Regardless of the order you choose, be consistent. Summer employment or part-time work should be identified as such. If you held a job for less than a year, specify months in the dates of employment.

It is important to include a brief description of the responsibilities you had in each job. This often reveals more about your abilities than the job title. Remember, too, that you do not have to mention the names of former supervisors or how much you earned. You can discuss these points during the interview or explain them on an application form.

The functional resume, on the other hand, emphasizes what you can do rather than what you have done. It is useful for people who have large gaps in their work history or who have relevant skills that would not be properly highlighted in a chronological listing of jobs. The functional resume concentrates on qualifications—such as familiarity with particular equipment, organizational skills, or managerial experience. Specific jobs may be mentioned, but they are not the primary focus of this type of resume.

***Explain Special Skills*** You may wish to include a third section called "Related Skills," "Professional Qualifications," or "Related Qualifications." This is useful if there are points you want to highlight that do not apply directly to educational background or work experience. Be sure these points are relevant to the kind of work you are seeking. This section is most effective if you can mention any special recognition, awards, or other evidence of excellence. It is also useful to mention if you are willing to relocate or can work unusual hours.

***Have References Available*** Employers may also want to know whom they can contact to find out more about you. At the start of your job search, you should ask three or four people if you may use them as references. If you haven't seen these people for a while, you may want to send them a copy of your resume and let them know what kind of position you're seeking. Your references should be the kind of people your potential employer will respect, and they should be able to comment favorably on your abilities, personality, and work habits. You should indicate whether these people are personal references or former work supervisors. Avoid using any relatives. You can list the names and addresses of your references at the end of your resume or in a cover letter. Or, you can simply write, "References available upon request." Just be sure you have their names, addresses, and phone numbers ready if you are asked.

***Present Yourself Concisely*** Tips for making your resume concise include using phrases instead of sentences and omitting unnecessary words. When

**Reena Singh**
48-10 River Run Drive
Boston, MA 54321
(707) 321-4567
rsingh@email.com

October 14, 2005

Mr. Patrick Campbell
Vice President
Precision Engineering Systems
Route 212
Boston, MA 54321

Dear Mr. Campbell:

I am writing with regard to your listing with the Engineer's Placement Service for a manager in your hydraulics division. I am an experienced mechanical engineer and have just received a master's degree in business administration. I would like to apply for the position.

In addition to my business administration training, I have had teaching experience with high school and graduate school students. As a result, I feel confident about my ability to coordinate and supervise employees in a professional and productive manner.

I have a solid background in hydraulics including work on a prototype assembly line belt, which was based on hydraulic systems. This project has since been duplicated for other clients.

I enclose my resume for your reference and would be pleased to meet with you to discuss the position.

Very truly yours,

Reena Singh

Reena Singh

Enclosure

*Alex Morton*
112 Hamilton Road
San Francisco, CA 12345
(505) 123-4567
ajmorton@email.com

August 22, 2005

Ms. Jennifer Chang
Employment Officer
California University School of Medicine
23 Spencer Boulevard
San Francisco, CA 12345

Dear Ms. Chang:

I am writing at the suggestion of Professor Loretta Kingsley at Southern California State University. Professor Kingsley has been my academic adviser for three years and is aware of my interest in working in biological research. As you may recall, she was affiliated with the Department of Genetics at California University School of Medicine for six years, and she thought you might know whether any suitable positions are available for which I might qualify.

I am a recent graduate in biology from Southern California State University. My laboratory experience both in the university and in private industry has included a solid background in chemistry, genetics, enzymology, and histology. I have become skilled at tissue culture techniques and preparation of slides for analysis. I am most interested in expanding my knowledge to new areas and techniques.

I enclose my resume and would be interested to know whether any laboratory positions are available at the School of Medicine at this time.

Very truly yours,

Alex Morton

Alex Morton

Enclosure

appropriate, start a phrase with a verb, such as "maintained" or "coordinated." There is no need to say "I"—that is obvious and repetitive.

***Present Yourself Well*** Employment counselors often recommend that resumes be no longer than one page because employers won't take the time to read a second page. If you've held many positions related to your occupation, go on to the second page, but don't include beginning or irrelevant jobs. If you have a lot of work experience, limit the education section to just the essentials.

You should also concentrate on the appearance of your resume. A traditional resume should be printed on a good grade of 8½" x 11" white paper. Consult a resume preparation guide for specific information about the best ways to format a resume that will be processed by e-mail or other electronic means. If you don't have access to a computer and printer, you can pay someone to type your resume, but it is up to you to read it carefully and ensure that it is error-free. Be sure that it is neatly typed with adequate margins. The data should be spaced and indented so that each item stands out. This enables a busy executive or personnel director to see at a glance the facts of greatest interest.

These suggestions for writing a resume are not hard-and-fast rules. Resumes may be adapted to special situations. For example, people with a variety of work experience often prepare several versions of their resumes and use the experience that's most relevant when applying for a particular job.

If this is your first resume, show it to someone else, perhaps a guidance counselor, for constructive advice. Make sure there are no spelling or punctuation mistakes anywhere on the page. No matter what, be truthful while emphasizing your assets. You can do that by showing the abilities, skills, and specific interests that qualify you for a particular job. Don't mention any weaknesses or deficiencies in your training. Do mention job-related aptitudes that showed up in previous employment or in school. Don't make things up; everything that's in your resume can, and often will, be checked.

## Writing Cover Letters

Whenever you send your resume to a prospective employer, whether it's on paper or in e-mail form, you should send a cover letter with it. This is true whether you are writing to apply for a specific job or just to find out if there are any openings.

A good cover letter should be neat, brief, and well written, with no more than three or four short paragraphs. Since you may use your resume for a variety of job openings, your cover letter should be very specific. Your goal is to get the person who reads it to think that you are an ideal candidate for a particular job. If at all possible, send the letter to a specific person—either the personnel director or the person for whom you would be working. If necessary, call the company and ask to whom you should address the letter.

Start your letter by explaining why you are writing. Say that you are inquiring about possible job openings at the company, that you are responding to an advertisement in a particular publication, or that someone recommended that you should write. (Use the person's name if you have received permission to do so.) Let your letter lead into your resume. Use it to call attention to your qualifications. Add information that shows why you are well suited for that specific job.

## Completing the Application Form

Many employers ask job applicants to fill out an application form. This form usually duplicates much of the information on your resume, but it may ask some additional questions. Give complete answers to all questions except those that are discriminatory. If a question doesn't apply to you, put a dash next to it.

You may be given the application form when you arrive for an interview, or it may be sent to your home. When filling it out, print neatly in ink. Follow the instructions carefully. For instance, if the form asks you to put down your last name first, do so.

The most important sections of an application form are the education and work histories. As in your resume, many applications request that you write these in reverse chronological order, with the most recent experience first. Unlike your resume, however, the application form may request information about your earnings on previous jobs. It may also ask what rate of pay you are seeking on the job you are applying for.

Be prepared to answer these and other topics not addressed on your resume. Look at the sample application form, and make note of the kinds of questions that you are likely to be asked—for example, your Social Security number, the names of previous supervisors, your salary, and your reason for leaving. If necessary, carry notes on such topics with you to an interview. You have a responsibility to tell prospective employers what they need to know to make an informed decision.

***Neatness Counts*** Think before you write on an application form so you avoid crossing things out. An employer's opinion of you may be influenced just by the general appearance of your application form. A neat, detailed form may indicate an orderly mind and the ability to think clearly, follow instructions, and organize information.

1 Always print neatly in blue or black ink. When completing an application at home, type it, if possible.

2 Read the application carefully *before* you start to fill it out. Follow instructions precisely. Use standard abbreviations.

3 If you aren't applying for a specific job, indicate the kind of work you're willing to do.

4 You don't have to commit to a specific rate of pay. Write "open" or "negotiable" if you are uncertain.

5 Traffic violations and so on do not belong here. Nor do offenses for which you were charged but not convicted.

6 If a question doesn't apply to you, write "NA" (for not applicable) or put a dash through the space.

7 Take notes along to remind you of school names, addresses, and dates.

8 If you're short on "real" employment, mention jobs such as babysitting, lawn mowing, or any occasional work.

9 Your references should be people who can be objective about you, such as former employers, teachers, and community leaders.

10 Under the heading "Reason for Leaving," a simple answer will do. Avoid saying "better pay"—even if it's so.

## APPLICATION FOR EMPLOYMENT

| NAME (LAST) | (FIRST) | (MIDDLE) | SOCIAL SECURITY NO. | | |
|---|---|---|---|---|---|
| PRESENT ADDRESS | CITY | STATE | ZIP CODE | AREA CODE | TELEPHONE NO. |
| PERMANENT ADDRESS | (IF DIFFERENT FROM ABOVE) | | | AREA CODE | TELEPHONE NO. |
| POSITION APPLIED FOR | DATE AVAILABLE | | | E-MAIL | |
| SALARY OR WAGE DESIRED | WILL YOU RELOCATE? | REFERRED BY | | | |
| ARE YOU A U.S. CITIZEN? YES ______ NO ______ | IF NOT A U.S. CITIZEN, LIST VISA NUMBER AND EXPIRATION DATE: NUMBER ______ DATE ______ | | | | |
| WITHIN THE LAST FIVE YEARS HAVE YOU BEEN CONVICTED OF A FELONY? | ☐ YES ☐ NO | IF YES, GIVE DETAILS ON BACK PAGE | HAVE YOU EVER BEEN EMPLOYED BY OUR COMPANY? IF YES, GIVE DETAILS ON BACK PAGE | ☐ YES ☐ NO | |

| EDUCATION | INSTITUTION NAME AND ADDRESS | DID YOU GRADUATE? | MAJOR FIELD OF STUDY | CLASS STANDING |
|---|---|---|---|---|
| HIGH SCHOOL | | | | |
| COLLEGE OR UNIVERSITY | | | | |
| GRADUATE STUDY | | | | |
| OTHER | | | | |

### EMPLOYMENT RECORD

*PLEASE LIST ALL EMPLOYMENT STARTING WITH MOST RECENT. ACCOUNT FOR ALL PERIODS (INCLUDING U.S. ARMED FORCES, PERIODS OF UNEMPLOYMENT, AND VOLUNTARY SERVICES).*

| LIST YOUR MOST RECENT POSITION HELD | MAY WE CONTACT YOUR PRESENT EMPLOYER? ☐ YES ☐ NO | |
|---|---|---|
| EMPLOYER'S NAME AND COMPLETE ADDRESS/PHONE | DATES EMPLOYED: FROM / TO | POSITION TITLE |
| | | NAME AND TITLE OF SUPERVISOR |
| | SALARY: START / FINAL | REASON FOR LEAVING |
| EMPLOYER'S NAME AND COMPLETE ADDRESS/PHONE | DATES EMPLOYED: FROM / TO | POSITION TITLE |
| | | NAME AND TITLE OF SUPERVISOR |
| | SALARY: START / FINAL | REASON FOR LEAVING |
| EMPLOYER'S NAME AND COMPLETE ADDRESS/PHONE | DATES EMPLOYED: FROM / TO | POSITION TITLE |
| | | NAME AND TITLE OF SUPERVISOR |
| | SALARY: START / FINAL | REASON FOR LEAVING |

### PERSONAL REFERENCES

| NAME | ADDRESS | PHONE NUMBER |
|---|---|---|
| 1. | | |
| 2. | | |
| 3. | | |

***Know Your Rights*** Under federal and some state laws, an employer cannot demand that you answer any questions about race, color, creed, national origin, ancestry, sex, marital status, age (with certain exceptions), number of dependents, property, car ownership (unless needed for the job), or arrest record. Refer to the information on job discrimination in this essay for more information about your rights.

## PRESENTING YOURSELF IN AN INTERVIEW

If your qualifications, as presented in your resume, cover letter, and application, are a strong match for the requirements of the job, you may be invited to a job interview. On the basis of this meeting, the prospective employer will decide whether or not to hire you, and you will decide whether or not you want the job.

### Prepare in Advance

Before an interview, there are a number of things you can do to prepare. Begin by giving thought to why you want the job and what you have to offer. Then review your resume and any lists you made when you were evaluating yourself so that you can keep your qualifications firmly in mind.

Learn as much as you can about the organization. Check with friends who work there, read company brochures, search the Internet, or devise other information-gathering strategies. Showing that you know something about the company and what it does will indicate your interest and demonstrate that you are a well-informed job candidate.

Try to anticipate some of the questions an interviewer may ask and think about how you would answer. For example, you may be asked: Will you work overtime when necessary? Are you ready to go to night school to improve some of your skills? Preparing answers in advance will make the process easier for you. It is also wise to prepare any questions you may have about the company or the position for which you are applying. The more information you have, the better you can evaluate both the company and the job.

Employers may want you to demonstrate specific skills for some jobs. An applicant for a job in a lumber mill or a mine, for example, might be required to demonstrate mechanical ability. Prospective technicians might be expected to demonstrate mathematical skills.

On the appointed day, dress neatly and in a style appropriate for the job you're seeking. When in doubt, it's safer to dress on the conservative side, wearing a shirt and tie rather than a turtleneck or wearing a dress or blouse and skirt rather than pants and a T-shirt. Be on time. Find out in advance exactly where the company is located and how to get there. Allow extra time in case you get lost, get caught in a traffic jam, can't find a parking spot, or encounter another type of delay.

### Maintain a Balance

When your appointment begins, remember that a good interview is largely a matter of balance. Don't undersell yourself by sitting back silently, but don't oversell yourself by talking nonstop about how wonderful you are. Answer all questions directly and simply, and let the interviewer take the lead.

Instead of saying, "I'm reliable and hardworking," give the interviewer an example. Allow the interviewer to draw conclusions from your example.

It's natural to be nervous before and during a job interview. However, you need to try to relax and be yourself. You may even enjoy the conversation. Your chances of being hired and being happy if you get the job are better if the employer likes you as you are.

Avoid discussing money until the employer brings it up or until you are offered the job. Employers usually know in advance what they are willing to pay. If you are the one to begin a discussion about the salary you want, you may set an amount that's either too low or too high.

Be prepared to ask questions, but don't force them on your interviewer. Part of the purpose of the interview is for you to evaluate the company while you are being evaluated. For instance, you might want to ask about the company's training programs and its policy on promotions.

Don't stay too long. Most business people have busy schedules. It is likely that the interviewer will let you know when it's time for the interview to end.

Don't expect a definite answer at the first interview. Employers usually thank you for coming and say that you will be notified shortly. Most employers want to interview all the applicants before they make a hiring decision. If the position is offered at the time of the interview, you can ask for a little time to think about it. If the interviewer tells you that you are not suitable for the job, try to be polite. Say, "I'm sorry, but thank you for taking the time to meet with me." After all, the company may have the right job for you next week.

### Follow Up after the Interview

If the job sounds interesting and you would like to be considered for it, say so as you leave. Follow up after the interview by writing a brief thank-you note to the employer. Express your continued interest in the position and thank the interviewer for taking the time to meet with you.

It's a good idea to make some notes and evaluations of the interview while it is still fresh in your mind. Write down the important facts about the job—the duties, salary, promotion prospects, and so on, which will help you make a decision should you be offered the job. Also evaluate your own performance in the interview. List the things you wish you had said and things you wish you had not said, which will help you prepare for future interviews.

Finally, don't hesitate to contact your interviewer if you haven't heard from the company after a week or two (unless you were told it would be longer). Write a brief note or make a phone call in which you ask when a decision might be reached. Making such an effort will show the employer that you are genuinely interested in the job. Your call will remind the interviewer about you and could work to your advantage.

## TAKE CHARGE

Job hunting is primarily a matter of organizing a well-planned campaign. Scan the classified ads, search through online job banks, watch for trends in local industry that might be reported in the news, and check with people you know in the field. Take the initiative. Send out carefully crafted resumes and letters. Respond to ads. Finally, in an interview, state your qualifications and experience in a straightforward and confident manner.

## TRADE AND PROFESSIONAL JOURNALS

The following is a list of some of the major journals in the fields of engineering, science, technology, and social science. These journals can keep you up to date with what is happening in your field of interest. These publications can also lead you to jobs through their own specialized classified advertising sections.

### Astronomy and Aerospace

*The Astrophysical Journal*, Steward Observatory, University of Arizona, 933 North Cherry Avenue, Tucson, AZ 85721.
*http://www.journals.uchicago.edu/ApJ*

*Aviation Week and Space Technology*, 1200 G Street, Suite 922, Washington, DC 20005.
*http://www.aviationnow.com*

*Popular Science*, 2 Park Ave., 9th Floor, New York, NY 10016.
*http://www.popsci.com*

### Chemistry, Physics, and Mathematics

*American Mathematical Monthly*, Amherst College, P.O. Box 5000, Amherst, MA 01002-5000.
*http://www.maa.org*

*Physics Today*, American Institute of Physics, One Physics Ellipse, College Park, MD 20740-3842.
*http://www.physicstoday.org*

*Science*, 1200 New York Avenue, NW, Washington, DC 20005.
*http://www.sciencemag.org*

*Scientific American*, 415 Madison Avenue, New York, NY 10017.
*http://www.sciam.com*

### Engineering and Technology

*Airconditioning, Heating & Refrigeration News*, 2401 W. Big Beaver Rd., Suite 700, Troy, MI 48084.
*http://www.achrnews.com*

*ASEE Prism*, American Society for Engineering Education, 1818 North Street, NW, Suite 600, Washington, DC 20036-2479.
*http://www.prism-magazine.org*

*Chemical Engineering*, 110 William Street, New York, NY 10038.
*http://www.che.com*

*Electronic News*, Reed Business Information, 1101 S. Winchester Boulevard, Bldg. N, San Jose, CA 95128.
*http://www.reed-electronics.com/electronicnews*

*Mechanical Engineering*, Three Park Avenue, New York, NY 10016-5990.
*http://www.memagazine.org*

*Power Engineering*, PennWell, 1421 S. Sheridan Road, Tulsa, OK 74112.
*http://pepei.pennnet.com/*

### Life Sciences

*American Journal of Public Health*, 800 I St., NW, Washington, DC 20001-3710.
*http://www.ajph.org*

*BioScience*, American Institute of Biological Sciences. 1313 Dolly Madison Boulevard, No. 402, McLean, VA 22101.
*http://www.bioscience.org*

*Conservation Biology*, Blackwell Publishing Inc., Commerce Place, 350 Main Street, Malden, MA 02148.
*http://www.blackwellpublishing.com*

*Environmental Science & Technology*, 1155 16th Street NW, Washington, DC 20036. *http://pubs.acs.org/journals/esthag/index.html*

*International Journal of Plant Sciences*, University of Chicago, 1101 E. 57th Street, Chicago, IL 60637. *http://www.journals.uchicago.edu/IJPS/journal/index.html*

*Physiological and Biochemical Zoology*, Department of Ecology and Evolutionary Biology, 321 Steinhaus Hall, University of California at Irvine, Irvine, CA 92697-2525. *http://www.journals.uchicago.edu/PBZ/journal/index.html*

*The Quarterly Review of Biology*, C-2615 Frank Melville Jr. Memorial Library, Stony Brook University, Stony Brook, NY 11794-3349. *http://www.journals.uchicago.edu/QRB/journal*

## Social Sciences

*American Anthropologist*, Department of Anthropology, University of Texas at San Antonio, 6900 North Loop 1604 W, San Antonio, TX 78249-0649. *http://www.aaanet.org/aa/index.htm*

*American Antiquity*, Society for American Archaeology, 900 Second Street NE, No. 12, Washington, DC 20002-3560. *http://www.saa.org/publications/amantiq/amantiq.html*

*The American Journal of Sociology*, 5835 S. Kimbark Avenue, Chicago, IL 60637-1684. *http://www.journals.uchicago.edu/AJS/journal/home.html*

*American Political Science Review*, 1527 New Hampshire Avenue NW, Washington, DC 20036. *http://www.apsanet.org/section_327.cfm*

*American Sociological Review*, Department of Sociology, University of Pennsylvania, 3718 Locust Walk, Philadelphia, PA 19104-6209. *http://www.asanet.org*

*Archaeology*, 656 Beacon Street, 4th Floor, Boston, MA 02215. *http://www.archaeology.org*

*Political Science Quarterly*, 475 Riverside Drive, Suite 1274, New York, NY 10115-1274. *http://www.psqonline.org*

*Social Science Quarterly*, Blackwell Publishing, Inc., 350 Main Street, Malden, MA 02148. *http://www.blackwellpublishing.com*

# Aerospace Engineering and Operations Technician

**Education and Training**
High school plus two years of training

**Salary**
Median—$52,250 per year

**Employment Outlook**
Good

## Definition and Nature of the Work

The aerospace industry is based on aeronautics, the science of flight, and on astronautics, the science of space travel. Both aircraft and spacecraft are produced in this industry. Aerospace engineering and operations technicians construct, test, and maintain aircraft and space vehicles. They may work on rockets, missiles, helicopters, and airplanes. They may adjust test equipment for accuracy and determine causes of equipment malfunctions. Using computer and communications systems, aerospace engineering and operations technicians often record and interpret test data. Technicians in the aerospace industry may work on many kinds of projects.

Most aerospace engineering and operations technicians work for companies that build aircraft and space vehicles. These companies have contracts to build this equipment for private airlines or the federal government. Some aerospace engineering and operations technicians work for the National Aeronautics and Space Administration (NASA), universities, or research institutes. Although much of this industry is located on the West Coast, some companies in the aerospace industry are located in the South or along the East Coast.

Due to the complexity of the aerospace industry, there is great variety in the type of work available for technicians. Many technicians specialize in certain kinds of equipment, such as air intake valves for jet engines. Some spend several years working on small, one-of-a-kind parts used in spaceships. Others specialize in certain kinds of systems, such as hydraulic, electrical, or mechanical systems. They may also work with aircraft instruments, sheet metal, or landing gear.

No matter what kind of equipment they work on, aerospace engineering and operations technicians generally work as part of a team under the direction of scientists or engineers. Technicians perform much of the routine work, allowing the scientists and engineers to focus on tasks that make use of their more advanced training.

Aerospace engineering and operations technicians work in all phases of their industry including research and development, production, and sales. Some technicians prepare precise drawings or scale models. Others work with special instruments to take measurements, collect information, or perform laboratory tests. They may write reports, make cost estimates, or prepare plans for the manufacture of equipment. Some aerospace engineering and operations technicians work as field representatives. They offer assistance and advice to their company's customers, such as NASA or the armed services. Other technicians work as technical writers, preparing information for instruction manuals or catalogs.

## Education and Training Requirements

There are several ways to train to become an aerospace engineering and operations technician. In high school you should take as many math and science classes as possible. You can then attend a college or technical school and take a two-year program in engineering or aerospace technology. Some schools have work-study programs in which you attend classes while working in the industry. Some companies in the aerospace industry offer on-the-job training programs. Apprenticeship programs, such as those given in drafting and electronics, may lead to a technician's job. Graduates of technical schools run by the armed services may also be able to find jobs as aerospace engineering and operations technicians. In addition, there are home-study courses that can qualify you for a job as a technician in the aerospace industry. Technicians may have to pass a security clearance before they can work on defense projects.

## Getting the Job

Private companies often recruit technicians through placement offices at colleges and technical institutes. These companies may also send notices of job openings to separation centers at military bases. You can apply directly to companies or research centers in the aerospace industry. You can also contact NASA for information about applying for a civil service job. In addition, job openings may be listed in newspaper classifieds and job banks on the Internet.

## Advancement Possibilities and Employment Outlook

Aerospace engineering and operations technicians usually advance to higher-paying positions as they gain experience. Sometimes they become supervisors of other technicians or workers. Experienced technicians can also become sales or technical representatives for their companies. Technicians who continue their education can become engineers. Some technicians become teachers in technical schools. Others become technical writers.

Overall employment of engineering technicians is expected to increase about as fast as the average for all occupations through 2014. The field depends to a large extent on levels of government spending for defense and space programs, and changes in government spending priorities can quickly alter the employment picture. Jobs in this area are similarly sensitive to the economy. Research and development funds tend to decline during recessions, reducing job opportunities.

## Working Conditions

Aerospace engineering and operations technicians usually work in modern, well-equipped plants, laboratories, or offices. At times they must work in small spaces, such as the inside sections of space vehicles. Production lines or testing centers can be very noisy. Workers are given ear protectors if the noise level is dangerous. Aerospace engineering and operations technicians sometimes work nights and weekends, but thirty-five- to forty-hour weeks are standard. At times technicians must work longer hours to complete a project on time. When their projects are completed, aerospace engineering and operations technicians must find other jobs. They may have to move to a new area to find a job requiring their special skills.

Aerospace engineering and operations technicians generally work as part of a team that includes scientists, engineers, and technologists. They must be able to work well with others. They should also have an aptitude for science and mathematics and be able to concentrate on the details of their work. Technicians need to be responsible people who can work well with their hands. Some aerospace engineering and operations technicians belong to unions.

## Earnings and Benefits

Earnings depend on the education and experience of the aerospace technician, the location, and the kind of job. Salaries are generally higher than those received by other kinds of science and engineering technicians. In 2004 the average annual salary for aerospace engineering and operations technicians in the aerospace products and parts manufacturing industry was $52,250. Benefits include paid holidays and vacations, health insurance, and pension plans.

### Where to Go for More Information

American Institute of Aeronautics and Astronautics
1801 Alexander Bell Dr., Ste. 500
Reston, VA 20191-4344
(800) 639-2422
http://www.aiaa.org

American Society for Engineering Education
1818 N St. NW, Ste. 600
Washington, DC 20036-2479
(202) 331-3500
http://www.asee.org

# *Alternative Fuels Vehicle Technician*

### Education and Training
High school plus training

### Salary
Median—$38,000 per year

### Employment Outlook
Very good

## Definition and Nature of the Work

Alternative fuels vehicles are cars, vans, trucks, and buses that run on fuels other than gasoline or diesel. At present, the two types of alternative fuels vehicles in greatest use are those that run on compressed natural gas (CNG; natural gas under high pressure) and those that run on liquefied petroleum gas (LPG; hydrocarbon gases under low pressure; propane).

Federal law mandates that a growing percentage of public vehicle fleets—such as buses maintained by local governments—consist of alternative fuels vehicles, primarily because they are less polluting than traditional gas-powered vehicles. Many states also have enacted laws requiring the use of alternative fuels vehicles. There is a growing need for skilled technicians to convert standard vehicles to either CNG or LPG vehicles and to maintain and repair alternative fuels vehicles.

Alternative fuels vehicle technicians are employed by local and state agencies, independent automotive repair shops, car and truck dealers, public and private fleets, and service stations. They need a basic understanding of standard automotive and truck mechanics. In addition, they must be able to diagnose and repair problems specific to CNG and LPG vehicles. They should also be able to convert existing vehicles to either CNG or LPG using standard conversion kits. Like standard automotive, truck, and bus mechanics, alternative fuels vehicle technicians use computers to diagnose engine problems. They also use a wide variety of tools to repair and maintain vehicles.

A good technician combines solid mechanical skills with a flair for diagnosing and solving problems. Alternative fuels vehicle technicians need good communication skills for speaking with coworkers and customers. They must also be able to read and understand technical information.

## Education and Training Requirements

Alternative fuels vehicle technicians need a high school education and training in automotive mechanics, plus additional specialized training in CNG and/or LPG technology. Recommended school classes include mathematics and physics, with course work covering friction, hydraulics, pneumatics, and electronics.

Students interested in CNG and LPG training can look for programs certified by the National Institute for Automotive Service Excellence (ASE) and supervised by the National Automotive Technicians Education Foundation (NATEF). To become certified by the ASE, students must complete an accredited course and pass a written examination. To maintain certification, technicians must take a test every five years.

## Getting the Job

ASE certification is highly recommended for workers interested in employment as alternative fuels vehicle technicians. Schools offering ASE-approved courses usually provide job placement services for students. Positions are also advertised in local newspapers. To find out about opportunities for alternative fuels vehicle technicians, inquire at local car dealers, service stations, and government offices in your area.

## Advancement Possibilities and Employment Outlook

Currently there are approximately 370,000 ASE-certified alternative fuels vehicle technicians working throughout the automotive industry. As more alternative fuels vehicles come into use, either through government mandate or market decisions, the number of technicians needed to convert and maintain those vehicles is expected to grow. Job opportunities for automotive mechanics in general are expected to be very good for individuals who complete automotive training programs, because employers report difficulty in finding workers with the right skills.

Experienced alternative fuels vehicle technicians may move into supervisory positions as fleet managers, chief mechanics, and shop managers or owners. Technicians may also find teaching opportunities.

## Working Conditions

Alternative fuels vehicle technicians usually work in modern garages equipped with good ventilation, lights, and adequate climate control. Technicians who maintain fleets may also work outdoors making roadside repairs. Like all automotive technicians, alternative fuels vehicle technicians often work in uncomfortable positions. The job may involve lifting heavy objects and handling greasy parts. Modern garages are, however, usually safe working places.

Technicians generally work a standard forty- to forty-eight-hour workweek. Some technicians, especially those maintaining public fleets, may work night shifts to keep the vehicles on the road.

## Earnings and Benefits

Alternative fuels vehicle technicians can expect earnings and benefits comparable to other automobile and truck mechanics. According to the Bureau of Labor Statistics, the median annual income for automotive mechanics working for either the government or car dealerships was approximately $38,000 in 2004.

### Where to Go for More Information

National Energy Services Association
6430 FM 1960 West, No. 213
Houston, TX 77069
(713) 856-6525
http://www.nesanet.org

Natural Gas Vehicle Coalition
1100 Wilson Blvd., No. 850
Arlington, VA 22209-2297
(703) 527-3022
http://www.ngvc.org

National Automotive Technicians Education Foundation
101 Blue Seal Dr., Ste. 101
Leesburg, VA 20175
(703) 669-6650
http://www.natef.org

# Cable Television and Telecommunications Technician

## Definition and Nature of the Work

Cable television and telecommunications technicians install, maintain, and upgrade cable systems. They also perform repair work and respond to service problems at the homes of cable users. Their main goal is to keep a cable system operating efficiently.

Cable technicians generally start out as cable system installers. Installers prepare a subscriber's home for cable reception by connecting the cable system to one or more television sets or to one or more computers for high-speed Internet service. Installers explain to subscribers how to operate the cable system and how they can upgrade or downgrade their services. If a customer no longer wants the cable system, installers remove it. Installers may also be responsible for servicing feeder lines, which connect the main cable to small groups of homes, and droplines, which are the direct cable lines to a subscriber's home. In general, installers perform light troubleshooting work when customers have minor problems with their cable units.

Trunk technicians must have more advanced technical skills than installers. Trunk technicians continuously maintain the main line, or trunk line, of the cable system. This work is very important because the trunk line is the main artery of a cable system and a malfunction could shut down service in a large area. Trunk technicians are responsible for correcting any technical failure in the trunk line, the feeder amplifier, or the booster.

Service technicians respond to problems reported by a subscriber. These technicians generally repair amplifiers, cable poles, or lines. They may also correct electrical malfunctions occurring in the cable system. They practice preventive maintenance by electronically scanning the cable system periodically. By catching minor problems early, they can prevent major disruptions in cable service later.

Not all cable television and telecommunications technicians work in the field. Bench technicians, who are highly specialized electronics technicians, operate the cable system's repair facility. They examine broken and malfunctioning cable equipment, repair it, record the repairs, and return the equipment to the field.

Chief cable technicians are the most highly skilled of the cable technician staff. They supervise the work of other technicians. They are ultimately responsible for ensuring high-quality signal delivery to customers. Chief cable technicians also set employee performance standards, conduct interviews, and handle personnel matters. They do not work out in the field unless serious or complex problems arise.

## Education and Training Requirements

Cable television and telecommunications technicians need at least a high school education, an aptitude for math, and an interest in installing or repairing electronic equipment.

**Education and Training**
High school plus training

**Salary**
Median—$17.36 per hour

**Employment Outlook**
Poor

A cable television technician needs to have training in many areas. *(© Martha Tabor/Working Images Photographs. Reproduced by permission.)*

Most cable television and telecommunications technicians begin their careers as installers. Training is available for high school graduates at trade schools or from a cable company's on-the-job training program. Some trade schools offer a five- to seven-week course in electronics repair and maintenance. Trunk, service, and bench technicians have specialized telecommunications training; junior colleges and technical institutes offer programs that usually last one to two years. Chief cable television and telecommunications technicians need at least two years of electronics training and a considerable amount of experience in the field.

The number of vocational schools that train cable television and telecommunications technicians is limited. The cable industry provides on-the-job training, as well as special training schools for technicians. Some community agencies and educational institutions also offer technical training programs for cable technicians.

## Getting the Job

Schools that offer courses in cable maintenance often have placement offices that can help candidates find jobs. The majority of employment opportunities come from areas that already have cable service or are about to get it. The National Cable and Telecommunications Association (NCTA) provides lists of these areas. State and local government officials can help prospective cable technicians determine what opportunities exist locally.

*The Television and Cable Factbook,* published by Warren Communications, lists all the cable systems in the United States and Canada. Copies of the print edition can be found at most large libraries. Also available online, *The Factbook* is considered the industry's leading source of up-to-date information.

## Advancement Possibilities and Employment Outlook

Cable television technicians generally advance by gaining experience in cable maintenance and servicing. Installers, trunk technicians, service technicians, and bench technicians can advance to become chief cable technicians with increased on-the-job experience or electronics training. Some technicians may elect to continue their college training and become professional engineers. Those who have the necessary teaching skills may train new cable television and telecommunications technicians.

The employment outlook for cable technicians is slower than the average through the year 2014. Most areas of the country that can be served by cable systems have already been wired, and fewer installations will be needed in the coming years. However, technicians will still be needed to service existing cable lines and to replace old wiring with fiber optic cable. Steady customer demand for high-speed Internet connections may increase the demand for cable technicians; however, the increasing use of wireless Internet systems, along with the option of satellite television, will most likely counteract any job growth in the cable television and telecommunications field. Jobs will become available as workers retire or leave their jobs for other reasons.

## Working Conditions

Installers, service technicians, and trunk technicians spend most of their time outside installing or maintaining cable lines, while bench technicians perform their tasks inside the cable system's repair facility. Chief technicians normally do not go into the field unless a problem arises.

All technicians in this field should enjoy working with the public because it is a consumer-oriented industry. Cable television technicians generally work five days per week, but they may have to work some overtime.

### Earnings and Benefits

The earnings of cable technicians depend on the worker's experience, education, and place of employment. According to the U.S. Bureau of Labor Statistics, the median salary of a cable television and telecommunications technician is $17.36 per hour. Chief cable technicians earn more. Benefits include paid holidays and vacations, health insurance, and retirement plans. Cable technicians also receive extra pay for overtime.

**Where to Go for More Information**

Communications Workers of America
501 Third St. NW
Washington, DC 20001-2797
(202) 434-1100
http://www.cwa-union.org

National Cable and Telecommunications Association
1724 Massachusetts Ave. NW
Washington, DC 20036
(202) 775-3550
http://www.ncta.com

## Chemical Technician

**Education and Training**
High school plus two years of training

**Salary**
Median—$18.35 per hour

**Employment Outlook**
Fair

### Definition and Nature of the Work

Chemical technicians assist chemists and chemical engineers who develop, produce, and use chemical products, equipment, and related items. Most chemical technicians work for private companies, especially those that make chemicals, drugs, rubber, and steel. Chemical technicians also work for government agencies, universities, and hospitals. Because the chemical industry is so broad, technicians often specialize in one particular area, such as food processing or the production of drugs.

Most chemical technicians work in research and development. They work in experimental laboratories and are usually supervised by chemists. Many research and development chemical technicians conduct a variety of routine to complex laboratory procedures. For example, they may collect and analyze samples of air and water to monitor pollutants in them. They may also produce compounds using complex chemical processes.

Other chemical technicians are process control technicians. These chemical technicians work in manufacturing or other industrial plants, developing new products or new methods. They also look for ways to improve existing products or methods. Chemical technicians assist chemists by setting up and performing tests on these products and methods. Then they record the results. They measure batches according to formulas and set machine controls for temperature and flow. Depending on their employer, technicians may test products ranging from oil additives to breakfast cereals. They may do tests to find out what elements are present in a sample of steel, for instance. Or they may test how well a new kind of soap cleans in samples of water that range from very soft to very hard.

Chemical technicians help engineers make final product designs, install equipment, and train workers on the production line. Sometimes technicians act as supervisors on a production line. Or they may work in quality control, where they test raw materials, methods, and finished products to make sure that they meet the standards set for them. Other chemical technicians work in technical sales or as customer service representatives. Some are technical writers.

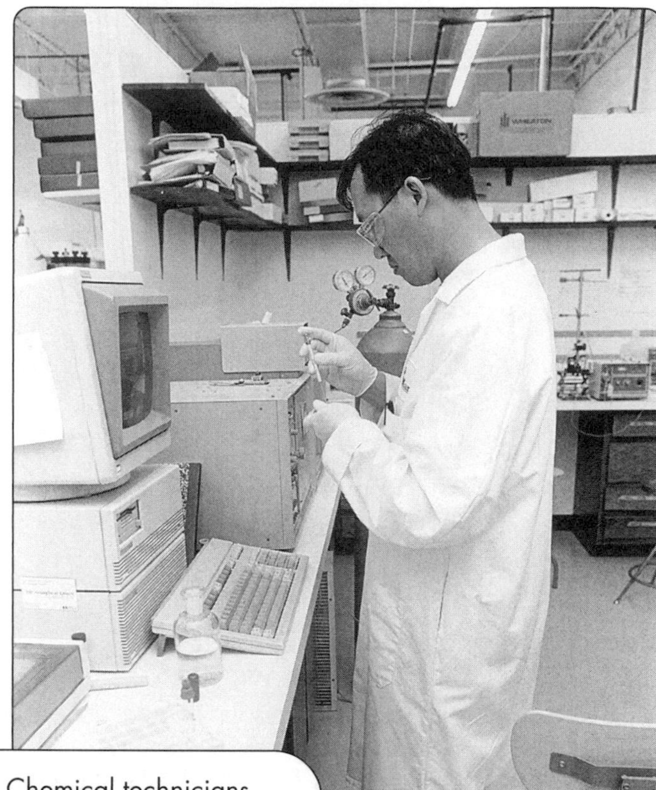

Chemical technicians may test products ranging from oil additives to breakfast cereals, depending on the company for which they work. *(© Martha Tabor/Working Images Photographs. Reproduced by permission.)*

Chemical technicians use a wide variety of equipment in their work. Sometimes they use the traditional laboratory equipment, such as test tubes, beakers, and Bunsen burners. In production they may deal with pipelines, tanks, valves, and pumps that handle large amounts of materials. They also use computers and other complex electronic equipment. They are often responsible for keeping this equipment in good working condition.

## Education and Training Requirements

Some companies give on-the-job training courses to high school graduates who have a good background in science and mathematics. Upon completion of these courses, employees may receive an associate of arts degree. They begin as trainees or assistants and advance to technician's jobs as they gain experience. Other companies prefer to hire chemical technicians who have attended a college or technical institute for two or more years. Courses in mathematics, chemistry, computer skills, and chemical engineering are useful. Some schools have two-year programs in chemical technology or process technology. Other schools offer related programs such as science technology, laboratory technology, or chemical engineering technology. Many companies pay part or all of the tuition for courses that technicians take to improve their job skills.

## Getting the Job

If you attend a college or technical institute offering courses in chemistry, your instructors and school placement office may be good sources for job leads. The state employment service or union office may be able to help you find a job with a company that will apprentice you to be a technician. Local chapters of the American Chemical Society may also keep job listings. You can apply directly to places that hire chemical technicians. These companies often list job openings in newspaper classifieds or job banks on the Internet.

## Advancement Possibilities and Employment Outlook

Technicians who show that they can accept responsibility and work without supervision are often given promotions. They can become supervisors of other workers. Technicians who take additional courses increase their chances for advancement. Some get bachelor's, master's, or doctoral degrees and become chemists or chemical engineers.

Job growth for chemical technicians is projected to be slower than average through 2014 as overall employment in the chemical industry is expected to slow. Job opportunities for chemical technicians will be best in the pharmaceutical industry.

## Working Conditions

Most chemical technicians work in clean, well-lighted, and well-ventilated laboratories. Workers are protected from dangerous fumes and chemicals. Sometimes they must spend hours on their feet or seated in front of a laboratory bench. Many laboratories are operational seven days a week, twenty-four hours a day. The beginning technician is usually assigned shift work. Experienced technicians work day shifts but may come in at odd hours to complete an experiment, inspect equipment, or solve a production problem. Sometimes they may be assigned night or weekend shifts, especially if they are working on a production line. Some technicians belong to unions.

Chemical technicians usually work in small teams with other technicians, chemists, or engineers. They must be able to work well with these people as well as with the production workers that they may be supervising. They must be able to follow directions exactly and need to pay close attention to safety. Their work requires a great deal of patience.

## Earnings and Benefits

Earnings vary depending on education, experience, location, and kind of job. Chemical technicians earn salaries that are about equal to those earned by other kinds of science and engineering technicians. In 2004 chemical technicians earned a median hourly income of $18.35. Benefits generally include paid holidays and vacations, health insurance, and pension plans.

**Where to Go for More Information**

American Chemical Society
1155 Sixteenth St. NW
Washington, DC 20036
(800) 227-5558
http://www.acs.org

American Chemistry Council
1300 Wilson Blvd.
Arlington, VA 22209-2307
(703) 741-5000
http://www.americanchemistry.com

# *Electrical and Electronics Engineering Technician*

**Education and Training**
High school plus two years of training

**Salary**
Median—$46,310 per year

**Employment Outlook**
Good

## Definition and Nature of the Work

Electrical and electronic engineering technicians help design, develop, test, manufacture, and repair electrical and electronic equipment. Electrical components of equipment provide power. Electronic components control the equipment, although many types of equipment still are controlled with electrical devices.

Electrical and electronic engineering technicians generally work under the supervision of electrical engineers. Technicians perform a wide variety of different tasks depending on the needs of their employer. Some electrical and electronic engineering technicians work for power companies that generate and transmit electricity, or they work for companies that use electricity to power machinery and lights. Others are employed by manufacturers of electrical equipment or telephone and telegraph companies. Still others have jobs with private firms that design and build factories, houses, and other buildings. A few technicians work as safety inspectors. Electrical and electronic engineering technicians work in all areas of the country. Most work for private companies. However, some work for public institutions that use electricity or for government agencies that regulate the electrical industry.

Many electrical and electronic engineering technicians work where electricity is generated. They are often employed by public utility companies, but some work for companies and institutions that generate their own electricity. These employers may include large industries, military bases, and institutions such as hospitals and colleges. Electrical and electronic engineering technicians are often directly involved in the generation of electricity. They may monitor switch-

Much of the work of electronics engineering technicians involves troubleshooting. They test circuits and parts to find out why a piece of equipment is not working properly. *(© Chuck Savage/ Corbis.)*

boards to make sure that the plant is operating efficiently. Sometimes they test and inspect generators, transformers, and other equipment. They may supervise crews of electrical workers who do routine work in the generating station. They often use their knowledge of electrical engineering technology to diagnose electrical problems. They may make repairs themselves or direct other electrical workers to do them.

Some electrical and electronic engineering technicians work for industrial plants that use electricity. They often study a plant's needs. They consult with engineers and offer advice on lighting and other uses of electrical power in the plant. They may plan, direct, and record tests done on electrical equipment, or recommend changes in equipment that is not operating efficiently. Sometimes they help companies solve production problems. For example, they may suggest a backup source of energy in case the circuits become overloaded at a particular point in the production process.

Electrical and electronic engineering technicians often work with electrical engineers in the design of new electrical equipment, ranging from small household appliances to huge power generating plants. They perform a variety of tasks to assist the engineers, such as assembling and testing experimental electrical parts or making changes in parts according to an engineer's instructions. They may also prepare wiring diagrams, layout drawings, or engineering specifications for new equipment. Once a design for new equipment has been perfected, electrical and electronic engineering technicians may direct the crew of workers who produce or install it.

Electrical and electronic engineering technicians work with such hand tools as wrenches, screwdrivers, wire cutters, pliers, and soldering irons. They also use precise instruments such as voltmeters, which measure electricity. In addition, they must be able to read and understand blueprints, as well as engineering handbooks.

## Education and Training Requirements

You can get training in electrical technology at a technical institute, community college, and extension divisions of colleges. Most programs take about two years to complete. The armed services also run schools designed to prepare enlisted personnel for technical work in this field. A number of companies offer on-the-job training. Sometimes these company-sponsored training programs include some formal schooling at a college or technical institute. Training programs vary considerably in quality, so you should check out a prospective program thoroughly.

## Getting the Job

Private companies looking for trained electrical and electronic engineering technicians often send lists of their job openings to placement offices at schools that offer courses in electrical technology. You can also apply directly to utility companies and other companies that hire technicians. Your state employment service may be able to help you find a job with a private company that will give you on-the-job training. State employment services are also good sources of information about jobs with government agencies. Sometimes positions for electrical and electronic engineering technicians are listed in newspaper classifieds or job banks on the Internet.

## Advancement Possibilities and Employment Outlook

Electrical and electronic engineering technicians often specialize and become highly skilled in one area of electrical technology. Technicians can become supervisors and managers of crews of electrical workers. Experienced technicians can also advance to positions as technical writers, sales representatives, and instructors in technical schools. Many technicians continue their education and become engineers.

Employment for skilled electrical and electronic engineering technicians is expected to grow at an average rate through 2014. This is due to the increasing demand for more sophisticated electrical systems. However, employment may be influenced by varying economic conditions. Those with practical work experience and knowledge of new technology will have the best opportunities.

## Working Conditions

Even though electric current can be dangerous, the safety record of the electrical industry is good. In general, working areas are in laboratories, offices, manufacturing or industrial plants, or on construction sites. Electrical and electronic engineering technicians working in generating plants or on production lines may be exposed to high noise levels. Most engineering technicians work at least forty hours a week. Some may be exposed to hazards from equipment, chemicals, or toxic materials.

Electrical and electronic engineering technicians must be able to work well as part of a team. They often come into direct contact with engineers, other electrical workers, and users of electricity. They need to be able to get along with all of these people. They should also be able to work by themselves at times. Their work requires them to pay close attention to details. They should also work well with their hands and have an aptitude for science and mathematics.

## Earnings and Benefits

Earnings vary depending on education, experience, location, and kind of job. Median annual earnings of electrical and electronic engineering technicians were $46,310 in 2004. Benefits generally include paid holidays and vacations, health insurance, and pension plans.

### Where to Go for More Information

Accreditation Board for Engineering and Technology
111 Market Place, Ste. 1050
Baltimore, MD 21202-4012
(410) 347-7700
http://www.abet.org

National Institute for Certification in Engineering Technologies
1420 King St.
Alexandria, VA 22314-2794
(888) IS-NICET
http://www.nicet.org

# Electrical and Electronics Installer and Repairer

**Education and Training**
High school plus training

**Salary**
$15.54 to $25.86 per hour

**Employment Outlook**
Fair to good

## Definition and Nature of the Work

Electrical and electronics installers and repairers are sometimes called electronics technicians. As their name suggests, these workers install and repair electrical and electronic equipment. The electrical components of equipment provide power. The electronic components control the equipment, although many types of equipment still are controlled with electrical devices.

Most electrical and electronics installers and repairers work for private companies. They work in all sections of the country in many different industries. They may work in research and development laboratories, repair shops, or plants that make electronic equipment. Many work as customer service technicians. They may install, repair, and service equipment in people's homes or in the hospitals, offices, and other places where it is used. Some electronics technicians work as teachers or aides who answer questions raised by students or customers. Others are mechanical writers who prepare instruction and repair manuals.

Electrical and electronics installers and repairers understand the basic laws of electricity and electrical circuits, as well as the principles of electronics technology. Since the electronics field is so broad and changes so fast, many technicians specialize in one area.

Some electrical and electronics installers and repairers work in the production of electronic equipment. Part of their job often includes testing equipment, making sure that it meets the proper specifications. This is known as quality control. Technicians sometimes assemble some of the more complex electronic parts.

Many electrical and electronics installers and repairers work at troubleshooting. They test circuits and parts to find out why a piece of equipment is not working properly and then fix the problem.

## Education and Training Requirements

You can get training in electronics technology at many colleges and technical institutes, in schools run by the armed services, and from home-study courses. It takes about two years to complete many of these programs. Students can usually specialize in one field, such as communications or medical equipment. You can also become an electrical and electronics installer and repairer through on-the-job training offered by many companies. These companies usually prefer to train people who have taken science and mathematics courses in high school or college or who have work experience in the electronics industry. There are also some formal apprenticeship programs. These programs take from two to four years to complete and combine on-the-job training with classroom instruction. Some electrical and electronics installers and repairers who work with radio transmitting equipment must be licensed by the Federal Communications Commission (FCC).

## Getting the Job

If you attend a two-year program at a college or technical institute, your school placement office may be able to help you find a job. State employment services may also help graduates find work as electrical and electronics installers and repairers. If you are not a graduate of a special school, state agencies can sometimes help you to get a position that offers on-the-job training. You can also apply directly to companies that hire electrical and electronics installers and repairers. Jobs are often listed in newspaper classifieds and job banks on the Internet.

## Advancement Possibilities and Employment Outlook

Experienced electrical and electronics installers and repairers can advance in many ways. They can become managers or supervisors at repair shops or open their own shops. They can also become quality control managers for firms that make electronic equipment or may become advanced specialists in their field. Some technicians who obtain additional education become engineers. Other experienced technicians become sales representatives or technical writers. There are also opportunities for advancement in the teaching of electronics.

Overall employment of electrical and electronics installers and repairers is expected to grow more slowly than average for all occupations through 2014. However, average employment growth is projected for electrical and electronics installers and repairers of commercial and industrial equipment, and of motor vehicle electronic equipment. Opportunities will be best for those applicants who have had postsecondary school training that includes practical work experience.

## Working Conditions

Working conditions for electrical and electronics installers and repairers vary. They usually work thirty-five to forty hours a week, but they may have to work night shifts, overtime, or weekends. Many electrical and electronics installers and repairers work on factory floors, where there is noise, dirt, vibration, and heat. Others service equipment in offices or stores, or travel to customers' locations. In some cases technicians are members of unions.

Electrical and electronics installers and repairers should have an aptitude for science and mathematics. They need to have mechanical ability and must work well with their hands. They should be able to communicate their ideas and get along well with other workers, as well as with customers. They must be willing to study to keep up with new developments in their field. They should also enjoy doing detailed work.

## Earnings and Benefits

Earnings vary depending on education, experience, location, and kind of job. In 2004 the median hourly wage of electrical and electronics repairers for commercial and industrial equipment was $20.48; of electric motor and power tool technicians was $15.54; of powerhouse, substation, and relay technicians was $25.86; of motor vehicle technicians was $12.79; and of transportation equipment technicians was $19.25. Benefits generally include paid holidays and vacations, health insurance, and retirement plans. Electronics technicians who must travel in their work often receive an expense allowance.

### Where to Go for More Information

Association of Communications & Electronics Schools International
5241 Princess Anne Rd., Ste. 110
Virginia Beach, VA 23462
(800) 798-2237
http://www.acesinternational.org

Electronics Technicians Association International
5 Depot St.
Greencastle, IN 46135
(800) 288-3824
http://www.eta-sda.org

International Society of Certified Electronics Technicians
3608 Pershing Ave.
Fort Worth, TX 76107-4527
(800) 946-0201
http://www.iscet.org

# Electromechanical Engineering Technician

**Education and Training**
High school plus two years of training

**Salary**
Median—$41,440 per year

**Employment Outlook**
Good

## Definition and Nature of the Work

Electromechanical engineering technicians work with equipment that uses electric power to operate mechanical controls. Technicians who work on this equipment understand the basic laws of electricity and electronics as well as mechanics. They design, develop, test, and manufacture electrical and computer-controlled mechanical systems. Their work often overlaps the work of electrical and electronics engineering technicians, and mechanical engineering technicians.

Most electromechanical engineering technicians work in the computer and office machines industries. Electromechanical equipment in these industries includes photocopy and facsimile machines as well as computers and related hardware. Electromechanical engineering technicians working in the computer and office machines industries work on the design and manufacture of new equipment. They also work as customer engineers who service computers and office machines.

Electromechanical engineering technicians work in a wide variety of other industries that use electromechanical equipment, such as automatic pilot systems, elevator controls, vending machines, and guided missile systems. Electromechanical equipment is used to take photographs of distant stars and regulate cancer treatments. It is also used in many manufacturing processes. Often the electromechanical equipment measures the size, shape, color, weight, or temperature of a product. It is generally linked to systems that adjust the manufacturing process automatically. For example, electromechanical devices used in the manufacture of paper control the texture of the fibers as well as the thickness of the final product. Electromechanical controls are also used in steel rolling mills and factories that make ball bearings, plastics, and many other kinds of goods.

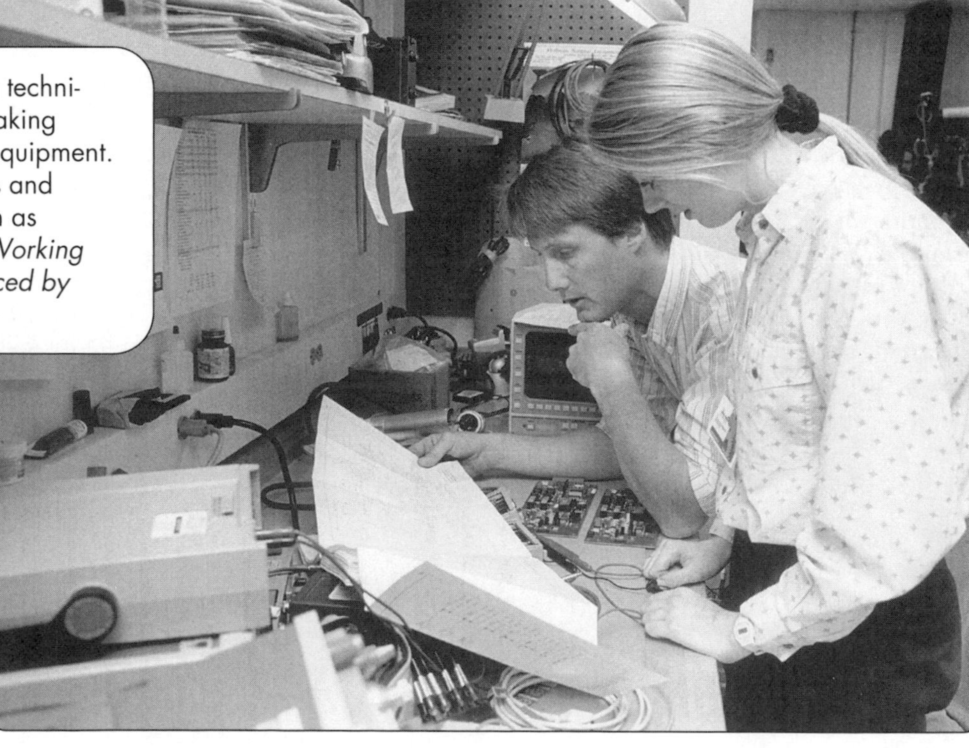

Electromechanical engineering technicians consult manuals when making repairs on electromechanical equipment. They also work with hand tools and precise testing equipment, such as voltmeters. *(© Martha Tabor/Working Images Photographs. Reproduced by permission.)*

Still other technicians work in factories in which electromechanical equipment is made. Many electromechanical engineering technicians work with the mechanical and electrical engineers who design and develop new equipment. They help the engineers by performing tests, recording information, preparing written reports, and taking care of other details. Technicians may also be directly involved in the production of new electromechanical equipment.

## Education and Training Requirements

Many colleges and technical institutes offer training that can lead to a career as an electromechanical engineering technician. Some of these schools have specific training programs in electromechanical technology. Others offer programs in related areas, such as electronics or electrical or mechanical engineering technology. Most companies prefer to hire technicians who are graduates of one of these programs, which usually take two years to complete and provide the graduate with an associate degree. A few employers will hire people with less education, provided they have a good background in science and mathematics. Because the field of electromechanical technology is changing so rapidly, technicians should keep up with new trends throughout their careers.

## Getting the Job

Your technical school or college may be able to help you find a job as an electromechanical engineering technician. You can also apply directly to companies that hire electromechanical engineering technicians. Your state employment service may be able to help you with job information. Jobs are often listed in newspaper classifieds or job banks on the Internet.

## Advancement Possibilities and Employment Outlook

Electromechanical engineering technicians can advance by specializing. They can also become supervisors or managers of a group of technicians or other workers. Some technicians advance by becoming technical writers, sales representatives, or instructors. Those who continue their educations can become engineers.

Overall employment of engineering technicians is expected to increase about as fast as the average for all occupations through 2014. Trained technicians should be in demand. Most job openings will occur from the need to replace workers who retire or leave the field.

## Working Conditions

Working conditions may vary according to the type of job. Electromechanical engineering technicians usually work with engineers in small teams. They may work in modern shops or laboratories, and they usually work regular forty-hour weeks.

In some kinds of jobs electromechanical engineering technicians need to work well under pressure. Most jobs require them to get along well with other people—either customers or their coworkers. Electromechanical engineering technicians need to be careful and accurate workers who can follow detailed instructions. They should be good at science and mathematics and must work well with their hands.

### Where to Go for More Information

American Society for Engineering Education
1818 N St. NW, Ste. 600
Washington, DC 20036
(202) 331-3500
http://www.asee.org

Accreditation Board for Engineering and Technology
111 Market Place, Ste. 1050
Baltimore, MD 21202-4012
(410) 347-7700
http://www.abet.org

National Institute for Certification in Engineering Technologies
1420 King St.
Alexandria, VA 22314-2794
(888) IS-NICET
http://www.nicet.org

## Earnings and Benefits

Salaries vary depending on the education and experience of the technician and the type and location of the job. In 2004 the median annual wage for electromechanical engineering technicians was $41,440. Benefits generally include paid holidays and vacations, health insurance, and retirement plans.

# *Electronic Home Entertainment Equipment Installer and Repairer*

**Education and Training**
High school

**Salary**
Median—$13.44 per hour

**Employment Outlook**
Poor

## Definition and Nature of the Work

Electronic home entertainment equipment installers and repairers set up and service televisions and radios, VCR and DVD equipment, video cameras, and stereo components such as CD players. Some technicians also install home theaters, satellite television dishes, home security systems, and intercoms.

Most of their work involves fixing electronic entertainment equipment that malfunctions because of defective parts, faulty circuits, or poor connections. Technicians use test instruments to find the problem. These instruments include voltmeters, signal generators, frequency counters, and oscilloscopes. Electronic home entertainment equipment installers and repairers also use hand tools in their work. These include screwdrivers, pliers, wire cutters, soldering irons, and wrenches. Another aid is the repair manual, which shows how the wiring of a given machine is laid out. These diagrams help technicians determine which circuits need repairing and how to make the right electrical connections.

Electronic home entertainment equipment installers and repairers may work for the firms that manufacture the equipment or the stores that sell them. Some own their own shops. These workers often make house calls, fixing the faulty equipment on the spot with tools and parts they store in their trucks or vans. More difficult jobs are usually done in the shop, where the technicians use their test equipment.

## Education and Training Requirements

Students interested in a career as an electronic home entertainment equipment installer or repairer should have training in electronics. High schools, vocational schools, and junior colleges offer courses in electronics repair. These training programs last from one to two years and usually include math, physics, schematic reading, and actual repair work.

Some technicians learn the trade in three-year or four-year apprenticeships. The people who sell or repair equipment may offer on-the-job training.

In addition to the initial training, technicians must attend seminars, study manuals, and read technical journals so that they are able to repair new types of equipment—such as digital consumer electronics—that hit the market. Techni-

A home entertainment equipment repairer works in a shop, repairing television sets, radios, and VCRs. He uses electronic equipment to diagnose problems. *(© Martha Tabor/ Working Images Photographs. Reproduced by permission.)*

cians must have excellent eyesight and color vision, normal hearing, and good hand-eye coordination.

## Getting the Job

Interested individuals should apply directly to the service centers of companies that make and sell the equipment and inquire about on-the-job training. Classified ads in local newspapers, Internet job sites, and state employment offices also feature job listings.

Trade and technical schools often help their graduates find jobs. Because 98 percent of all homes in the United States have television sets, most areas of the country have repair shops that hire technicians.

## Advancement Possibilities and Employment Outlook

Electronic home entertainment equipment installers and repairers who work for large companies can advance to supervisor or service manager, depending on schooling and work experience. Workers who open their own shops need at least two or three years' experience, a considerable amount of start-up money, a background in running a business, and good customer relations skills.

The need for electronic home entertainment equipment installers and repairers will grow more slowly than the average through 2014. Due to the declining costs of electronic products, it is often cheaper to replace televisions, VCRs, and stereo equipment than to pay for repairs. Technicians who can install and repair expensive digital equipment are most likely to find jobs, since consumers feel that costly, high-end items such as high-definition digital televisions and digital camcorders are worth repairing.

According to the U.S. Bureau of Labor Statistics (BLS), there were about 47,000 electronic home entertainment equipment installers and repairers working in the United States in 2004. Most work in electronics repair shops and service centers or in stores that sell and service electronic products.

## Where to Go for More Information

Association of Communications and Electronics Schools International, Inc.
5241 Princess Anne Rd., Ste. 110
Virginia Beach, VA 23462
(800) 798-2237
http://www.acesinternational.org

Electronics Technicians Association International
5 Depot St.
Greencastle, IN 46135
(765) 653-8262
(800) 288-3824
http://www.eta-i.org

International Society of Certified Electronics Technicians
3608 Pershing Ave.
Fort Worth, TX 76107-4527
(817) 921-9101
(800) 946-0201
http://www.iscet.org

National Electronics Service Dealers Association
3608 Pershing Ave.
Fort Worth, TX 76107-4527
(817) 921-9061
http://www.nesda.com

## Working Conditions

Service technicians generally work in pleasant places—shops, offices, and homes. Working for a large company or repair shop means job security and a regular forty-hour week. Electronic home entertainment equipment installers and repairers who own their own businesses typically put in longer hours, including nights and Saturdays.

Because technicians often travel to make repairs, they sometimes lift and carry heavy equipment. In addition, their work involves some danger from electric shock or falls from roofs.

## Earnings and Benefits

Salaries depend on schooling, experience, and whether a worker belongs to a union. According to the BLS, in 2004 the median wage for electronic home entertainment equipment installers and repairers was $13.44 per hour.

Benefits depend on the employer. Some provide paid vacations and holidays. Others pay or help pay for health and life insurance programs. Union members receive full benefits, including medical and health insurance, paid vacations, and retirement plans.

# *Hydraulic and Pneumatic Technician*

**Education and Training**
High school plus two years of training

**Salary**
$20,000 to $50,000 per year

**Employment Outlook**
Good

## Definition and Nature of the Work

Hydraulic and pneumatic technicians are sometimes called fluid power technicians, because they maintain and repair equipment and machines that use pressurized fluids to carry power from one place to another. Hydraulic and pneumatic systems are two types of fluid power systems. Hydraulic systems use "wet" fluids, such as oil and water. Pneumatic systems use "dry" fluids, such as pressurized air or other gases.

About three-fourths of the factories in this country use hydraulic or pneumatic power systems. These fluid power systems run over half the machines and equipment used in industry. They are also important in transportation vehicles, for example, in automatic transmissions, power brakes, and power steering. In addition, fluid power is used for tasks as varied as opening supermarket doors and raising and lowering the flaps on airplane wings.

Hydraulic and pneumatic technicians work in factories, laboratories, and offices all across the country. Most are employed by private industry. A few work in independent research centers. Those working in private industry are often on the maintenance or research and development staffs of companies that use fluid power in manufacturing. Technicians might help engineers to design, test, and install a fluid power system for a one-of-a-kind machine that is used to bolt fenders on automobiles. Others in private industry may work on fluid power equipment used in such products as trucks, airplanes, and automatic doors.

Hydraulic and pneumatic technicians also work as service representatives for companies that make hydraulic or pneumatic equipment. These technicians often travel from plant to plant. They might, for example, service machines that use air pressure to drive nails and turn screws. Sometimes these technicians help to sell their company's equipment. Other technicians work in shops. They might repair hydraulic cylinders used in farm equipment or bulldozers.

Most hydraulic and pneumatic technicians use hand tools, electronic calculators, and measuring devices. They sometimes carry or lift bulky equipment. They often read and interpret instruments, computer data, technical manuals, and blueprints. Hydraulic and pneumatic technicians may also do some technical writing or drafting. In some cases they specialize in one field.

## Education and Training Requirements

Many hydraulic and pneumatic technicians learn their skills through on-the-job training. However, many companies prefer to hire beginners who have some postsecondary formal training in industrial technology, mechanics, or a related field in which fluid power is part of the curriculum. Relatively few schools offer programs specifically in fluid power. Such training programs usually take about two years to complete. The armed services also train some enlisted personnel in fluid power. This training usually deals with the use of fluid power in aircraft or armored vehicles. Certification is available through the Fluid Power Society (FPS).

## Getting the Job

Many hydraulic and pneumatic technicians get their first jobs through the placement offices at their schools. Your state employment service may be able to help you find a position as a fluid power technician. You can also apply directly to companies that use fluid power in manufacturing or materials handling or that make or distribute fluid power equipment. Sometimes jobs for technicians are listed in the classified section of the newspaper or in job banks on the Internet.

## Advancement Possibilities and Employment Outlook

Experienced hydraulic and pneumatic technicians can become supervisors of maintenance crews in plants that use hydraulic or pneumatic equipment. Technicians can also advance to careers in sales, management, technical writing, or teaching. With the continued reliance on fluid power systems in American industry, the employment outlook for skilled technicians in this field is expected to remain favorable.

## Working Conditions

Working conditions for hydraulic and pneumatic technicians vary with their employers and their jobs. Many technicians install, test, or repair equipment in factories. Although their basic workweek is thirty-five to forty hours long, these technicians may be required to work some night or weekend shifts and some overtime. At times they may have to do heavy lifting. There is some danger of electric shocks, burns, and cuts. Factory technicians usually work alone or in pairs. Those that work in laboratories or shops are often parts of teams that include technicians, skilled workers, and engineers. They usually work regular hours. Sometimes they must travel to inspect equipment in the field. In many cases technicians must deal with a wide variety of customers, as well as with their coworkers. Some technicians belong to unions.

Hydraulic and pneumatic technicians should have mechanical ability. They should enjoy learning how machines and other equipment work. Technicians must also be good at mathematics and science. In addition, they often need to communicate their ideas to others in oral or written form or through drawings and graphs. They must study to keep up with changes in the industry.

## Earnings and Benefits

Earnings depend on education, experience, location, and kind of job. In 2005 beginning hydraulic and pneumatic technicians usually earned from $20,000 to $30,000 per year. Experienced hydraulic and pneumatic technicians earned from $30,000 to $50,000 per year. Benefits usually include paid holidays and vacations, health insurance, and retirement plans.

### Where to Go for More Information

Fluid Power Educational Foundation
3333 N. Mayfair Rd., Ste. 211
Milwaukee, WI 53222
(414) 778-3364
http://www.fpef.org

Fluid Power Society
1930 E. Marlton Pike A-2
P.O. Box 1420
Cherry Hill, NJ 08034
(800) 303-8520
http://www.ifps.org

National Fluid Power Association
3333 N. Mayfair Rd., Ste. 211
Milwaukee, WI 53222-3219
(414) 778-3344
http://www.nfpa.com

# *Mechanical Engineering Technician*

**Education and Training**
High school plus two years of training

**Salary**
Median—$43,400 per year

**Employment Outlook**
Good

## Definition and Nature of the Work

Mechanical engineering technicians assist mechanical engineers and sometimes scientists in all phases of the design, development, production, testing, operation, and maintenance of mechanical equipment, tools, and industrial machinery. Mechanical engineering technology is a broad field. Technicians work on products that range from automobile engines, air conditioners, and power saws, to nuclear reactors, elevators, and printing presses. They also work on the machines and tools needed to make such products. Sometimes they are concerned with tiny parts for delicate instruments. At other times they deal with huge gears for machines such as bulldozers.

Mechanical engineering technicians have a wide variety of titles. Sometimes they are just called mechanical technicians. If they specialize, they may be called automotive technicians or diesel technicians depending on their field. Others are known as tool designers, mechanical drafters, or production technicians depending on the job they do within their field. Mechanical engineering technicians work in plants and factories in all sections of the country. Most work for private companies that make tools and machinery. Others work for government agencies or consulting firms.

Many mechanical engineering technicians work in design and development. They usually work closely with the mechanical engineers who create or im-

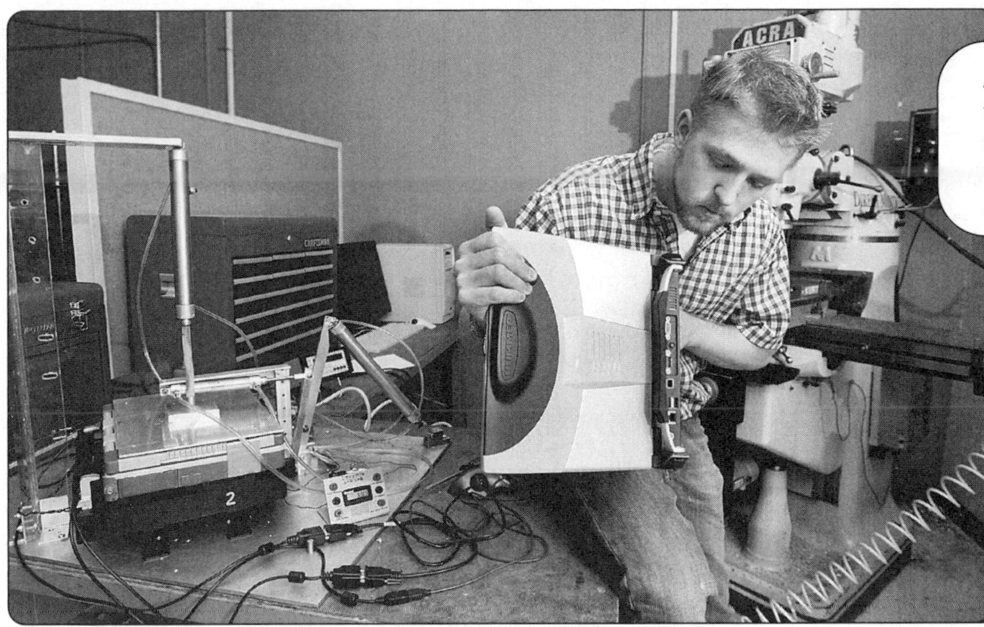

A mechanical engineering technician looks over mechanical equipment. *(Jeff T. Geen/Getty Images News/Getty Images.)*

prove products ranging from mechanical pencils to complex spaceships. Many of these technicians spend much of their time at drawing boards. They prepare drawings, or layouts, of the product being developed—for example, an engine for an automobile. They have to make detailed drawings of each screw, nut, bolt, and gear to be used in the engine. They estimate how much it will cost to make the engine and how well it will work. They take into account the friction, stress, strain, and vibration that the various parts of the engine will have to endure. Mechanical engineering technicians often use complex instruments, testing equipment, and gauges in their work. They test models of the engine, write up reports, and suggest better ways to make the engine.

Other mechanical engineering technicians work in production. They help to make layouts of each step to be taken and each part to be made in the production of, for example, the automobile engine. Specialists in tool design make drawings of the tools, jigs, dies, and other devices needed to mass-produce each part for the engine. They often improve the design of existing tools. Other mechanical engineering technicians make estimates of the cost of labor and the best use of plant space. They help with any production problems that may arise. Sometimes they test machinery or the parts being made for the engine. They do studies of the manufacturing process to find out whether it could be done in a better or cheaper way. Many technicians supervise other workers.

Mechanical engineering technicians are also involved in the installation, operation, and maintenance of machinery used to manufacture other products. Some technicians work in technical sales. Others are employed as technical writers.

## Education and Training Requirements

You can become a mechanical engineering technician in several ways. Some technicians receive their training from a vocational high school. Others attend a community college or technical institute. Most employers prefer to hire graduates of two-year programs in mechanical engineering technology. In some jobs in this field, such as tool design, there are formal apprenticeship programs that combine classroom instruction with on-the-job training. Apprenticeship programs generally take from two to four years to complete. Nearly all workers in the field of mechanical engineering technology need some on-the-job training to prepare them to meet the specific needs of their employers.

## Getting the Job

Mechanical engineering technicians often get their first jobs with the help of their school placement office. Many companies list openings for mechanical engineering technicians in newspaper classifieds or job banks on the Internet. You can apply directly to companies that hire technicians. Your state employment service may also be able to help you find a job in mechanical engineering technology.

## Advancement Possibilities and Employment Outlook

Advancement depends on ability, education, and experience. Most technicians are given more responsibility as they gain experience. Some become supervisors of other technicians. Mechanical engineering technicians who further their education can become mechanical engineers. Some technicians advance by moving into technical sales work or technical writing.

Overall employment of engineering technicians is expected to increase about as fast as average for all occupations through 2014. The continuing demand for improved industrial machinery and tools should cause demand for mechanical engineering technicians to grow. Many skilled technicians will be needed to help create complex new products. Technicians familiar with new technology and those having an associate's degree or extensive job training in engineering technology should have the best opportunities.

## Working Conditions

Because they are involved in all phases of manufacturing and design, mechanical engineering technicians work under a variety of conditions. Some spend most of their time in an office at a drawing board. Others do much of their work in a foundry, die-casting room, machine shop, or other manufacturing area. Although these technicians sometimes work near powerful, fast-moving machinery, they are seldom in danger. The safety record of manufacturing plants is good.

Mechanical engineering technicians who specialize in design usually work thirty-five to forty hours a week on day shifts. Technicians who specialize in production sometimes work night shifts. In some cases overtime work is required. Some mechanical engineering technicians belong to unions.

Technicians in this field should be able to get along well with others since they often work as part of a mechanical engineering team. They must be able to work with drawings and follow directions exactly. An interest in machines and in solving mechanical problems is an asset in this field.

## Earnings and Benefits

Salaries vary depending on the education and experience of the technician, the location, and the kind of job. Mechanical engineering technicians earn salaries that are similar to those of other kinds of engineering technicians. In 2004 the median annual earnings of mechanical engineering technicians was $43,400 per year.

### Where to Go for More Information

American Society for Engineering Education
1818 N St. NW, Ste. 600
Washington, DC 20036-2479
(202) 331-3500
http://www.asee.org

American Society of Mechanical Engineers
Three Park Ave.
New York, NY 10016-5990
(800) 843-2763
http://www.asme.org

# Metallurgical Technician

## Definition and Nature of the Work

Metallurgical engineering is a subdivision of materials engineering. "Materials" refers to substances such as metals, ceramics, plastics, semiconductors, and composites that are used in the development of products. Materials engineers are involved in selecting and creating materials that meet certain mechanical, electrical, and chemical requirements.

Metallurgy is the science and technology of metals. Metallurgical technicians are involved in the many processes that transform natural ores into finished metal products. Metals are generally found in ore, which is a mixture of metals and other substances. Metals are removed from ore and treated before they are ready to be made into finished products.

Most metallurgical technicians work in the iron and steel industry. Some work with other metals, such as aluminum or copper. Technicians are also employed by companies that manufacture goods containing metal, such as automobiles and electrical equipment. Some technicians work for government agencies.

Metallurgical technicians work as part of an engineering team. They usually assist metallurgical engineers, metallurgists, or materials scientists. Sometimes metallurgical technicians are called materials science technicians. They work in all phases of the development and production of metal goods. Some also work in related fields, such as technical sales.

Many metallurgical technicians work in research and development. They help engineers and scientists develop and test new processes and alloys. Alloys are created by fusing together a metal and one or more other elements. Steel, for example, is an alloy of iron and small amounts of carbon and other substances. Brass is an alloy that contains copper and zinc. Technicians measure the hardness, strength, flexibility, and other properties of metals and alloys. They build and test models of new metal processing equipment. They perform tests that show how metals and alloys change as they are heated, forged, or welded. Technicians test these materials to see how well they can be worked and how well they can withstand heat and corrosion. Metallurgical technicians use many kinds of special testing equipment, including hot-stage microscopes, spectrographs, metallographs, and X-ray machines. This equipment helps them to examine metal samples closely.

Some metallurgical technicians work in production. They often supervise crews operating the huge furnaces and other equipment used to remove fairly pure metals from ore or scrap materials. Technicians are sometimes in charge of crews operating equipment that converts the metals into materials needed by other industries. Wires and cables, I-beams, and sheets of aluminum are examples of these finished products. Some technicians make adjustments to complex machines such as the D-gun, or detonation gun, which is used to apply tiny particles of metallic mixtures to such goods as carving knives and the blades of jet engines. Technicians also work in quality control. They take samples of metals and alloys during production and test them to make sure that they are of high quality. They use equipment such as carbon analyzers, pyrometers, and special microscopes.

## Education and Training Requirements

To become a metallurgical technician, you usually need to complete a two-year program in metallurgy or materials science. Some community colleges and technical institutes offer these programs.

**Education and Training**
High school plus two years of training

**Salary**
Median—$43,400 per year

**Employment Outlook**
Fair

## Getting the Job

Your school placement office or your instructors may be able to help you find a job as a metallurgical technician. Your state employment service may also help you to find work in the field. You may find it necessary, however, to apply directly to firms that hire metallurgical technicians. Sometimes these firms list job openings in newspaper classifieds and job banks on the Internet.

## Advancement Possibilities and Employment Outlook

As they gain experience, technicians can advance to positions of more responsibility. Technicians in research, for example, are often promoted as they learn to use more complex testing equipment. Production technicians can take charge of larger crews. Technicians sometimes become supervisors of other technicians. They can also advance by transferring from one department to another. Production technicians, for example, may find opportunities in their company's research or marketing departments. Some technicians continue their educations and move into engineering jobs. The employment outlook for metallurgical technicians is only fair, because some industries that employ metallurgical technicians are expected to experience employment declines.

## Working Conditions

Conditions vary with the kind of work done. Many metallurgical technicians spend most of their time in laboratories. They usually work as part of a team with other technicians, engineers, or scientists. They must use precise instruments and keep careful records. Laboratory technicians usually work thirty-five to forty hours a week. Quality control technicians may have to work rotating shifts. Technicians involved in production often work in plants with crews of workers. They may work rotating shifts and some overtime. Often these technicians must wear hard hats and protective clothing and glasses. Some metallurgical technicians belong to unions.

Metallurgical technicians should have an interest in science and mathematics. They must be careful workers who can handle a wide variety of equipment ranging from heavy furnaces to sensitive instruments. They should also be able to get along with scientists and engineers, as well as with production workers and the other technicians who may be part of their team.

## Earnings and Benefits

Salaries vary depending on the education and experience of the metallurgical technician, the location, and the kind of job. Metallurgical technicians earn salaries that are similar to those earned by other kinds of science and engineering technicians. In 2004 the median annual earnings of mechanical engineering technicians (used here as an estimate of a metallurgical technician's salary) was $43,400. Benefits usually include paid holidays and vacations, health insurance, and pension plans.

### Where to Go for More Information

American Iron and Steel Institute
1140 Connecticut Ave. NW, Ste. 705
Washington, DC 20036
(202) 452-7100
http://www.steel.org

The American Society for Metals (ASM) International
9639 Kinsman Rd.
Materials Park, OH 44073-0002
(800) 336-5152
http://www.asm-intl.org

# Nuclear Technician

**Education and Training**
High school plus two years of training

**Salary**
Median—$28.46 per hour

**Employment Outlook**
Fair

## Definition and Nature of the Work

Nuclear technicians work in the field of nuclear energy. Nuclear energy is produced from the splitting of atoms, a process called nuclear fission. Radioactivity is the spontaneous emission of energy and/or high-energy particles from the nuclei of atoms when they are split. In the United States, uranium-235 (U-235), found in the form of ore, is used as nuclear fuel.

The fission of U-235 releases several particles, which can then penetrate other U-235 nuclei, and so on. If this series of reactions occurs slowly, as it does in nuclear power plants, the energy emitted can be captured for a variety of uses such as providing electricity. In 2005 the United States Department of Energy reported in its *Annual Energy Review* that nuclear energy supplied 20 percent of America's energy needs in the previous year. The radioactivity emitted during nuclear fission can also be an important tool in fields such as health and manufacturing. However, radioactivity can also damage human tissue. Moreover, if nuclear reactions occur all at once, the energy emitted is explosive, as in a nuclear (atomic) bomb.

There are several kinds of nuclear technicians. Some technicians do more than one type of work. Nuclear reactor operators maintain and control the nuclear reaction process in reactors. They often work at remote-control instrument panels. Nuclear reactor operators also help to load and unload the nuclear fuels used in reactors. Accelerator operators set up and control particle accelerators, such as cyclotrons, that produce artificial radioactivity. Particle accelerators are used in nuclear research. They focus and speed up electrically charged particles of atoms as these particles bombard the nuclei of other atoms. Radiation monitors, who are sometimes called health physics technicians, measure and monitor the radiation levels of work areas and equipment. They keep records and enforce safety regulations to ensure that the amount of radiation at a nuclear facility remains within the limits established by health physicists.

Radiographers use X-ray machines or other sources of radioactivity to make radiographs of metal castings, welds, and other objects. Radiographers process the radioactive film and use it to distinguish cracks and other flaws in the objects that they have radiographed. Hot-cell technicians use remote control equipment to do procedures or tests in hot cells. Hot cells are rooms encased in lead or concrete shields to prevent dangerous radiation from escaping. Technicians often use a "slave manipulator"—a set of mechanical arms and hands—to work by remote control with radioactive materials that are inside the hot cell. Sometimes hot-cell technicians put on special protective suits and enter the hot cell to set up experiments or to reduce the level of radioactivity there.

Decontamination workers use special equipment to measure radioactivity. They decontaminate work areas and materials—that is, they reduce the amount of radioactivity to a safe level. Waste treatment operators and waste disposal workers process and dispose of hazardous radioactive wastes. Radioisotope production operators test radioisotopes and prepare them for shipment. Radioisotopes are radioactive forms of elements. They emit radiation that can be measured with special instruments. They are used in science, agriculture, manufacturing, and medicine.

Nuclear technicians also work in a variety of other jobs. For example, some technicians measure radiation levels in the environment. Others trace radioactive substances in scientific experiments. Still other nuclear technicians work in the health field. Radiation treatment, for example, is often used by hospitals on patients with cancer.

## Education and Training Requirements

Most employers of nuclear technicians hire workers who have an associate's degree from a community college or technical school, or a minimum of two years of specialized training in nuclear technology. Most workers need on-the-job training in addition to their formal schooling. Throughout their careers, workers must continue to study new developments, because the field changes rapidly.

Nuclear reactor operators must be licensed by the federal government. It usually takes about a year of job experience to get ready for the government's operating and written tests. You must also pass a medical examination to qualify for licensing. Licenses must be renewed every two years.

Some technicians work on projects that are restricted because they are vital to national security. These workers must obtain a security clearance.

## Getting the Job

If you attend a school that offers courses in nuclear technology, the school placement office may be able to help you find a job as a nuclear technician. You can apply directly to government agencies, power companies, laboratories, or factories that make or use nuclear equipment. State employment agencies may also be able to give you information about job opportunities in the field of nuclear energy.

## Advancement Possibilities and Employment Outlook

Nuclear technicians can advance by gaining experience and taking on more responsibility. Some become supervisors of other workers. Others get further training and become technical specialists. A few take more advanced college courses and become nuclear engineers. Technicians with the necessary skills can become instructors who train new workers. They can also become technical writers who prepare operating or repair manuals.

The employment outlook in the nuclear energy field is fair. Openings will be concentrated in the defense, medical, and waste management and safety standards areas of the field. However, public concern over the safety of nuclear energy, and the move toward finding alternative energy sources, could result in a slower growth rate in the field.

## Working Conditions

Nuclear technicians work in modern laboratories, plants, and offices. Since some employees work close to radioactive materials, many precautions are taken to keep them safe from radiation poisoning. The nuclear energy field has an excellent safety record. Many nuclear technicians work thirty-five to forty hours a week. In many cases they must work or be on call on night, holiday, and weekend shifts. Some workers are unionized.

Nuclear technicians must be careful and responsible workers. They should work well as part of an engineering team. They should also have an aptitude for science and mathematics. Due to the possible dangers of radiation, good judgment is an essential quality in this field.

## Earnings and Benefits

Earnings for technicians working in the field of nuclear energy depend on education, experience, and place of employment. In 2004 the median hourly wage for nuclear technicians was $28.46 per hour. Benefits generally include paid holidays and vacations, health insurance, and retirement plans.

### Where to Go for More Information

American Nuclear Society
555 N. Kensington Ave.
La Grange Park, IL 60526
(708) 352-6611
http://www.ans.org

Nuclear Energy Institute
1776 I St. NW, Ste. 400
Washington, DC 20006-3708
(202) 739-8000
http://www.nei.org

# *Pharmaceutical Technician*

### Education and Training

High school plus two years of training

### Salary

$15.97 to $18.35 per hour

### Employment Outlook

Very good

## Definition and Nature of the Work

Pharmaceutical technicians assist scientists in the pharmaceutical industry. They are sometimes called drug technicians. Their jobs vary depending on their employer's needs. Most pharmaceutical technicians work for private companies that make finished drugs, such as vitamin pills, tranquilizers, antiseptics, antibiotics, and veterinary medicines. These drugs are used in disease prevention, therapy, and diagnosis. Some drug technicians work for companies that make biological products, including serums, vaccines, and toxins. Others work for firms that make large amounts of the chemical and botanical compounds that are used in finished drugs.

Pharmaceutical technicians who work in research and development programs are usually supervised by a scientist, veterinarian, or physician. These professionals work in such fields as chemistry, biochemistry, microbiology, or pharmacology. They often direct the pharmaceutical technicians, who do much of the routine work involved in developing new drugs. In some cases, however, experienced technicians are allowed to work independently on complicated procedures after they have been given instructions. They often help prepare laboratory experiments and record the results. They may operate electronic equipment that tests samples of chemicals and drugs. Technicians may prepare cultures of bacteria for testing, or they may observe and report the results of testing. Some technicians prepare drugs that are given to test animals. Technicians are usually expected to keep records, fill out forms, and keep laboratory equipment clean and in good working condition. Sometimes they have to make calculations or look up needed information.

Pharmaceutical technicians involved in production or quality control may work in a laboratory or on a production line. They often assist professionals such as pharmacists, chemists, and chemical, mechanical, or industrial engineers to put efficient methods of production and testing into practice. Pharmaceutical technicians often must operate complex scientific instruments. They may tend fermenting tanks used in the production of antibiotics, or they may mix and assemble compound drugs. Sometimes they perform tests that determine whether liquids, powders, or tablets contain the right amount of each ingredient and meet other requirements. Technicians are often required to prepare cost esti-

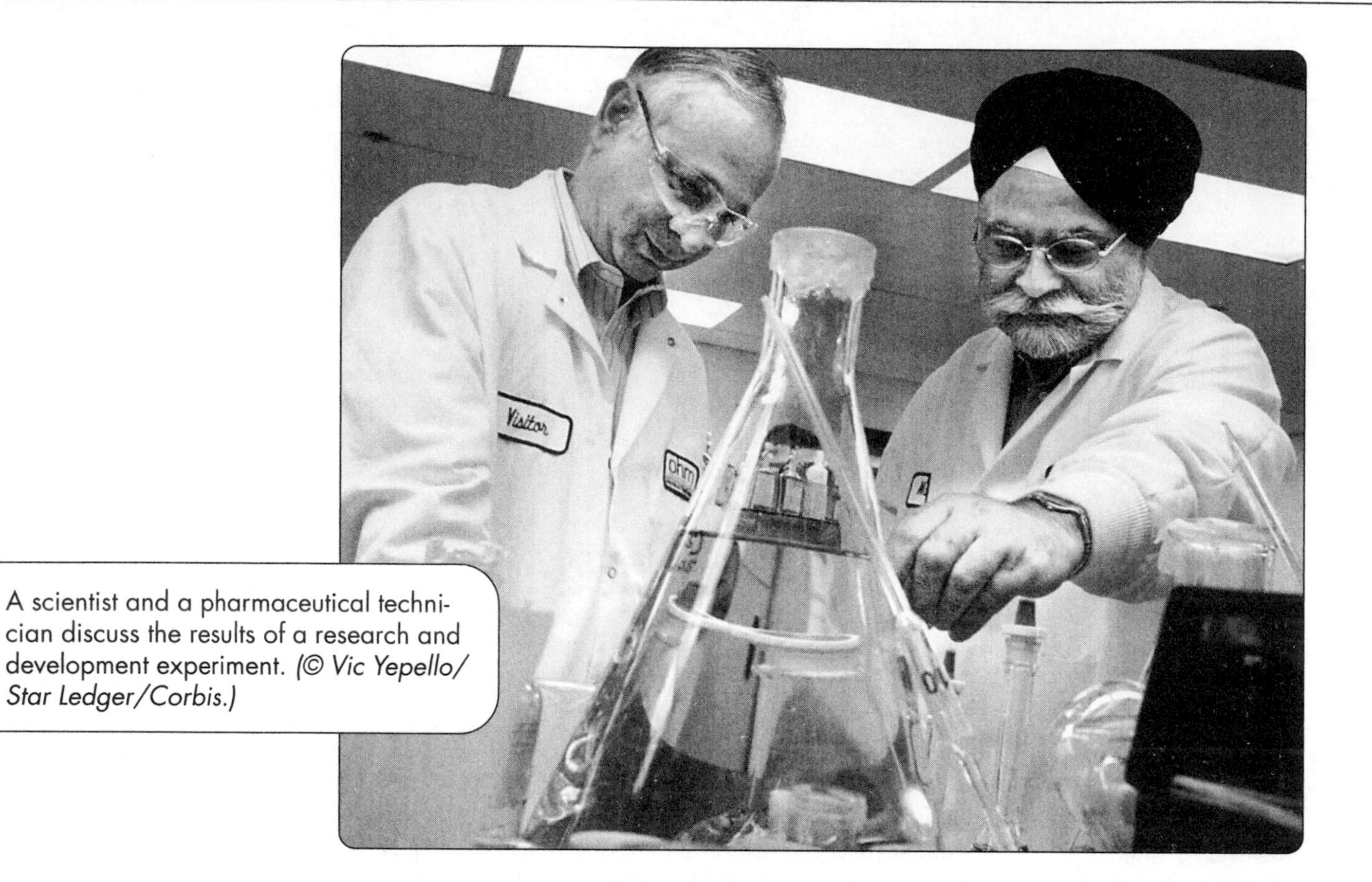


A scientist and a pharmaceutical technician discuss the results of a research and development experiment. *(© Vic Yepello/Star Ledger/Corbis.)*

mates, make drawings, take measurements, and write up reports. They may also devise work schedules and supervise other workers.

## Education and Training Requirements

Many companies prefer to hire people who have attended a college or technical institute for two years. You may also need some on-the-job training. For some jobs, employers prefer to hire people who have a bachelor's degree in one of the biological sciences. College courses that would be useful in the drug industry include chemistry, biology, engineering, and veterinary science. Some colleges offer pre-pharmacy courses.

## Getting the Job

If you graduate from a two-year program at a college or technical institute, your school placement office can help you find a job in the drug industry. You can also apply directly to companies in the drug industry. These companies often list job openings in newspaper classifieds and job banks on the Internet.

## Advancement Possibilities and Employment Outlook

As they gain experience, technicians are usually given more responsibility. They often become supervisors of other workers. They can increase their chances for advancement by taking more courses related to their work. Some technicians may decide to pursue a five-year pharmacy degree program. Others take the one-year certification programs offered in some states. Pharmaceutical technicians can also advance by going into technical writing or sales work.

The employment outlook for pharmaceutical technicians is very good. There will be some increase in the total number of technicians employed in the drug industry. There will also be openings to replace workers who leave the field. The drug industry is only slightly affected by changes in the economy. Employment levels tend to be stable.

## Working Conditions

The plants and laboratories in which pharmaceutical technicians work are usually clean and well lighted. Safety practices protect technicians from dangerous fumes, chemicals, and disease cultures. Technicians who work in laboratories may work alone or in small teams. Those who work in production may work alone, or they may come into contact with many other workers. They must be able to work well either independently or as part of a team. Pharmaceutical technicians usually work thirty-five to forty hours a week. Some technicians, especially those in production or quality control programs, may work weekends and night shifts. Technicians in the drug industry seldom do any heavy labor, but they may spend hours at a time on their feet or seated at a laboratory bench. Technicians need to be careful workers who can follow directions. Some drug technicians belong to unions.

## Earnings and Benefits

Salaries for technicians in the pharmaceutical industry vary depending on education, experience, location, and the kind of job. Pharmaceutical technicians earn salaries that are similar to those of biological and chemical technicians. In 2004 the median hourly wage of biological technicians was $15.97. In 2004 chemical technicians earned a median hourly income of $18.35. Benefits generally include paid holidays and vacations, health insurance, and retirement plans.

### Where to Go for More Information

Pharmaceutical Research and Manufacturers of America (PhRMA)
1100 Fifteenth St. NW, Ninth Fl.
Washington, DC 20005
(202) 835-3400
http://www.phrma.org

American Association of Pharmaceutical Scientists
2107 Wilson Blvd., Ste. 700
Arlington, VA 22201-3042
(703) 243-9650
http://www.aapspharmaceutica.com

# *Photonics Technician*

### Education and Training

High school and two years of training

### Salary

Median—$55,000 per year

### Employment Outlook

Excellent

## Definition and Nature of the Work

Photonics technicians are trained in the use of devices and systems associated with fiber optics and lasers, and with their applications. The job title comes from the word "photon," which is a unit of light. Photonics is the science of using light to generate energy, detect information, or transmit information. Photonics technicians install and troubleshoot lasers, optical systems, fiber optic devices, telecommunications equipment, photonics manufacturing equipment and simple control systems.

Fiber optics is the technology by which light and images are transmitted through hair-thin strands of plastic-coated glass fiber. The light in these fibers may be generated by lasers, which concentrate light into a narrow, intense beam. Fiber optics offers a fast, reliable, and inexpensive means of telecommunication. Lasers have applications in numerous other fields, as well. For example, they are used by physicians in diagnosing and treating a variety of conditions and diseases, and by the military in navigation and weaponry equipment.

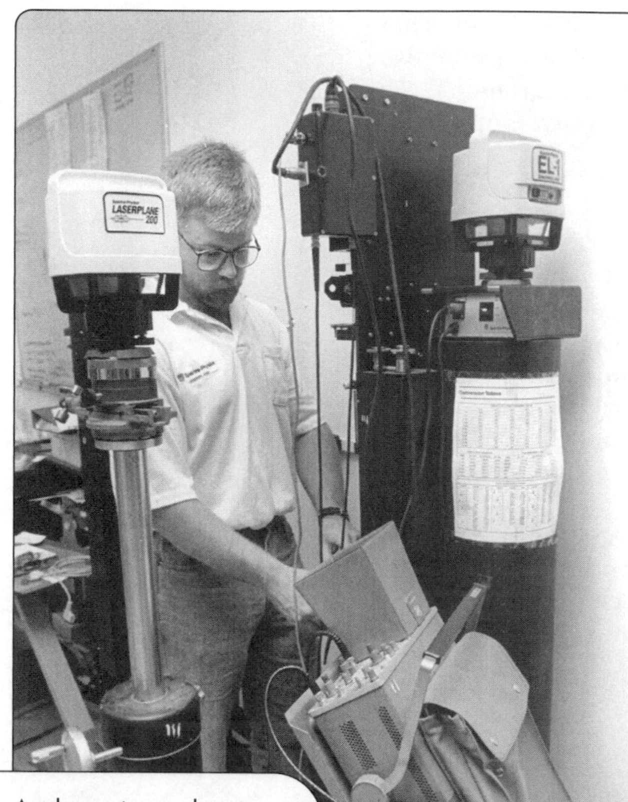


A photonics technician repairs and calibrates laser equipment. *(© Martha Tabor/ Working Images Photographs. Reproduced by permission.)*

Photonics technicians may work for telecommunications firms and for optical fiber producers. They help electrical and chemical engineers and scientists deal with problems relating to fiber optics light sources. Using a special instrument called a spectrometer, these technicians measure light frequencies emitted by lasers. They also help engineers set up electrical and electronic experiments. Results are calculated through the use of computer-aided design systems. Photonics technicians may also assist in the development of new fiber optics designs and applications.

Some photonics technicians work with chemists and materials scientists to develop production methods aimed at purifying optical fiber. Others assist chemical and mechanical engineers in finding methods to reduce production costs.

Photonics technicians may work with engineers and scientists concerning the development, installation, and operation of laser systems. There are basically two types of laser systems: gas and solid-state. Some photonics technicians work with semiconductor laser systems, which are the most compact and reliable of all laser systems. Many assist engineers in dealing with methods to improve information flow and telecommunications systems. Computer and telephone systems are the primary information flow systems that they help to design, test, and install.

Other photonics technicians work with the larger and more costly gas-type laser systems, which are used primarily in the robotics and materials processing industries and in medical applications. Photonics technicians are also employed by the Department of Defense and companies that manufacture lasers for the department under contract.

## Education and Training Requirements

Educational requirements vary depending on the type of job you want and the employer for whom you want to work. You can train to become a photonics technician at a college or technical institute that offers a program in this field. Most technicians' programs take two years to complete. Fiber optics and laser manufacturing companies may hire graduates of two-year associate degree programs who have specialized in physics or electronics. Many companies provide on-the-job training to high school graduates who have a strong background in mathematics and physics. They often train technicians who have worked in related fields, especially those with experience in the electronics industry. The armed forces also train some enlisted personnel in laser installation and operation.

## Getting the Job

If you attend a two-year program at a college or a technical institute, your school placement office may be able to help you find a job. State employment agencies may also help graduates find jobs as photonics technicians. If you are not a graduate of a specialized school, state agencies can sometimes help you locate a position that offers on-the-job training. You can also apply directly to companies that hire photonics technicians. Jobs are often listed in newspaper classifieds, job banks on the Internet, and trade journals that specialize in laser and optics technology.

## Advancement Possibilities and Employment Outlook

Experienced photonics technicians can advance in several ways. Some may become supervisors of other technicians. Others may advance by moving into positions in sales, training, or technical writing. Technicians who receive additional education can become photonics engineers.

The employment outlook for photonics technicians is excellent. Currently there is a shortage. The demand for trained technicians in this rapidly growing field will be high as new laser and fiber optics applications are designed and implemented in telecommunications and many other areas.

## Working Conditions

Working conditions for photonics technicians vary. They generally work thirty-five- to forty-hour workweeks, often in modern offices and laboratories. Technicians who install laser and fiber optics materials may work alone or with customers. Technicians who work with scientists and other engineers usually work in small teams. Although their hours are regular, some overtime and occasionally some weekend work may be necessary. In some cases, photonics technicians are members of labor unions.

Photonics technicians should enjoy working with their hands and with electronic components. They should also be able to work well both with fellow team members and customers. Because the laser and fiber optics field is changing rapidly, technicians will need to upgrade their skills continually by taking courses related to the latest technological developments.

## Earnings and Benefits

Earnings for photonics technicians vary depending on the applicant's experience and the kind of job. These technicians generally earn salaries that are higher than those of other kinds of engineering technicians, and in recent years their salaries have risen considerably. According to a leading photonics publication, *Photonics Spectra*, the median salary for photonics technicians in 2004 was $55,000. Benefits generally include paid holidays and vacations, health insurance, and retirement plans. Technicians who install or repair fiber optics systems often receive an allowance for travel expenses.

### Where to Go for More Information

Laser Institute of America
13501 Ingenuity Dr., Ste. 128
Orlando, FL 33826
(800) 345-2737
http://www.laserinstitute.org

Optical Society of America
2010 Massachusetts Ave. NW
Washington, DC 20036
(202) 223-8130
http://www.osa.org

Photonics.com
Laurin Publishing Co., Inc.
Berkshire CommonP.O. Box 4949
Pittsfield, MA 01202-4949
(413) 499-0514
http://www.photonics.com

# Precision Instrument and Equipment Repairer

**Education and Training**
High school plus two years of training

**Salary**
$13.47 to $21.25 per hour

**Employment Outlook**
Fair to good

## Definition and Nature of the Work

Precision instrument and equipment repairers, sometimes called instrumentation technicians, help install, repair, and maintain complex instruments. These instruments are varied and include watches and clocks, musical instruments, photographic equipment, and medical equipment. Other kinds of precision instruments and equipment include those used in communications systems, scientific research, environmental protection, and many industrial processes. Precision instruments are used to measure heat, temperature, pressure, and other factors. They are used to control such things as the speed, thickness, and flow of liquids, gases, or electricity. Some instruments store information that guides automated processes.

Precision instrument and equipment repairers are employed in a variety of industries. Many work for companies that do chemical and medical research. In the chemical industry, for example, some technicians install special instruments that measure and regulate the temperature, pressure, acidity, or flow of chemical processes needed to make products ranging from nylon fibers to house paint. Other precision instrument and equipment repairers fix the complex heart-lung and kidney dialysis machines used in medical care. Precision instrument and equipment repairers may be employed by firms that make precision instruments, colleges and universities, or government agencies. They need wide knowledge in the physical sciences, as well as in electrical and mechanical engineering technology. Their special field is known as instrumentation technology.

Some precision instrument and equipment repairers work under the direction of scientists and engineers. They assist them in the design and development of sensitive instruments. Precision instrument and equipment repairers help nuclear engineers test and perfect instruments. Some instruments in nuclear reactors, for example, measure radiation, heat, pressure, and rates of change. These instruments are designed to make automatic adjustments to keep the reactor running safely and smoothly. Other technicians help metallurgical, biomedical, and other kinds of engineers to develop instruments for their special fields.

Precision instrument and equipment repairers often handle troubleshooting, which is the diagnosis of problems with one instrument or an entire system of related instruments. For example, they might be asked to find out what is wrong with an instrument used in modern cryosurgery, which is surgery done at extremely low temperatures. Precision instrument and equipment repairers use special tools and electronic equipment in their work. Sometimes technicians travel from one job site to another to service complex instruments. Some precision instrument and equipment repairers teach in technical schools or sell instruments to manufacturers, hospitals, and other customers. Others help to write technical manuals for the users of complex instruments.

## Education and Training Requirements

Most precision instrument and equipment repairers receive their training from colleges or technical institutes. Some of these schools have programs in instrumentation technology. Programs vary in length from one to four years. Most are two-year programs, however. Students can also get their training in a related field, such as electronics, electrical, or mechanical technology. Most employers give some on-the-job training to help employees meet the needs of their particular industries.

## Getting the Job

Your instructors or the placement office at your college or technical school can help you find a job in the instrumentation field. State employment services, newspaper classifieds, and job banks on the Internet are other good sources for job leads. You can also apply directly to companies that hire precision instrument and equipment repairers.

## Advancement Possibilities and Employment Outlook

Precision instrument and equipment repairers often begin by making simple adjustments to instruments. As they gain skill and experience, they advance to more difficult tasks, such as troubleshooting. Some become supervisors. Others advance by moving into jobs in sales, teaching, or technical writing. Repairers who further their education can become engineers.

Overall employment growth is projected to be about as fast as average for all occupations through 2014. In some job specialties, such as repairers of watches, clocks, and cameras, opportunities will decline because people often replace these items with newer technology rather than repair them.

## Working Conditions

Working conditions vary greatly because of the wide variety of industries that employ precision instrument and equipment repairers. For example, precision instrument and equipment repairers working in a nuclear power plant face conditions that are very different from those experienced by technicians who are part of a team searching for new sources of petroleum. Technicians sometimes work in laboratories or on production lines. Their work is usually varied. Although their basic workweek is thirty-five to forty hours long, they may sometimes have to put in some overtime or shift work. Some precision instrument and equipment repairers belong to unions.

Because very precise work is needed in the instrumentation field, workers should be patient, careful, and able to work well with tools. They should be good at science and mathematics. In addition, they should be able to work as part of an engineering team.

## Earnings and Benefits

Earnings vary with the education and experience of the instrumentation technician and with the location and type of job. In 2004 median hourly earnings for precision instrument and equipment repairers ranged from $13.47 per hour to $21.25 per hour. Benefits usually include paid holidays and vacations, health insurance, and pension plans.

### Where to Go for More Information

National Association of Professional Band Instrument Repair Technicians
P.O. Box 51
2026 Eagle Rd.
Normal, IL 61761
(309) 452-4257
http://www.napbirt.org

Instrument Society of America
67 Alexander Dr., Box 12277
Research Triangle Park, NC 27709
(919) 549-8411
http://www.isa.org

Association for the Advancement of Medical Instrumentation
1110 North Glebe Rd., Ste. 220
Arlington, VA 22201-4795
(703) 525-4890
http://www.aami.org

# Robotics Technician

**Education and Training**
High school plus two years of training

**Salary**
$30,400 to $50,500 per year

**Employment Outlook**
Excellent

## Definition and Nature of the Work

Robotics, or flexible automation, is the technology involving the design, maintenance, and use of robots. Robotics technicians work as part of the team that produces robots, which are machines designed to perform tasks in place of a living agent. Most robots are "manipulators"—machines that function in place of a human hand and arm. They may also function as "walking" machines, or teleoperators, using remote control or sensory manipulators. Robots are usually directed by microprocessors, which are tiny computers that are installed in these machines.

Robotics technicians assist manufacturing, mechanical, and electronics engineers in all phases of robotic design, development, production, testing, and operations. Robot maintenance technicians are employed either by the manufacturers and distributors of robots or by the robot users. These technicians are often responsible for the initial installation of the robot. They may then establish an in-house maintenance and repair program. If employed by the robot manufacturer or distributor, maintenance technicians usually respond to service calls. These members of the robotics team work closely with engineers and other technical workers.

Robotics technicians who are trained in computer programming sometimes perform low-level programming and reprogramming of the robots. The technicians often act as the liaison between robotics engineers and the customers who purchase the machines. They may also install the robots at the manufacturing plant or other site where they will be used.

A robotics technician repairs the damaged electronics on a patient's bionic arm. *(© McPherson Colin/ Sygma/Corbis.)*

Technical workers called robot assemblers construct the robot for the robot manufacturer according to the design worked out by the robotics engineer. Generally, these workers receive in-house training for this job.

Robot operators actually operate the robots. Some of the larger users of robots provide their own specialized in-plant training programs to instruct their workers in the systems and equipment used to power and control the robots.

Another group of robotics technicians works as robotics trainers. Robotics trainers must have extensive experience installing and maintaining robots. They supervise trainees and less experienced technicians in all aspects of robotics design, installation, and maintenance. Trainers are employed at companies that manufacture robotic systems. They may also provide instruction at trade and technical schools, vocational schools, and some high schools.

## Education and Training Requirements

For all jobs in this field you will need at least a high school education with a good background in science and mathematics. Most robotics technicians earn a two-year associate's degree in robot technology. Many colleges, technical institutes, and trade schools offer programs in this field. Your studies will concentrate on hydraulics, pneumatics, electronics, CADD/CAM (computer-assisted design and drafting, and computer-assisted manufacturing) systems, and microprocessors. Robotics manufacturers generally provide additional on-the-job training.

Robot maintenance technicians must often complete an apprenticeship training program to learn how to service the robots. These programs, which usually take two years to complete, combine classroom instruction with on-the-job training. Training includes instruction on how to maintain hydraulic valves and how to operate electronic systems. Although some of the instruction is highly technical, the skills that are taught generally are not very different from those needed to maintain other complex machinery.

Robot manufacturers and vendors often provide training programs to teach employees how to assemble or operate robots and their related electronics systems. Most robot operators need only minimal training. Typically, experienced machine operators require only one week of formal training to adapt their skills to routine operating and monitoring of robots. If you want to become a robotics trainer, you will need at least a two-year associate's degree in robotics technology together with extensive practical experience in robot design, installation, and maintenance work.

## Getting the Job

If you attend a program at a college or technical institute, your school placement office may be able to assist you in finding a job. State employment agencies should also be able to help. You can apply directly to companies that hire robotics technicians, including robot manufacturers and robot suppliers and distributors. Jobs are often listed in newspaper classifieds, job banks on the Internet, and trade journals that specialize in robotics.

## Advancement Possibilities and Employment Outlook

Experienced robotics technicians can advance in many ways. They can become robotics trainers and teach other technicians how to design and maintain robots. With additional education they can become robotics engineers. Other experienced technicians can become sales representatives. Robotics technicians who demonstrate managerial skills and receive advanced technical training may be able to work as independent consultants.

The job outlook for robotics technicians and technical workers is excellent. The demand for skilled technicians in this field is high.

## Working Conditions

Most robotics technicians work forty hours per week and some work overtime. Generally, they work alone or in pairs. Some technicians travel to customers' plants to service or install equipment. Others spend their time working in-house with engineers and scientists. Robot maintenance technicians, assemblers, and operators often work in noisy plants. Maintenance technicians may be expected to be on call around the clock in plants where robots are in twenty-four-hour use. Operators may have to work night shifts. In some cases robotics technicians belong to labor unions.

### Where to Go for More Information

Robotics International of the Society of Manufacturing Engineers
One SME Dr.
P.O. Box 930
Dearborn, MI 48121-0930
(800) 733-4763
http://www.sme.org/ri

## Earnings and Benefits

Earnings vary widely depending on education, experience, and the kind of job. The average salary for a robotics technician ranged from $30,400 to $50,500 per year in 2002. Benefits generally include paid holidays and vacations, health insurance, and retirement plans.

# *Semiconductor Processor*

**Education and Training**
High school plus two years of training

**Salary**
Median—$13.85 per hour

**Employment Outlook**
Poor

## Definition and Nature of the Work

Semiconductor processors, sometimes known as integrated circuit technicians, are production workers who manufacture semiconductors. Semiconductors (also known as integrated circuits, computer chips, and microchips) are tiny electronic systems produced on minute slices of silicon. Semiconductors are used in computers, DVD players, cell phones, household appliances, and video games, along with many other products.

Manufacturing computer chips is a difficult and complex process. Semiconductor processors usually specialize in one part of the larger manufacturing process. To manufacture computer chips, first semiconductor disks, or wafers, of varying sizes are manufactured. The circuitry of the microchips is layered on the wafers. When the circuitry is completed, each wafer is cut into many individual chips.

Semiconductor processors make wafers by imprinting the microscopic patterns of the circuitry on the wafers. They then etch out the patterns with acids and fill in the etched patterns with metals that conduct electricity. After giving the wafer a chemical bath, the semiconductor processor applies another layer of microscopic circuitry to the wafer. Wafers usually have from eight to twenty layers of circuitry.

The manufacture of computer chips takes place in "cleanrooms"—production areas that are free of airborne matter, which could damage the chips. All semiconductor processors working in cleanrooms wear special lightweight garments that fit over their clothing to prevent lint and other particles from contaminating semiconductor processing worksites.

## Education and Training Requirements

The education and training necessary for a semiconductor processor varies somewhat depending on the specific position. Some routine technical jobs require only a high school diploma along with the training provided on the job. However, most employers prefer to hire graduates of specialized two-year training programs, which are offered by community colleges and technical schools.

## Getting the Job

Semiconductor processors are often hired after completing a technical program. Students in their last semester at a community college or technical

A semiconductor processor works with an engineer to develop new designs for microchips. *(© Martha Tabor/ Working Images Photographs. Reproduced by permission.)*

school should check with their placement offices for job openings. Newspaper classifieds, job banks on the Internet, and state employment agencies are good resources. You can also apply directly to a microchip manufacturer for an entry-level position.

## Advancement Possibilities and Employment Outlook

With additional training and experience, semiconductor processors can advance from one area of the process to a more demanding one. If they further their education, they can become supervisors or circuit designers.

Employment of semiconductor processors is projected to decline between 2004 and 2014. The computer chip fabrication process is becoming more automated, requiring fewer workers. In addition many newer manufacturing facilities are being constructed in other countries.

## Working Conditions

Semiconductor processors work in clean, well-lighted, dust-free environments. They use highly specialized equipment but sometimes work with potentially dangerous acids and other chemicals.

## Earnings and Benefits

Salaries for semiconductor processors vary somewhat depending on their education and training and the difficulty of the tasks performed. The median wage of electronic semiconductor processors was $13.85 in 2004. Full-time semiconductor processors usually receive standard benefits, including health insurance, paid holidays and vacations, and retirement plans.

### Where to Go for More Information

Electronic Industries Association
2500 Wilson Blvd.
Arlington, VA 22201
(703) 907-7500
http://www.eia.org

Electronics Technicians Association International
5 Depot St.
Greencastle, IN 46135
(800) 288-3824
http://www.eta-sda.com

Maricopa Advanced Technology Education Center
2323 W. 14th St., Ste. 540
Tempe, AZ 85281
(480) 517-8650
http://matec.org/index.htm

# Telecommunications Central Office Technician

**Education and Training**
Varies—see profile

**Salary**
Median—$23.96 per hour

**Employment Outlook**
Poor

## Definition and Nature of the Work

Telecommunications central office technicians keep the complex and sophisticated equipment used in the telecommunications industry working properly. They are in charge of installing, maintaining, and repairing the electronic and electromechanical switching equipment in the central offices of telecommunications companies. Installers set up the intricate systems, and craft workers keep the switching equipment in fine running condition. Used equipment is replaced before it breaks down so that the telecommunications system never stops working.

Most central office installers are employed by telecommunications equipment manufacturers. Others work for telecommunications companies or contractors that coordinate large installations. Central office equipment installers, also called equipment installation technicians, set up, rearrange, and change communications equipment associated with the complex switching and dialing operations vital to telecommunications central offices. Using equipment work order information, blueprints, circuit diagrams, and floor plans, installers set up new central offices, add equipment to existing offices, and replace outdated equipment. Once the installation is complete, it is the installers' responsibility to verify that everything works properly. Using sophisticated equipment, they test each piece of equipment, determine the cause of any difficulty, and correct the problem.

Central office craft workers are usually employed by telecommunications companies. They are generally divided into three categories: the frame wirer, the central office repairer, and the test desk technician. Frame wirers, sometimes referred to as frame attendants, connect, disconnect, and rearrange wires that run from the telecommunications lines and cables to the central office. Central office repairers, also known as switching equipment technicians, test, repair, and

A telecommunications central office technician locates a problem at a control station. *(Photograph by Kelly A. Quin. Thomson Gale. Reproduced by permission.)*

maintain all types of local and long-distance switching equipment that automatically connects telecommunications customers. Most of the switching systems are electromechanical—that is, they contain many moving parts that require frequent cleaning, oiling, and replacement. Newer switching systems, which use digital electronics, have few moving parts and require practically no maintenance. Test desk technicians, sometimes called trouble locators, use specially designed testing equipment to locate problems in telecommunications lines. They supervise the troubleshooting procedures used by both the inside and the outside repair crews to clear problems from subscribers' lines.

## Education and Training Requirements

Candidates for central office technician positions were traditionally selected from inside and outside telecommunications companies. They received both formal classroom instruction and on-the-job training. As of the early 2000s, however, most companies preferred workers who had already acquired these skills through the military or through other job experience. In addition to experience, employers look for people who have completed an associate's degree or postsecondary vocational school program in telecommunications technology, electronics, or related subjects.

Persons considering a job as a central office technician should have the analytical skills and judgment to resolve complex mechanical problems. Candidates must be able to work in a team environment and have the patience to follow detailed instructions. Solid reading comprehension, logic, and mathematical skills are necessary to understand company manuals and follow circuit diagrams.

New workers may receive a combination of formal instruction, on-the-job training, and practical experience by observing and helping experienced technicians.

## Getting the Job

Individuals interested in this type of work should apply directly to the personnel offices of telecommunications equipment manufacturers or large installation contractors. Candidates should also contact local telecommunications companies because they frequently hire installers and offer excellent training programs. To get a job as a central office craft worker, students should apply directly to the nearest telecommunications company employment office.

## Advancement Possibilities and Employment Outlook

There are several avenues of advancement for central office technicians, and particularly for craft workers. After one or two years of satisfactory performance, frame wirers may be selected to train for a more skilled job such as that of test desk technician or central office repairer. The central office craft worker can advance to a supervisory position and then to a position as an engineering assistant or administrative staff worker. The central office installer can also advance to engineering assistant.

The employment of central office technicians is projected to decline through the year 2014. Although there will be a need for telecommunications services and equipment due to the growth in both population and demand, newer electronic switching equipment requires little maintenance and is relatively easy to install. In addition, with computerization, more companies are centralizing their maintenance forces in switching control centers. However, the growing popularity of voice-over Internet protocol (VoIP), expanded multimedia offerings such as video on demand, and growth in other telecommunications services will provide new job opportunities. Mobile maintenance crews can be dis-

### Where to Go for More Information

Communications Workers of America
501 Third St. NW
Washington, DC 20001-2797
(202) 434-1100
http://www.cwa-union.org

International Brotherhood of Electrical Workers
900 Seventh St. NW
Washington, DC 20001
(202) 833-7000
http://www.ibew.com

United States Telecom Association
607 Fourteenth St. NW, Ste. 400
Washington, DC 20005
(202) 326-7300
http://www.usta.org

patched to clear trouble conditions, thereby reducing the need for on-site central office repairers. This trend is expected to continue.

## Working Conditions

Telecommunications central offices are generally comfortable and clean. Because communications systems operate twenty-four hours a day, seven days a week, central office craft workers have schedules that include late shifts, holidays, and weekends. Those craft workers who are assigned to mobile work forces must travel within their assigned territories. Central office installers are also expected to do some traveling.

## Earnings and Benefits

According to the U.S. Bureau of Labor Statistics, the median salary for telecommunications central office technicians is $23.96 per hour. Experienced technicians who belong to unions earn more. For technicians covered by a union contract, the contract provides for health and life insurance, educational benefits, retirement plans, and overtime pay.

# *Telephone Service Technician*

**Education and Training**
Varies—see profile

**Salary**
Median—$23.96 per hour

**Employment Outlook**
Poor

## Definition and Nature of the Work

Telephone service technicians are one of the largest groups of telephone company workers. They repair and install telephone lines and small switchboard systems at customers' houses and offices. Working from trucks that carry the equipment they need, these technicians spend much of their time traveling from one location to another. Although many service technicians do a variety of work, most specialize in one kind of job.

Telephone installers put new phone lines in homes and offices. They install inside wiring and connect it to the service wires outside. They may have to climb a telephone pole to complete the necessary connections. The next step involves installing the terminal box, which usually requires drilling holes through walls to make connections. Once this task is complete, a telephone can be plugged in and used.

Telephone repairers test, clean, and fix or replace faulty wiring. Working closely with the central office, they locate and analyze problems with customers' inside lines. Repairers track down the source of the trouble by connecting a test set to the phone line and then testing it with the central office.

Many telephone installers become PBX installers. PBX, an acronym for private branch exchange, refers to a switchboard. PBX installers set up the telephone systems found in offices. The PBX installer's job is similar to the job of the telephone installer but requires more training. A PBX system makes it possible for private companies to direct clients' calls to the proper extensions, and it allows people who work in the same office to call each other at their desks. PBX installers also set up the equipment that radio and television stations use for broadcasting.

PBX repair workers are called in when private switchboards break down. They find out where the trouble lies and get the system up and running again. PBX repair workers also fix teletypewriters—machines that send written messages through the telephone system—as well as radio and television broadcasting equipment.

## Education and Training Requirements

Education requirements for telephone service technicians vary according to the employer. Some employers require their workers to receive certification in electronics. Others require only a high school diploma or its equivalent. Most employers require potential workers to pass a test of mechanical ability. Candidates for the job must have good eyesight and cannot be color-blind. Telephone companies often offer on-the-job training, which includes classroom instruction and observation of experienced workers.

## Getting the Job

Interested individuals should apply directly to the telephone companies in their area for telephone service technician openings. Most telephone service workers start out as installers and must work their way up to the position of technician. Line workers and cable splicers often apply for these jobs as well.

## Advancement Possibilities and Employment Outlook

Training is a continual process for all telephone service technicians, and there are several possibilities for promotion. Telephone installers and repairers can become PBX installers and repair workers. Many service technicians advance by becoming skilled in both installation and repair work. With further training, service workers can become supervisors, sales and customer service workers, and communications equipment technicians. Promotions are given to reward length of service as well as ability.

Employment opportunities for telephone service technicians are expected to decline through the year 2014. Modern prewired buildings and plug-in telephones have nearly eliminated the need for telephone installers. Telephone repair will consist mainly of replacing worn-out wires. Reliable, self-monitoring, high-capacity equipment has been designed to reduce the frequency of breakdowns, further decreasing the need for repairs. However, there will be jobs for those qualified to work on PBX and other private systems. The growing popularity of voice-over Internet protocol (VoIP) systems, expanded multimedia offerings such as video on demand, and the growth of other telecommunications services will place additional demand on telecommunications networks.

## Working Conditions

Telephone service workers usually work forty hours per week but must put in overtime during emergencies. They generally work independently out in the field while their supervisors remain in the central office. Telephone service technicians deal directly with the public when they go to homes and offices, so

### Where to Go for More Information

Information Technology and Telecommunications Association
P.O. Box 278076
Sacramento, CA 95827-8076
(415) 777-4647
http://www.tca.org

International Brotherhood of Electrical Workers
900 Seventh St. NW
Washington, DC 20001
(202) 833-7000
http://www.ibew.com

United States Telecom Association
607 Fourteenth St. NW, Ste. 400
Washington, DC 20005
(202) 326-7300
http://www.usta.org

they need a considerable amount of patience and a pleasant demeanor. They also spend a lot of time stooping, kneeling, or crouched over to access phone lines. PBX workers can make repairs indoors because they do not have to work on outside wiring. Telephone installers and repairers work both indoors and outdoors.

### Earnings and Benefits

Pay scales vary in different parts of the country. According to the U.S. Bureau of Labor Statistics, the median hourly salary for a telephone service technician is $23.96. Experienced technicians earn more. Benefits include overtime pay, paid vacations and holidays, and insurance and retirement plans.

## *Wireless Communications Technician*

**Education and Training**
High school plus formal training

**Salary**
Average—$45,000 per year

**Employment Outlook**
Good

### Definition and Nature of the Work

Wireless communications technicians help to build and maintain the infrastructure supporting wireless communications systems. Wireless communications systems encompass two-way radios, cellular phones, beepers, wireless Internet (WiFi) access, hand-held computers, vehicle location equipment, marine radios, satellite systems and related equipment, and other personal communications devices. Technicians are needed to maintain the complex networks relaying wireless signals as well as to maintain and repair personal communications devices themselves.

Wireless communications technicians must be familiar with electronics, digital radio technology, and cellular systems. They use measuring and diagnostic tools to test, adjust, and repair electronic equipment.

Technicians must be able to read work orders that describe equipment failures, and they must be able to talk to equipment operators to determine what problems exist with the equipment. If the equipment has serious problems, technicians must be able to use schematic drawings and other written specifications to locate and repair problems.

Field technicians visit sites where wireless communications break down—either work sites where personal communication devices are used or relay sites maintained by the wireless network itself. Field technicians also do regular maintenance work on personal communication devices used by corporate clients as well as periodic work to maintain the wireless networks.

Bench technicians work at repair facilities, in stores, or in service centers, where they repair wireless communication devices. Bench technicians often deal directly with consumers, advising them when it makes more sense to replace rather than repair a wireless communications device.

Some wireless communications technicians work exclusively as field technicians or bench technicians. However, the majority are employed as both.

The wireless communications industry offers employment opportunities with large telecommunications companies as well as with small-scale shops. Wireless communications technicians working for small-scale businesses may have other responsibilities in addition to equipment maintenance and repair. These responsibilities might include the purchasing of office equipment, office administration, and sales.

## Education and Training Requirements

Employers prefer college graduates with formal training in electronics. Many community and technical colleges also offer programs in wireless communications technology, which take one to two years to complete. In addition, many workers in the field receive formal training and work experience in the armed forces. Formal training usually involves courses in mathematics, circuit theory, digital systems, electronics, microwave technology, and computer science. Adequate training also involves hands-on experience in which students perform diagnostic work and maintenance on equipment.

Rapidly evolving technology makes continuing education essential for wireless communications technicians. Workers in this industry must be willing and able to upgrade their skills constantly, both through informal on-the-job training and through formal continuing education courses.

## Getting the Job

After receiving formal training through school or the military, job applicants can apply directly at local offices of telecommunications companies or smaller wireless service providers. Colleges and technical schools usually provide career development services to help students find jobs. Many positions in this field are posted on Internet job and career Web sites, including those maintained by telecommunications companies.

## Advancement Possibilities and Employment Outlook

Once they are on the job, wireless communications technicians can advance to positions in service management or as business administrators. Some technicians may become "troubleshooters" who specialize in specific equipment and help other technicians deal with specific types of problems. Technicians with an entrepreneurial bent may start their own businesses that provide technical service and support.

Wireless communications technicians are expected to be in great demand as the wireless industry grows and more telecommunications businesses compete for wireless consumers.

## Working Conditions

Bench technicians generally work in clean, well-lighted, air-conditioned surroundings. They may work in stores or electronics repair workshops.

Field technicians face a variety of working conditions, including working outdoors in bad weather and working on ladders or on telephone poles. In addition, technicians may work shifts, including weekends and holidays, to repair and maintain wireless networks.

## Where to Go for More Information

Information Technology and
Telecommunications Association
74 New Montgomery St., Ste. 230
San Francisco, CA 94105-3411
(415) 777-4647
http://www.tca.org

Telecommunications Industry Association
2500 Wilson Blvd., Ste. 300
Arlington, VA 22201
(703) 907-7700
http://www.tiaonline.org

Wireless Communications Association
International
1333 H St. NW, Ste. 700 W
Washington, DC 20005
(202) 452-7823
http://www.wcai.com

## Earnings and Benefits

Salaries for wireless communications technicians increase with experience and training. Entry-level technicians employed by a telecommunications company may earn up to $35,000 per year. Mid-level technicians earn between $40,000 and $45,000 per year, whereas top technicians may earn an annual salary between $45,000 and $60,000.

Wireless communications technicians generally receive benefits packages that include paid vacations and sick leave, health and life insurance, and retirement plans. Many employers also offer bonuses as incentives for meeting customer service goals.

# Job Profiles Some Specialized Training/Experience

## Biological Technician

**Education and Training**
Associate's or bachelor's degree

**Salary**
Median—$15.97 per hour

**Employment Outlook**
Good

### Definition and Nature of the Work

Biological technicians assist scientists who study living things and their life processes. Like agricultural technicians and medical laboratory technicians, biological technicians work in the life sciences. Their field is biology, which is a very broad life science area. Biological technicians may be called biology technicians, biological aides, laboratory technicians, or laboratory assistants.

Biological technicians help life scientists by gathering information, materials, and samples. They set up scientific apparatus, do calculations, and draw simple graphs and charts. Technicians often perform tests and experiments. They keep records and report the results of these tests and experiments to the scientists. Sometimes they are responsible for cleaning and maintaining laboratory equipment, such as test tubes, microscopes, scales, and animal cages. Workers who

Biological technicians work mainly in laboratories in colleges and universities. *(© Brownie Harris/Corbis.)*

spend most of their time caring for laboratory animals, such as mice and guinea pigs, are known as laboratory animal care technicians.

The duties of biological technicians vary according to the area of biology in which they work. Some technicians, for example, work in microbiology. They help scientists who study microscopic organisms and may do experiments with molds, viruses, or bacteria. They may, for example, study the role of bacterial membranes in causing disease. Some technicians work primarily with insects. They may, for example, study the control of insects and help scientists develop new insecticides or new ways to use one kind of insect to control another.

Biological technicians are needed wherever laboratory work in biology is done. They work primarily in laboratories in colleges and universities. Some are employed in medical or agricultural research centers. Some work for government agencies or nonprofit research organizations. Others have jobs in private industry, especially in the drug, chemical, and food processing industries.

## Education and Training Requirements

You can train to become a biological technician at a college or technical school that offers a program in laboratory technology. You can specialize in one area, such as animal science or plant science. Most technicians' programs take two years to complete. You may also need some on-the-job training. For some jobs, employers prefer to hire people who have a bachelor's degree in one of the biological sciences. College students may work part time in a university or hospital laboratory and apply for full-time positions when they become available.

## Getting the Job

The placement office at your college or technical school can give you information about getting a job as a biological technician. State and private employment agencies may be able to put you in touch with laboratories that need technicians. You can also find job openings listed in newspaper classifieds, professional journals, or job banks on the Internet. You may want to apply directly to colleges and universities, government agencies, and companies that hire biological technicians. To get a government job, you will probably have to take a civil service test.

## Advancement Possibilities and Employment Outlook

Advancement depends on education, experience, and job performance. Biological technicians sometimes start as laboratory assistants. They generally receive more responsibility and higher salaries as they show that they can do their jobs well. Some become supervisors of other technicians. Others advance by getting jobs in areas related to laboratory work, such as technical writing or biological equipment sales. Technicians who get doctoral degrees can become scientists.

Overall employment of science technicians in general and biological technicians in particular is expected to increase about as fast as average for all occupations through the year 2014. The continued growth of the biotechnology industry will continue to create demand for biological technicians. The fastest employment growth of biological technicians, however, should occur in the pharmaceutical industry. An aging population will increase demand for innovative and improved drugs, further spurring demand for biological technicians.

## Working Conditions

Biological technicians generally work in laboratories that are clean, airy, well lighted, and well equipped. Depending on the specific job, however, they may have to spend some time outside the laboratory gathering samples and information or doing other tasks. For example, technicians who study plant life sometimes have to care for plants growing in outdoor fields. Technicians who deal with fish may have to take water samples and check fish in various rivers or lakes.

Biological technicians should be flexible workers who can follow the directions of scientists carefully, keep detailed and accurate logs of experimental procedures they conducted, and work as part of a scientific research team. Since laboratory tests often must be repeated many times, technicians must also have a great deal of patience. They generally work thirty-five to forty hours per week. In some cases they may have to work rotating shifts when test results have to be recorded around the clock, or they may have to come in at unusual times to carry out the experimental procedure.

## Earnings and Benefits

Earnings depend on the education and experience of the biological technician, the location, and the kind of job. In 2004 the median hourly wage of biological technicians was $15.97. In 2005 the average annual salary for biological technicians working for the federal government was $38,443. Benefits usually include paid holidays and vacations, health insurance, and pension plans.

**Where to Go for More Information**

American Institute of Biological Sciences
1444 I St. NW, Ste. 200
Washington, DC 20005
(202) 628-1500
http://www.aibs.org

# *Genetic Engineering Research Assistant*

**Education and Training**
Bachelor's degree

**Salary**
Median—$15.97 per hour

**Employment Outlook**
Good

## Definition and Nature of the Work

Genetic engineering research assistants work with research scientists in the development and testing of genetically engineered products. Genetic engineering is the science concerned with the manipulation or modification of genes in plants, animals, and microorganisms. Genetic engineering research typically involves isolating and altering genetic material from one organism and transplanting, or splicing, it to another. By applying this technology to medicine, scientists have produced purer and safer vaccines and other drugs for humans. In agriculture, they have developed new crop strains and increased crop yields.

Most genetic engineering research assistants work in the area known as research and development. They are employed by chemical or pharmaceutical companies or by firms that specialize in genetic engineering. The rest of the assistants usually work in medical research facilities, specializing in such fields as microbiology, pharmacology, genetics, and biochemistry.

Genetic engineering research assistants perform most of the routine duties related to experimentation and new product development. For example, they prepare cultures of microorganisms for experiments and run experiments designed by scientists. They may be asked to analyze the data and report the results.

Genetic engineering research assistants operate laboratory equipment, such as high-speed centrifuges, and gather data using various laboratory methods such

A genetic research assistant prepares samples for testing.
*(© CDC/PHIL/Corbis.)*

as gel electrophoresis. This method separates large molecules on the basis of size, electric charge, and other physical properties. Research assistants may also sterilize laboratory materials and media using an autoclave. They must maintain stringent cleanliness and sterility standards in the laboratories so that they do not contaminate any of the materials under research. The smallest of errors can ruin weeks, even months, of research.

Some genetic engineering research assistants work in process development areas. Here they may assist scientists and chemical engineers in "scaling up" a product from a small laboratory sample into a large-scale commercial quantity. Research assistants may help analytic chemists in performing assay testing on genetically engineered products to determine their quality, weight, and composition.

## Education and Training Requirements

Educational requirements vary depending on the job. For most research assistant positions in genetic engineering, you need a bachelor's degree in a biological science. Degree programs at colleges generally take four years to complete. In addition, the hiring company or institution usually provides on-the-job training.

## Getting the Job

If you attend a college or university, your school placement office may be able to help you find a job. State employment agencies may also be able to help. You can apply directly to firms in the genetic engineering field, such as pharmaceutical and chemical companies. These companies often list job openings in newspaper classifieds or job banks on the Internet. Research hospitals and medical schools may also list openings for genetic engineering research assistants.

## Advancement Possibilities and Employment Outlook

With increased experience, a genetic engineering research assistant can become a supervisor of other workers. Research assistants who continue their education and get an advanced degree can become genetic engineering scientists.

The employment outlook for genetic engineering research assistants is very good. Research scientists and their assistants will be in high demand as more and more applications for genetic engineering are found in medicine, agriculture, and private industry.

## Working Conditions

Genetic engineering research assistants typically work in clean, well-lighted laboratories. Some assistants may work wearing protective hooded clothing that filters out potentially contaminating materials. Assistants in laboratories may work alone or with other workers. Research assistants generally work a thirty-five to forty-hour week. In some cases, they might need to work at night or on weekends. Research assistants sometimes handle heavy equipment. They may also have to spend hours at a time on their feet or seated at a laboratory bench.

Genetic engineering research assistants must be able to follow instructions carefully and precisely. They should enjoy doing extremely meticulous work and maintaining accurate, detailed records.

## Earnings and Benefits

Salaries for research assistants in genetic engineering vary depending on education, experience, and the kind of work they perform. They make earnings similar to biological technicians. In 2004 the median hourly wage for biological technicians was $15.97 per hour. Benefits usually include paid holidays and vacations, health insurance, and pension plans.

### Where to Go for More Information

American Society of Human Genetics
9650 Rockville Pike
Bethesda, MD 20814-3998
(866) HUM-GENE
http://www.ashg.org/genetics

National Center for Biotechnology Information
National Library of Medicine, Building 38A
Bethesda, MD 20894
(301) 496-2475
http://www.ncbi.nlm.nih.gov

# Job Profiles Advanced Training/Experience

## *Aerospace Engineer*

**Education and Training**
Bachelor's degree

**Salary**
Median—$79,100 per year

**Employment Outlook**
Good

### Definition and Nature of the Work

Aerospace engineers design, develop, and test aircraft, missiles, and space vehicles and oversee their production. They often specialize in one kind of vehicle, such as passenger planes, helicopters, or rockets. In some cases, they also work with earthbound vehicles, such as deep-diving vessels that are used to do research in the oceans and high-speed trains that float above their tracks. Aerospace engineering includes aeronautical engineering, which is limited to aircraft, and astronautical engineering, which is limited to spacecraft.

Most aerospace engineers work in the aircraft industry. This industry includes companies that make engines, communications systems, electronic devices, and the many other parts used in aircraft. Some aerospace engineers work for government agencies, such as the Department of Defense or the National Aeronautics and Space Administration (NASA). Many also work for companies that are under government contract to produce equipment needed for missiles and spacecraft. Others work for commercial airline companies, research and development organizations, and consulting firms, as well as for colleges and universities.

Aerospace engineers work closely with other specialists. Scientists such as physicists or metallurgists do the research needed to create new materials. They study how the materials will react in certain conditions, such as the intense heat or speeds encountered in space travel. Aerospace engineers then use the research to develop designs. They test the designs and make changes before be-

Aerospace engineering includes astronautics, which is the science concerned with travel beyond the earth's atmosphere to the moon and other planets. *(AP Images.)*

ginning production of the equipment. They also supervise drafters and engineering technicians.

Aerospace engineering is a broad field. Its general area of concern overlaps with areas of other engineering fields, including mechanical, chemical, and electrical. There are also several areas of specialization within the field. Some aerospace engineers concentrate on structures and specialize in the design of new frameworks. They test the framework's ability to withstand heat, pressure, and other forms of stress in wind tunnels. This helps to develop strong and durable aircraft and other vehicles.

Other aerospace engineers work chiefly on guidance and control systems. These systems include automatic navigation equipment for submarines and the automated Instrumentation Landing Systems (ILS) for aircraft, which allow aircraft to land at night and in bad weather. Other special fields in aerospace engineering include propulsion, fluid mechanics, thermodynamics, celestial mechanics, and acoustics. In addition, some aerospace engineers specialize in one phase of a process during which new equipment is developed, produced, and distributed. For example, they may concentrate on design, production, or sales. Others may specialize in a particular type of aerospace product, such as commercial aircraft, military fighter jets, helicopters, spacecraft, or missiles and rockets. They may become experts in aerodynamics, thermodynamics, celestial mechanics, propulsion, acoustics, or guidance and control systems.

## Education and Training Requirements

Beginning aerospace engineers need at least a bachelor's degree in engineering. Degree holders in mathematics or the natural sciences may qualify for certain jobs. It usually takes four or five years to earn a bachelor's degree in engineering. A number of colleges offer undergraduate majors in aeronautical, astronautical, or aerospace engineering. Some jobs also require an advanced degree. Aerospace engineers must continue to study the latest developments in the field throughout their careers.

All states require licensing for engineers whose work affects life, health, or property, or for those who offer their services to the public. To become licensed as a professional engineer, you need a degree from an accredited school, four years of experience as an engineer, and a passing grade on a state examination. Some jobs in the aerospace industry require security clearance before you can start work.

## Getting the Job

If you are interested in working for private industry, you should contact aircraft manufacturers, commercial airlines, and companies that make aerospace parts and tools. If you are interested in space travel, you can contact NASA for job information. For most government jobs you need to apply through a civil service agency. You can also apply directly to universities, consulting firms, and research and development organizations. The placement office at your engineering college can also give you advice on finding a job. In some cases, openings for aerospace engineers are listed in newspaper classifieds and job banks on the Internet. Professional engineering journals are another good place to look for job information.

## Advancement Possibilities and Employment Outlook

Aerospace engineers who have the needed experience and education can advance to positions as managers or administrators. Some become sales engineers or college teachers. A few start their own engineering firms.

Employment opportunities for aerospace engineers is expected to grow more slowly than average for all occupations from 2004 to 2014. Military aerospace projects likely will generate new jobs, but the number of new jobs in the design and production of commercial aircraft will decrease. However, the employment outlook for aerospace engineers through 2014 is good because new graduates will be needed to replace aerospace engineers who retire or leave the occupation for other reasons. Aerospace engineers who keep up with broad developments in their field are more likely to get jobs than those who know only one narrow area of technology.

## Working Conditions

Aerospace engineers work under a variety of conditions—from quiet laboratories and offices to noisy airfields and manufacturing plants. They usually work at least forty hours a week. They may be required to work long hours to complete a project on time. When a project is completed, engineers sometimes must move to a new location to find a job using their special skills.

Aerospace engineers generally work in teams and share information and ideas. They need to work well with others and be able to communicate their ideas. Engineers are problem solvers and should enjoy facing the challenge of a difficult problem. They must be patient and creative and able to pay close attention to the details of their work.

### Where to Go for More Information

American Institute of Aeronautics and Astronautics
1801 Alexander Bell Dr., Ste. 500
Reston, VA 20191-4344
(800) 639-2422
http://www.aiaa.org

International Association of Machinists and Aerospace Workers
9000 Machinists Place
Upper Marlboro, MD 20772-2867
(301) 967-4500
http://www.iamaw.org

National Society of Professional Engineers
1420 King St.
Alexandria, VA 22314-2794
(703) 684-2800
http://www.nspe.org

## Earnings and Benefits

Earnings vary depending on the education and experience of the aerospace engineer and the location and nature of the job. Aerospace engineers earn salaries close to the average for all engineer. In 2005 the average starting salary for an aerospace engineer with a bachelor's degree was $50,993 per year. Engineers with master's degrees earned starting salaries of $62,930 per year, and those with doctoral degrees earned starting salaries of $72,529 per year. In 2004 the median annual income for all aerospace engineers was $79,100. Benefits generally include paid holidays and vacations, health insurance, and pension plans.

# *Air-Conditioning Engineer*

**Education and Training**
Bachelor's degree

**Salary**
Median—$67,110 per year

**Employment Outlook**
Good

## Definition and Nature of the Work

Air-conditioning engineers are mechanical engineers who work on systems that cool, heat, purify, circulate, humidify, and dehumidify air. Climate control systems are used in a wide range of indoor areas, from office buildings to tractor-trailer cabs. These systems help people work and live with maximum comfort and safety. Air-conditioning also helps machines and other equipment work properly. For instance, the humidity level in a print shop must be controlled so that the paper does not shrink and the ink prints clearly. Also, computer systems need to be kept at a certain temperature and humidity.

Air-conditioning engineers work on systems for homes, offices, hospitals, schools, stores, factories, theaters, airplanes, trains, ships, and cars. Each interior area has its own set of problems that the engineer must solve. For example, a space vehicle that is burning hot on one side from the direct rays of the sun and −400°F on the other side presents unique air-conditioning problems. Engineers can also encounter problems when developing systems for large areas such as glass-enclosed shopping malls.

Air-conditioning engineers work for manufacturers of air-conditioning equipment and for engineering and contracting firms. They work in industries that use air conditioners, such as the aerospace industry. Engineers also work for colleges, universities, and government agencies. Some have their own businesses.

Air-conditioning engineers usually specialize in a particular area of engineering, such as research and development. In this area, engineers design, test, and develop new kinds of air-conditioning equipment. Air-conditioning engineers who work in production plan every step of the manufacturing process. They estimate the costs of labor and supplies and often supervise the manufacturing of equipment. Other engineers work in sales. They work with customers to determine their needs and then sell them the appropriate air-conditioning systems. Engineers also supervise the installation, operation, and maintenance of air-conditioning systems. Some work as independent consultants who advise manufacturers, contractors, architects, and others on air-conditioning problems.

## Education and Training Requirements

To become an air-conditioning engineer you need at least a bachelor's degree in engineering. Most air-conditioning engineers have degrees in mechanical or electrical engineering. Some colleges have courses in air-conditioning engineering, but training in one of the traditional engineering fields provides adequate training. If your college has a work-study program, you might be able to combine job experience in the air-conditioning industry with your formal training. Some engineers go on to get a master's or doctoral degree. A master's degree requires an additional one or two years of full-time study, and a doctoral degree often involves four years of full-time study. Some engineers do graduate work on a part-time basis once they have their bachelor's degrees and a job. Employers usually encourage their employees to take courses that will improve their job performance, and they will often pay tuition. In addition, engineers need to continue studying and reading throughout their careers in order to keep up with advances in air-conditioning technology.

Engineers who offer their services to the public or whose work affects life, health, or property must be licensed by the state in which they work. They generally need a degree from an approved engineering college, about four years of work experience as an engineer, and a passing grade on a state examination before becoming licensed as a professional engineer.

## Getting the Job

Your college placement office can give you information about getting an engineering job. If you take part in a work-study program in college, you may be able to continue working for your employer after graduation. You can also apply directly to companies that hire air-conditioning engineers. Many employers advertise job openings in newspapers, Internet job banks, and trade and professional journals.

## Advancement Possibilities and Employment Outlook

Advancement in this field generally depends on education and experience. Many air-conditioning engineers become heads of research teams, managers, or even executives. Some start their own consulting or contracting firms. Mechanical engineers, including air-conditioning engineers, are projected to have an average rate of employment growth through 2014. Openings will result from a demand for new or upgraded energy-efficient climate control systems. The number of new jobs created each year also depends on the state of the economy.

## Working Conditions

Working conditions vary depending on the area in which the engineer is employed. Air-conditioning engineers working in research and development generally spend most of their time in offices and laboratories. They usually work forty hours per week. Engineers working in production usually spend more of their time on production lines or at construction sites. They often work rotating shifts. Most sales engineers travel frequently, and their hours are more flexible. Engineers can expect to work extra hours at times, especially when deadlines must be met. They also spend additional time learning about new developments in the field.

Engineers must be creative, innovative problem solvers. They should be good at science and mathematics and have the communication skills necessary to get their ideas across to other engineers, air-conditioning technicians, architects, and customers. They should also be able to work well in teams.

### Where to Go for More Information

Air-Conditioning and Refrigeration Institute
4100 North Fairfax Dr., Ste. 200
Arlington, VA 22203
(703) 524-8800
http://www.ari.org

Air Conditioning Contractors of America
2800 Shirlington Rd., Ste. 300
Arlington, VA 20006
(703) 575-4477
http://www.acca.org

American Society of Heating, Refrigeration and Air-Conditioning Engineers
1791 Tullie Circle NE
Atlanta, GA 30329-2305
(800) 527-4723
http://www.ashrae.org

## Earnings and Benefits

Earnings vary depending on the education and experience of the air-conditioning engineer, the location, and the type of job. Air-conditioning engineers earn salaries that are close to the salaries of materials engineers. In May 2004, the median annual salary of a materials engineer was $67,110. In 2005 the average starting salaries for a materials engineer with a bachelor's degree was $50,982 per year. Benefits usually include paid holidays and vacations, health insurance, and pension plans.

# *Anatomist*

**Education and Training**
Doctoral degree

**Salary**
Median—$65,110 per year

**Employment Outlook**
Good

## Definition and Nature of the Work

Anatomists are biological scientists who study the structure of living things. Most anatomists are biomedical researchers and educators focusing on human anatomical form and function. Many specialize in areas such as biological imaging, cell biology, genetics, molecular development, endocrinology (study of the glands that produce hormones), histology (study of tissues), neuroscience, forensics, microscopy, and physical anthropology (study of the physical characteristics, variability, and evolution of the human organism).

Most anatomists work in colleges, universities, or medical centers. They usually teach and do research. They help train scientists, as well as physicians, dentists, nurses, pharmacists, and other workers in the health field. Some work for government agencies or for medical and scientific publishing firms. Others are employed by private companies, such as firms that make artificial limbs or organs.

Although the work of anatomists varies widely, nearly all spend some time in laboratories studying the structures of plant or animal species. Anatomists may do basic research to further our knowledge about organisms in general. They may also do applied research to solve specific problems. The two kinds of research often overlap.

Anatomists often observe and dissect the large organs of plants and animals. They use microscopes and computers to examine smaller units, such as small organs, tissues, and cells. They also use special techniques to prepare their samples. Because their field is so broad, anatomists need to have some knowledge of other fields such as embryology, neurology, biomedical engineering, genetics, and pathology. They often work with experts in these fields. Anatomists are sometimes assisted by biological technicians.

Some anatomists specialize in the study of the anatomy of plant forms. These botanists concentrate on the internal structure of plants and the development of the various plant parts, such as stems, leaves, and flowers. They also study smaller units, such as plant cells and tissues.

Other anatomists concentrate on the anatomy of animals. They may be zoologists, veterinarians, or physicians. Some of these scientists do basic studies of the structures of animal life. Others make direct applications of anatomical principles to solve specific problems in a human or an animal. Anatomists have made significant contributions to medicine, ranging from the identification of neurons to the discovery of vitamin E. In the field of cytology, or the study of cells, anatomists have developed new techniques for studying samples of living material. They have also helped develop cinematography as a tool for research and teaching in biology.

Anatomy is a cornerstone of medicine. The work of anatomists will be vital in the development of artificial organs, such as kidneys and hearts, and in the transplantation of donated organs. Such varied fields as plastic surgery, space medicine, and environmental health will depend on the discoveries of anatomists.

## Education and Training Requirements

You generally need an advanced degree to become an anatomist. In college you should major in premedicine, biology, chemistry, or a related field and take a variety of courses in the biological, physical, and behavioral sciences. With a bachelor's degree you may be able to get a job as a biological technician, but your opportunities for advancement will be limited. If you have a master's degree in anatomy or a related field, you may be able to get a job in teaching or applied research, or in a field such as medical publishing. You usually need a doctoral degree to get a research and teaching position at a university or medical school.

Because anatomy is a broad field, you can get your specialized training in anatomy in one of three areas—biology, veterinary medicine, or medicine. Whichever area you choose, however, you are likely to spend at least eight years as a student after high school. Some anatomists get both a doctor of medicine (M.D.) degree and a doctoral (Ph.D.) degree. To keep up with new developments in anatomy and related fields, anatomists must continue to study throughout their careers.

## Getting the Job

Your professors or the placement office at your university or medical school can give you information about getting a job as an anatomist. Professional journals sometimes list openings for anatomists. You can also apply directly to research centers, private companies, or government agencies that hire anatomists. You sometimes need to pass a civil service exam to get a government job.

## Advancement Possibilities and Employment Outlook

Anatomists with a doctoral degree can advance to positions of assistant, associate, and full professor or to director of research in a university or medical center. Anatomists sometimes achieve distinction when their discoveries are important advances in science or medicine. They publish their research work in scientific and medical journals.

The employment outlook for anatomists with doctoral degrees is good through the year 2014; employment of biological scientists is projected to grow about as fast as average for all occupations through that year.

## Working Conditions

Anatomists generally work in clean, well-lighted laboratories. They often spend some time in offices and classrooms as well. Although the standard workweek may be forty hours long, many anatomists work more. However, their schedules are often somewhat flexible. Anatomists often need to spend time attending meetings, correcting papers and examinations, and studying to keep up with the new developments in anatomy and in related fields of science and medicine.

Anatomists must be able to work alone or as part of a team. Those who teach must be able to explain complex concepts in simple terms. Researchers need to be precise and careful. They should also be able to write and explain their findings to others.

## Earnings and Benefits

Earnings depend on the education and experience of the anatomist, as well as on the location and kind of job. In 2004 the median annual earnings of medical scientists in research and development were $65,110. In the federal government in 2005, general biological scientists in nonsupervisory, supervisory, and managerial positions earned an average salary of $69,908. Benefits usually include paid holidays and vacations, health insurance, and pension plans.

### Where to Go for More Information

American Association of Anatomists
9650 Rockville Pike
Bethesda, MD 20814-3998
(301) 634-7910
http://www.anatomy.org

American Association of Veterinary Anatomists
College of Veterinary Medicine
Auburn University
Auburn, AL 36849-5518
(334) 844-4546
http://www.vetanatomists.org

American Institute of Biological Sciences
1444 I St. NW, Ste. 200
Washington, DC 20005
(202) 628-1500
http://www.aibs.org

# Anthropologist

## Definition and Nature of the Work

**Education and Training**
Doctoral degree

**Salary**
Median—$43,890 per year

**Employment Outlook**
Good

Anthropologists are social scientists who study the origin and physical, cultural, and social development of human beings. Anthropologists study the language, traditions, beliefs, possessions, and values of people in various parts of the world and formulate hypotheses to explain their research and findings. They generally specialize in physical anthropology, archaeology, linguistics, or cultural anthropology.

Physical anthropologists attempt to understand the physical or biological development of the human species. Some study fossils to trace the evolution of human beings. Physical anthropologists also study how humans have been influenced by their heredity and environment. They are interested in the geographical distribution of human physical characteristics. They study measurements, blood types, and other information about large groups of people. Physical anthropologists need to have some knowledge of genetics, human anatomy, evolution, and other fields of biology. In fact, many physical anthropologists work in medical schools or in biology departments in colleges or universities.

Some anthropologists are archaeologists. They examine physical objects, such as tools, clothing, homes, and art left from past human cultures. They use these objects to determine the history, customs, and living habits of earlier civilizations. Most often archaeologists dig up objects that have become buried in the ground over the years. Archaeologists have made important contributions to the field of anthropology concerning the cultures of Native Americans, European cave dwellers, and early American settlers.

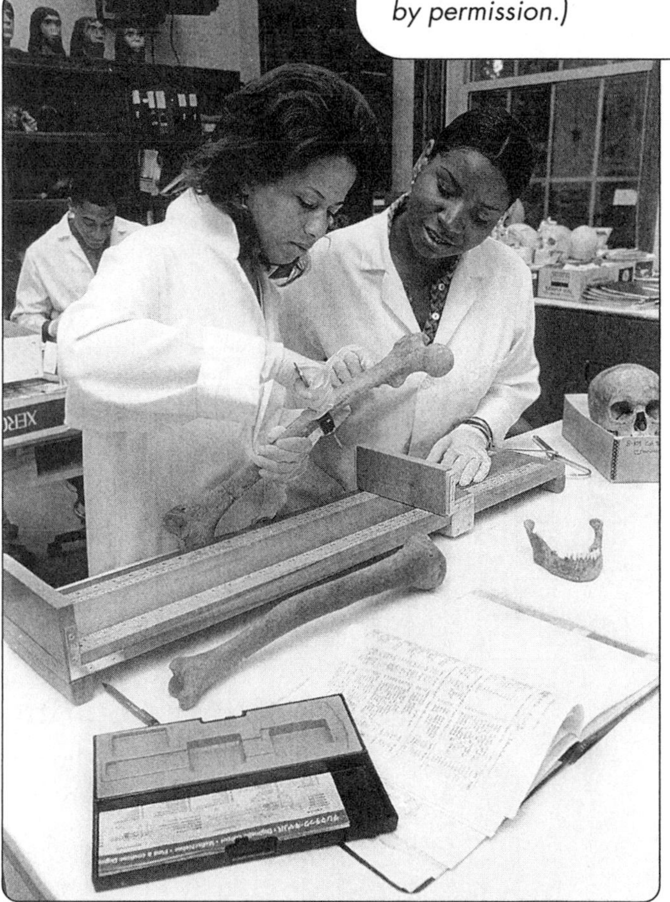

Physical anthropologists measure a human bone in an ongoing attempt to understand the physical or biological development of the human species. *(© Martha Tabor/ Working Images Photographs. Reproduced by permission.)*

Anthropologists known as linguistic anthropologists study the evolution of languages and their relation to one another. They sometimes visit communities with no written languages and study and record the spoken languages. Linguistic anthropologists also try to explain how the language is related to the ways in which the people in the community think and act.

Cultural anthropologists, who study the customs and cultures of living peoples, form the largest group of anthropologists. They study populations such as native tribes of Africa or America, people on remote islands of the Pacific, or segments of the populations of modern cities. Cultural anthropologists interview persons in the populations they study and observe their behavior. They often concentrate on one area of life, such as their religious beliefs, their music, or how they care for the aged. They keep careful records and try to draw conclusions about their ways of life.

Most anthropologists work in colleges and universities, where they teach and do research. Others work for museums. Government agencies employ a few anthropologists, usually in museums, national parks, and technical aid programs. Anthropologists also work for the Bureau of Indian Affairs and the

Army Corps of Engineers. Some anthropologists serve as consultants to government or industry. For example, they may write reports estimating the impact that the construction of a new dam would have on the people living in a valley upstream from the dam. They may prepare an estimate of the value of the archaeological sites that would be flooded by the resulting reservoir.

## Education and Training Requirements

A doctoral degree in anthropology is needed for most positions in this field. Individuals with a bachelor's or master's degree sometimes qualify for research or administrative positions in government or private firms.

If you want to be an anthropologist, you should major in anthropology in college. As early as possible, you should begin training in the use of statistics, in one or more foreign languages, and in a field related to the area of anthropology that especially interests you. For example, if you want to go into archaeology, you will need knowledge of geology and geography. For physical anthropology, you should be trained in genetics and human anatomy. It usually takes at least eight years of full-time study beyond high school to get a doctoral degree in anthropology. Part of this time is often spent doing fieldwork. In addition, anthropologists are expected to continue reading and studying throughout their careers so that they can keep up with new findings in the field.

## Getting the Job

Your professors and the placement office at your university can give you information about getting a job in anthropology. Students often have an opportunity to work as research assistants while in graduate school. Openings are sometimes listed in professional publications. You can also apply directly to colleges and universities, government agencies, and private firms that hire anthropologists.

## Advancement Possibilities and Employment Outlook

Anthropologists are highly trained specialists who usually advance by improving their skills and becoming experts in their fields. They often write books and articles about their findings. Many feel that the best form of advancement is winning the recognition of other anthropologists and of scholars in other fields. Anthropologists can also supervise teams doing research at archaeological sites. They can advance to the rank of full professor in a college or university, or they can become administrators.

Employment of anthropologists is expected to be average when compared with all occupations through 2014. The growth of environmental legislation has led to a corresponding rise in the need for qualified people to write impact statements. With many more qualified applicants than available openings, however, competition is expected to be keen. Most new jobs for anthropologists are likely to be in private industry or in government agencies. Very few jobs, with only limited advancement opportunities, will be available to those who have only a bachelor's or master's degree.

## Working Conditions

Anthropologists who are employed by colleges and universities usually spend much of their time in offices, classrooms, and libraries. Their working hours are flexible but often total more than forty hours a week. Most anthropologists also do some field work. This work may take them to study sites as diverse as the Arctic to study the Inuit or Eskimos, to Africa to dig at an archaeological site or observe monkeys in their natural habitat, or into a modern city to record the behavior and attitudes of members of a particular ethnic group. Anthropologists engaged in field work require good physical stamina. Most anthropologists find that the challenge of making new discoveries more than compensates for any lack of physical comfort on field trips. Anthropologists who work for museums or for businesses or government agencies face a wide variety of working conditions.

All anthropologists must be able to communicate their ideas to other people, whether these people are visitors to a museum, other scholars, or a management group in business or industry. They must be careful workers who have the patience to sift through bushels of earth looking for fossils and artifacts or to sort information looking for details about one area of human culture. Although much of their work is done independently, anthropologists should be able to work as part of a research team when necessary. They need to be adaptable people who can get along with people from cultures that are very different from their own.

## Earnings and Benefits

The earnings of anthropologists vary depending on the experience and skill of the anthropologist and the type of job. In 2004 anthropologists had median annual earnings of $43,890. Many anthropologists employed at colleges and universities add to their salaries by writing books or giving lectures. Benefits usually include paid holidays and vacations, health insurance, and pensions.

**Where to Go for More Information**

American Anthropological Association
2200 Wilson Blvd., Ste. 600
Arlington, VA 22201
(703) 528-1902
http://www.aaanet.org

# *Artificial Intelligence Specialist*

**Education and Training**
Master's or doctoral degree

**Salary**
Median—$74,980 per year

**Employment Outlook**
Excellent

## Definition and Nature of the Work

Artificial intelligence (AI) specialists program computers to "think." Some AI specialists work in cognitive simulation, in which computers are used to test hypotheses about how the human mind works. For example, the AI specialist might develop a computer program to simulate the way the human brain might recognize a face. The computer's ability to recognize a face would then be compared to a human's ability. However, most AI specialists work in applied AI. The goal of applied AI, or advanced information processing, is to program computer expert systems ("smart" systems)—those that can, for example, recognize a fingerprint for security purposes, recognize voices, interpret information, solve problems, and speak in a humanlike voice.

The development of expert systems enables computers to make specific judgments and give advice to users by incorporating human expertise. Computers are able to diagnose illnesses, evaluate psychological tests, locate natural resources, and perform many other important functions. Expert systems are used in the fields of medicine, law, geology, and accounting. In medicine, expert systems can make the knowledge and experience of top specialists available to all doctors. These specialists work with AI specialists to develop programs for the identification of diseases. AI scientists at naval research laboratories have even developed a robot that can be sent aboard an unmanned submarine to repair crippled vessels.

Artificial intelligence specialists work for the research centers of universities, small AI development companies, and the growing numbers of large corporations that are maintaining in-house AI groups. Some of these companies are interested in computer-aided instruction for their own personnel. Other companies may develop and sell instructional software created by AI specialists. The defense, electronics, computer, communications, and automotive industries are all interested in this field. Some academic researchers are forming their own small AI companies.

## Education and Training Requirements

The field requires a strong background in programming or systems analysis or fluency in several computer languages. Most artificial intelligence specialists have master's or doctoral degrees in computer science or cognitive science (a combination of psychology, psycholinguistics, computer science, anthropology, and philosophy). Some applicants with bachelor's degrees may be qualified for entry-level positions.

## Getting the Job

Try to gain practical experience by initiating a school project or by taking part in research efforts. This may help you break into the field. You can apply directly to university research centers or to companies that do AI research and development. You can also sign up with a recruiting firm.

## Advancement Possibilities and Employment Outlook

An AI specialist who has a bachelor's or master's degree can advance by earning a doctoral degree. Other forms of advancement include becoming head of a research group or moving into management. Some researchers start their own development companies.

Although artificial intelligence research began in the 1940s, the field is still in its infancy and has only recently started to gain momentum. More than half of the nation's one thousand largest corporations have invested significantly in AI developments, including machine vision systems, natural language, robotics, and voice-recognition systems. Job opportunities are expected to grow at a rate much faster than the average for all occupations. Computer software engineering in general is projected to be one of the fastest-growing occupations from 2004 to 2014.

At one time, specialists needed a background in operations research. The job market should be less restrictive in the future, accepting specialists from a range of disciplines including systems analysis, programming, and computer languages.

## Working Conditions

Patience and dedication are desirable qualities for AI specialists since programs often take years to develop. Research is almost always a team effort, so AI specialists must be able to work well with others. In addition, researchers often work closely with experts in many fields to benefit from their knowledge.

## Earnings and Benefits

Artificial intelligence specialists make salaries comparable to software engineers. Their median annual salary in 2004 was $74,980. Benefits usually include paid vacations and holidays, as well as health insurance.

### Where to Go for More Information

American Association for Artificial Intelligence
445 Burgess Dr.
Menlo Park, CA 94025-3442
(650) 328-3123
http://www.aaai.org

# Astronomer

## Definition and Nature of the Work

**Education and Training**
Doctoral degree

**Salary**
Median—$97,320 per year

**Employment Outlook**
Fair

Astronomers are sometimes called astrophysicists. They use the laws of physics and mathematics to learn about the nature of matter and energy throughout the universe, which includes the sun, moon, planets, stars, and galaxies. In addition, astronomers apply their knowledge to solve problems in navigation, space flight, and satellite communications. They also develop the instruments and techniques needed to observe and collect astronomical data.

Many astronomers work in colleges and universities where they do research and teach astronomy. Some work in observatories, planetariums, and museums where they help to explain what is known about the universe to the public. Others are employed by government agencies, such as the U.S. Naval Observatory or the National Aeronautics and Space Administration (NASA). A few work for companies in the aerospace industry.

Some astronomers primarily gather and analyze large quantities of data from observatories and satellites. They usually only spend a few weeks each year making observations with telescopes. For many years, satellites and other kinds of space-based instruments have greatly expanded the range of observation for astronomers. Most recently, new computer and telescope technologies are leading to a resurgence in ground-based observation techniques.

Astronomers must first decide which objects to observe and the methods and equipment to use. They may go to an observatory at a scheduled time and make and record their observations, or they may have assistants gather the data. Astronomers then analyze these observations, put them into numerical form, and if possible, explain them using existing hypotheses or theories.

Other astronomers spend most of their time working on new hypotheses, theories, or mathematical models. They often use computers to help them do the many calculations required to develop complex hypotheses about space. Such hypotheses may help explain some of the observations made by other astronomers.

Astronomers often specialize in one area, such as the sun, the solar system, or in the development of instruments and techniques. Their recent findings have included quasars, pulsars, black holes, and other mysterious phenomena in the far reaches of space.

The discoveries and theories of astronomers have been put to work in many useful ways. For example, they have improved weather forecasting, the measurement of time, and air and sea navigation. Astronomical study has been instrumental in the development of atomic theory and the exploration of space.

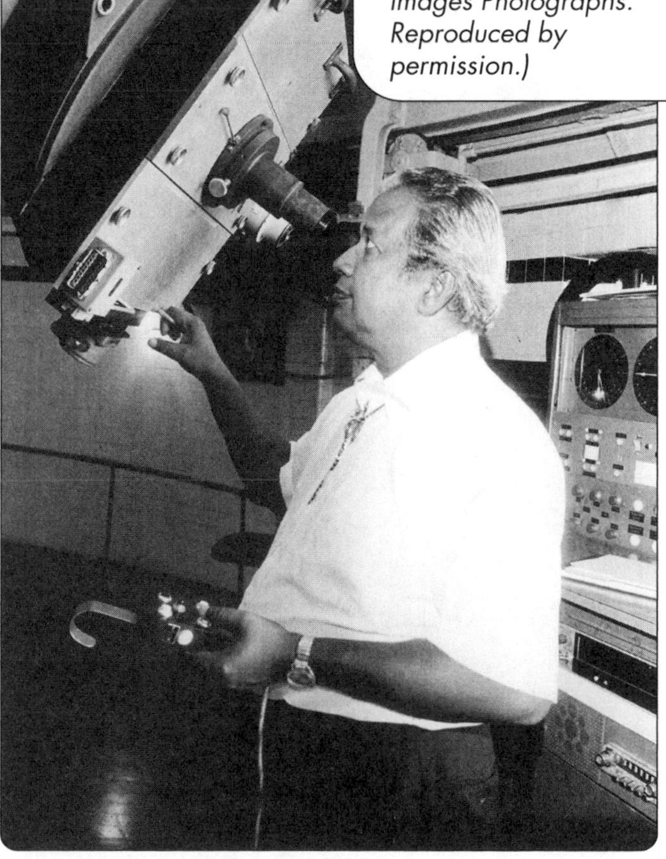

An astronomer at the Naval Observatory in Washington, D.C., adjusts a telescope. Astronomers are sometimes called astrophysicists. *(© Martha Tabor/Working Images Photographs. Reproduced by permission.)*

## Education and Training Requirements

There are a few openings as assistants or technicians in astronomy for those who have a bachelor's degree in physics or astronomy. There are more opportunities for those who have a master's degree in astronomy or a related field, such as physics or mathematics. To be an astronomer, a doctoral degree in astronomy or a closely related field, such as astrophysics, is usually required. It takes about four years to get a bachelor's degree and about another four years of full-time study to earn a doctoral degree. Astronomers also spend time studying throughout their careers to keep up with new discoveries in their field.

## Getting the Job

The astronomy department of your university will be able to give you advice and information about getting a job. You should apply directly to colleges and universities, national research centers, museums and planetariums, and other places that traditionally employ astronomers. Many of these jobs are advertised in professional journals. You should also consider applying for a job in places that have not traditionally employed astronomers. For example, a two-year college or high school may hire you, especially if you show enthusiasm for teaching and are prepared to teach other subjects in addition to astronomy. For some of these teaching jobs you may have to be certified by the state in which you teach. You may also be able to find other nontraditional jobs in industry, publishing, or scientific research. To find these kinds of jobs, you may first have to do a lot of searching on your own to determine the needs of employers.

## Advancement Possibilities and Employment Outlook

Astronomers with a doctoral degree can advance by moving into high-level positions in research and teaching. Many astronomers consider recognition as an expert in their special field to be the best form of advancement. They usually get this recognition only after spending years on research problems and having the results of their work published in scientific journals. Astronomers with only bachelor's degrees will find only limited opportunity for advancement in astronomy. A doctoral degree or a move into a related field, such as engineering or high school teaching, provides the best opportunities for advancement.

Employment of astronomers is expected to grow more slowly than the average for all occupations through 2014. Although government funding of astronomy research is expected to increase from 2004 to 2014, funding will still be limited. This limited funding will result in competition for basic research jobs. Most job openings will result from workers who retire.

## Working Conditions

Many astronomers work in well-equipped offices, laboratories, classrooms, and observatories with fellow scientists and students who share the same interests and goals. Others work with the general public to whom they try to convey their own interest in and enthusiasm for astronomy. Astronomers sometimes need to travel to remote observation sites and must often work at night. Most astronomers find their work exciting and personally rewarding because of the challenges it offers them. They usually devote long hours to their research and to the study needed to keep up with new developments in their field. They need to be patient and careful workers who can work for months or even years on the details of a research problem. They must also be able to communicate their findings to others.

## Earnings and Benefits

Salaries vary according to education, experience, and the type of employer. The median annual salary of astronomers was $97,320 in 2004. Benefits usually include paid holidays and vacations, health insurance, and pension plans.

**Where to Go for More Information**

American Astronautical Society
6532 Rolling Mill Place, Ste. 102
Springfield, VA 22152-2354
(703) 866-0020
http://www.astronautical.org

Universities Space Research Association
10211 Wincopin Circle, Ste. 500
Columbia, MD 21044-3432
(410) 730-2656
http://www.usra.edu

# *Biochemist*

**Education and Training**
Doctoral degree

**Salary**
Median—$68,950 per year

**Employment Outlook**
Good

## Definition and Nature of the Work

Biochemists are scientists who study the chemistry of living things. Their work includes studying the complex chemical combinations and reactions involved in metabolism, reproduction, growth, and heredity.

Some biochemists do basic research that expands scientific knowledge about the chemistry of living things. Others do applied research—that is, they work to create new products or to solve practical problems. In the field of medicine, for example, biochemists doing basic research may study the ways hormones are formed. Biochemists doing applied research may use the basic findings about hormone formation to develop synthetic hormones that can be produced on a large scale.

Biochemists working in medicine are sometimes called molecular biologists. They study bacteria, viruses, and other organisms to better understand the chemical basis of life. They also determine the effects of chemicals on medical problems such as cancer, aging, or obesity.

Biochemists in nutrition analyze food products to measure their vitamins, proteins, carbohydrates, and minerals. They research the effects of freezing or cooking and compute the caloric value of foods.

About half of all biochemists work for colleges and universities, where they teach or do research. Many are employed by private firms such as breweries, drug companies, petroleum producers, and manufacturers. Others work for nonprofit research centers or government agencies. A few biochemists are self-employed consultants who advise government or industry.

Although their jobs may differ widely, almost all biochemists do laboratory research at least some of the time. They plan research projects to test theories or to develop new products or processes. They are often assisted by laboratory technicians or research assistants. Biochemists perform a number of tasks, such as weighing chemicals, filtering liquids, distilling ingredients, and growing cultures of microorganisms. They use a variety of tools and instruments, including test tubes, beakers, flasks, electron microscopes, centrifuges, and spectrophotometers. Sometimes they make use of radioactive isotopes. Biochemists must use exact scientific methods in their work. They are often aided by computerized

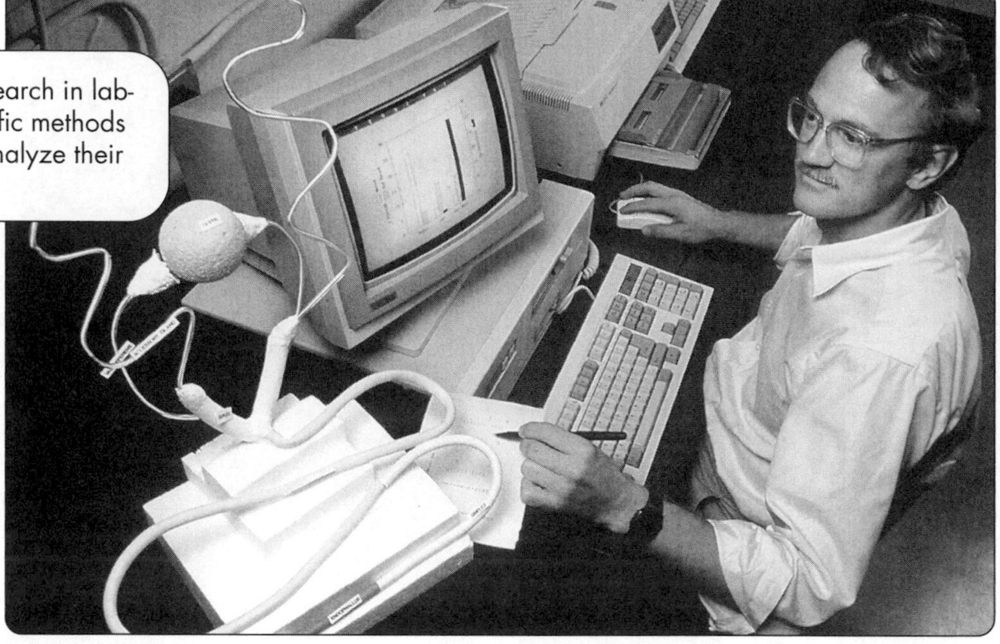

Biochemists conduct their research in laboratories and then use scientific methods and computer programs to analyze their data. *(USDA-ARS.)*

data. Biochemists generally write up their findings for scientific journals and report them before groups of scientists.

## Education and Training Requirements

High school students interested in biochemistry should take chemistry, biology, physics, mathematics, English, and a foreign language. By participating in science clubs, science fairs, and summer programs sponsored by the National Science Foundation, secondary school students can get experience in science-related work. You usually need a doctoral degree to become a biochemist. You should major in biochemistry, biology, or chemistry as an undergraduate and continue with specialized training in biochemistry in graduate school. Individuals with bachelor's degrees are sometimes hired as research assistants or technicians. They often do routine testing and analysis, but their opportunities for advancement are limited. People who have earned master's degrees in biochemistry are qualified for more responsible jobs in applied research and for some teaching jobs. You usually need a doctoral degree (Ph.D.) to teach and do research at a university or to move into a management or administration job. It generally takes four years to earn a bachelor's degree and another one or two years to receive a master's degree. You need to spend an additional three or four years for a doctoral degree. To keep up with new developments in the field, you should continue to read and study throughout your career.

Some biochemists get a doctoral degree in biochemistry after they have completed medical school and received the degree of doctor of medicine (M.D.). Medical training is needed by scientists who want to do certain kinds of research involving human beings.

## Getting the Job

Your professors and college placement service are probably the best sources for jobs in biochemistry. Recruiters from industry sometimes visit colleges to interview candidates. In addition, professional journals, newspaper classifieds, and Internet job banks often list openings for biochemists. You can also apply directly to research centers, private firms, and government agencies that hire biochemists. You may need to pass a civil service exam to get a government job.

## Advancement Possibilities and Employment Outlook

There are several ways for biochemists to advance, especially those with doctoral degrees. They can become supervisors of other biochemists or directors of research in laboratories run by universities, the government, or private industry. They can become professors and combine research and teaching. They can also advance to positions as executives in private companies or as higher administrators in colleges and universities. For many biochemists, the highest form of achievement is being recognized as an authority by others in the field. This recognition generally comes after they have done a great deal of research and have published the results of that research in scientific journals.

Employment of biological scientists in general is projected to grow about as fast as average for all occupations from 2004 to 2014, as biotechnological research and development continues to drive job growth. Biochemists do most of their work in biotechnology, so the job market for them through 2014 should be good. However, the federal government has recently tightened its budget and reduced the number of grants awarded to researchers. At the same time, the number of advanced degrees awarded has continued to increase. As a result, there will be considerable competition for research positions. Colleges and universities will add only a few positions each year.

Opportunities for those with bachelor's or master's degrees in biochemistry are expected to be better than the opportunities for those with doctoral degrees. Jobs will be plentiful in private industry, large hospitals, and medical centers. There will be a great number of sales-related positions in sales, marketing, and research management. Some recent advances in biochemistry have commercial applications, particularly in the expanding genetic engineering field. Increased public awareness and interest in preserving the environment and finding cures for such diseases as AIDS, cancer, heart disease, and arthritis are also likely to provide the stimulus for increased spending by private pharmaceutical and new biotechnology companies.

## Working Conditions

Biochemists generally work in well-lighted and well-equipped laboratories. Sometimes they spend time in offices and classrooms as well. The basic workweek is usually forty hours long. Hours are sometimes flexible, and they often total more than forty hours a week. Sometimes biochemists must work in rotating shifts if a project needs to be monitored around the clock. Biochemists also need to spend time reading and studying to keep up with other scientists' findings that are related to their own work.

Because biochemists work in a field that requires precision, they need to be careful and patient workers who can use scientific methods and equipment. They must be inquisitive as well as persistent. Often experiments are carried out over long periods of time. Biochemists should be imaginative and independent workers who can devise and carry out projects on their own. They also need the ability to work as part of a scientific team when a cooperative approach seems more useful for

### Where to Go for More Information

American Chemical Society
1155 Sixteenth St. NW
Washington, DC 20036
(800) 227-5558
http://www.acs.org

American Institute of Biological Sciences
1444 I St. NW, Ste. 200
Washington, DC 20005
(202) 628-1500
http://www.aibs.org

American Society for Biochemistry and Molecular Biology
9650 Rockville Pike
Bethesda, MD 20814-3996
(301) 634-7145
http://www.asbmb.org

solving a research problem. The ability to communicate their ideas, orally and in writing, is also essential for biochemists.

## Earnings and Benefits

Earnings depend on the education and experience of the biochemist as well as the location and type of job. The median annual income of biochemists was $68,950 in 2004. Benefits generally include paid holidays and vacations, health insurance, and pension plans.

# *Biologist*

**Education and Training**
Master's or doctoral degree

**Salary**
Average—$69,908 per year

**Employment Outlook**
Good

## Definition and Nature of the Work

Biologists study the origin, development, structure, and function of plant and animal life. The word biology comes from the Greek word *bios*, which means "mode of life." Like medicine and agriculture, biology covers a broad area within the life sciences. Biologists, also called biological scientists or life scientists, usually specialize in one area and are recognized and named by that specialty.

In many cases, biologists are recognized according to the kind of organism that they study. For example, biologists who study animals are often known as zoologists. Biologists who specialize in plants are called botanists. Those who work with microscopic forms of plant and animal life, such as bacteria, fungi, and viruses, are known as microbiologists.

Some biologists study aspects of life that are common to many living things. For example, anatomists study the structure of living things, ranging from single-celled plants and animals to human beings and redwood trees. Physiologists specialize in the study of the life functions of plants and animals. These functions include growth, respiration, and reproduction. Geneticists study heredity and how traits, or inherited characteristics, vary in all forms of life. They expand our knowledge about how traits originate and are passed on from one generation to another. Pathologists concentrate on the effects of diseases on the cells, tissues, and organs of plants and animals. Nutritionists study how food is used and changed into energy. They examine the ways in which living tissue is built and repaired by its use of vitamins, minerals, proteins, and other nutrients. Pharmacologists study the effects of drugs and other substances, such as poisons and dusts, on living organisms.

Some scientists work in areas that combine other sciences with biology. For example, biochemists specialize in the chemistry of living things. Biophysicists concentrate on the atomic structure and the electrical and mechanical energy of cells and organisms. Ecologists are life scientists who study the relationship of plants and animals to their environment.

Other life scientists specialize in the organisms in one kind of environment. Marine biologists, for example, study organisms that live in the ocean.

In addition to the many areas of specialization for biologists, there are also many different kinds of jobs. For example, some geneticists are hired to develop new breeds of animals, such as chickens that can provide better food for people.

Other geneticists teach biology and genetics to college students. Still other geneticists work for hospitals where they counsel people to help them understand how likely they are to pass on hereditary diseases to their children. Biologists of all kinds are employed by drug, chemical, and food processing companies; colleges and universities; government agencies; publishing firms; and research centers.

Although biologists have many different areas of specialization and work in many different kinds of organizations, almost all are skilled in basic research techniques. The majority of biologists do research as part of their jobs. Most biologists use microscopes, which enable them to see tissues and organisms not visible to the naked eye. Some biologists use computers to solve research problems. Others work in laboratories with animals, and some work in greenhouses. Biological technicians often assist biologists.

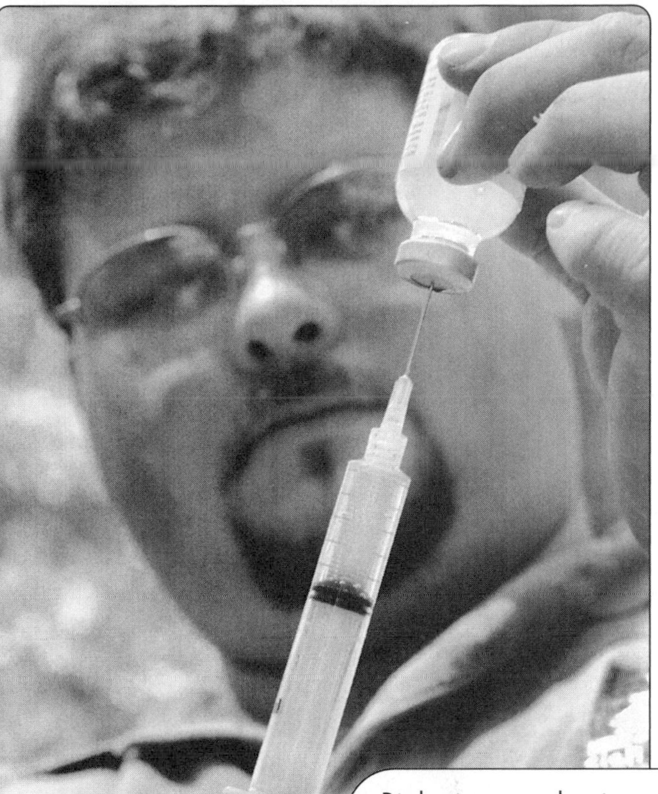

Biologists are classified according to the kind of organism they study. Pharmacologists study the effects of drugs on living organisms. *(© Steve Klaver/ Star Ledger/Corbis.)*

## Education and Training Requirements

If you graduate from college with a bachelor's degree in biology, you can get several kinds of jobs related to the field of biology. For example, you can become a sales or service representative, an inspector, or an advanced biological technician. In many states, a bachelor's degree will qualify you to teach biology in a high school. You must also meet your state's requirements for certification before you can get most teaching jobs.

On the other hand, you usually need an advanced degree to become a biologist. You should major in one of the sciences in college and receive specialized training in a life science in graduate school. People who have earned a master's degree in the biological sciences are qualified for some jobs in teaching and applied research. You usually need a doctoral degree for a teaching and research position at a university or a job as an administrator. It generally takes four years to earn a bachelor's degree and another one or two years for a master's degree. You need to spend an additional two to four years to receive a doctoral degree. Some biologists in fields such as pathology and pharmacology have a doctor of medicine (M.D.) degree instead of or in addition to a doctoral degree (Ph.D.). To keep up with new developments in the life sciences, biologists must continue to study throughout their careers.

## Getting the Job

Your college instructors or placement office may help you find a job as a biologist. You can also apply directly to corporations, colleges and universities, scientific and medical research centers, and government agencies. You must sometimes pass a civil service examination to get a government job. Professional journals, newspaper classifieds, and job banks on the Internet sometimes list openings for biologists.

## Advancement Possibilities and Employment Outlook

There are many possibilities for advancement in the field of biology, especially for those who have a doctoral degree. Some experienced biologists become directors of research teams. Some become managers or administrators. Those employed by colleges and universities can be promoted to the rank of full professor. They often write scientific articles and books. Many biologists advance by becoming experts in their special fields or by making important discoveries in their research. Some biologists develop laboratory devices, disease-resistant plants, or new drugs.

Employment of biological scientists is projected to grow about as fast as the average for all occupations from 2004 to 2014. However, the federal government has recently tightened its budget and reduced the number of grants awarded to researchers. At the same time, the number of advanced degrees awarded has continued to increase. As a result, there will be considerable competition for the highly desired research positions. Opportunities for those with bachelor's or master's degrees in biology are expected to be better than the opportunities for those with doctoral degrees. There will be a great number of positions in sales, marketing, and research management. Increased public awareness and interest in preserving the environment are also likely to provide the stimulus for increased spending by private companies.

## Working Conditions

Working conditions for biologists vary widely from job to job. Most spend at least part of their time in laboratories, which are usually clean, well lighted, and well equipped. Many spend some time in offices and classrooms. Depending on their area of specialization, biologists are also likely to do some fieldwork. For example, they may travel to Africa to observe monkeys in their natural environment. They may collect moss specimens near the Arctic Circle. They may also work in greenhouses or fields behind their laboratories. Although their basic workweek is often forty hours long, hours are sometimes flexible. Biologists usually spend extra hours completing research projects, writing up their findings, and reading to keep up with the many new developments in their field.

Biologists must be inquisitive and interested in solving specific scientific problems. They should enjoy doing research to expand scientific knowledge about living things. They must have the patience to work on long-term research projects. At times they have to work under pressure. They must be able to communicate their ideas and findings to others. In addition, they must be able to work well alone or as part of a scientific research team.

### Where to Go for More Information

American Institute of Biological Sciences
1444 I St. NW, Ste. 200
Washington, DC 20005
(202) 628-1500
http://www.aibs.org

Federation of American Societies for Experimental Biology
9650 Rockville Pike
Bethesda, MD 20814-3998
(301) 634-7000
http://www.faseb.org

## Earnings and Benefits

Earnings for biologists vary widely. They depend on the education and experience of the scientist, the location, and the kind of job. In the federal government in 2005, general biological scientists in nonsupervisory, supervisory, and managerial positions earned an average salary of $69,908. According to the National Association of Colleges and Employers, beginning salary offers for bachelor's degree recipients in biological and life sciences in 2005 averaged $31,258 per year. Benefits usually include paid holidays and vacations, health insurance, and pension plans.

# *Biomedical Engineer*

**Education and Training**
Master's degree

**Salary**
Median—$67,690 per year

**Employment Outlook**
Very good

## Definition and Nature of the Work

Biomedical engineers combine their knowledge of biology and medicine with engineering principles and practices to develop devices and procedures that solve medical and health-related problems. That is, biomedical engineers try to answer medical challenges by helping design and develop new equipment or methods.

Biomedical engineers help develop a wide variety of medical instruments and devices. For example, the heart-lung machine takes over the body's job of pumping and oxygenating the blood during surgery. Special lasers are used in delicate eye surgery. Sonar, or sound waves, can be used to measure diseased organs and detect tumors. Tiny radio transmitters that send out signals about changes in body temperature, internal bleeding, and digestion can be worn or swallowed .

Biomedical engineers also work to improve equipment, such as artificial limbs, heart valves, and kidney machines. They contribute to the development of such devices as heart pacemakers, which can be implanted in a patient's body to improve the heart's functioning.

Many biomedical engineers do research along with physicians, chemists, and other scientists in hospitals and universities. They are involved in the search for answers to questions such as how drugs affect muscle fibers and how the brain thinks, remembers, and sleeps. Engineers with advanced degrees or experience may teach in addition to doing research.

Some biomedical engineers work in hospitals where they help maintain and monitor complex medical systems. For example, they work with systems that can inform a hospital physician of the pulse rate, blood pressure, and other vital signs of a heart attack victim in an ambulance miles away.

Other biomedical engineers work for companies that make biomedical equipment. Government agencies, such as the National Aeronautics and Space Administration (NASA) and the National Institutes of Health (NIH), also employ biomedical engineers.

## Education and Training Requirements

You need at least a bachelor's degree in engineering to become a biomedical engineer. It usually takes four or five years to earn this degree. Most biomedical engineers get their degrees in such fields as industrial, electrical, mechanical, or chemical engineering. You will also need specialized biomedical training; a master's degree is suggested. You can take courses in biology, physiology, medical instrumentation, biochemistry, or biophysics. Or you can sometimes get on-the-job training. A few colleges and universities offer courses and degrees in biomedical engineering. You may want to go on to get an advanced degree in biomedical engineering or a related science. Since biomedical engineering draws on a wide variety of disciplines, a broad background is an asset in this field. You will need to continue studying throughout your career to keep up with new developments.

You may also need to be licensed by the state in which you work. You generally need a degree from an approved engineering college, about four years of experience as an engineer, and a passing grade on a state examination before you can be licensed as a professional engineer.

## Getting the Job

Your college placement office may be able to give you information about getting internships or jobs as a biomedical engineer. Professional journals, Internet job banks, and newspaper classifieds sometimes list openings in this field. You can also contact manufacturers of biomedical equipment as well as hospitals, universities, and government agencies that employ biomedical engineers.

## Advancement Possibilities and Employment Outlook

Advancement usually depends on education and experience. Biomedical engineers who work in research can become project leaders or administrators of entire research programs. They can also become managers in hospitals or manufacturing companies. Some form their own companies. Biomedical engineers who have a doctoral degree can teach in universities and medical schools.

The opportunities in biomedical engineering are expected to increase much faster than the average for all occupations through 2014. The aging population and a focus on health issues will increase demand for better medical devices and equipment designed by biomedical engineers. However, the number of degrees granted in biomedical engineering has increased greatly and those with only a bachelor's degree may face stiff competition for jobs. Therefore a graduate degree is suggested in this field.

## Working Conditions

Biomedical engineers work in modern, well-equipped hospitals, research centers, and manufacturing plants. Their basic workweek is generally forty hours, but in many cases they work longer to complete special projects.

Biomedical engineers usually work as part of a team. Since their field is so broad, they must be able to cooperate and communicate with specialists in other fields. Biomedical engineers should be interested in science and mathematics as well as medicine. They should enjoy solving problems and meeting challenges.

## Earnings and Benefits

In 2004 the median annual salary for biomedical engineers was $67,690. Benefits generally include paid holidays and vacations, health insurance, and retirement plans.

### Where to Go for More Information

Biomedical Engineering Society
8401 Corporate Dr., Ste. 140
Landover, MD 20785-2224
(301) 459-1999
http://www.bmes.org

National Society of Professional Engineers
1420 King St.
Alexandria, VA 22314-2794
(703) 836-4875
http://www.nspe.org

# Botanist

## Definition and Nature of the Work

**Education and Training**
Doctoral degree

**Salary**
Average—$62,207 per year

**Employment Outlook**
Good

Botanists are biological scientists who study plants. Their field, botany, is very broad. It encompasses the study of more than three hundred thousand species of plants ranging from ground-hugging mosses to giant redwood trees. In addition, there are many different ways to approach the study of plant life. Botanists usually specialize in one type or group of plants, or one approach to the study of plants.

Botanists are often classified according to the types of plants that they study. For example, agronomists specialize in the study of agricultural crops and grasses. Marine botanists study plants that grow in the ocean.

Many botanists examine aspects shared by different plant species. Plant taxonomists, for example, identify and classify plants. Sometimes they explore unknown areas in order to find new types of plants. Plant physiologists are experts on the life processes of plants. They study how plants grow, reproduce, and manufacture food. Plant physiologists are concerned with the effects of temperature, humidity, light, and other environmental conditions on plant life processes. Economic botanists search for and develop plants that can be sold as food, drugs, fibers, or other useful goods. There are many other kinds of botanists. Some plant science workers in related areas specialize in the practical applications of the findings of research scientists. They work in fields such as agriculture, conservation, forestry, horticulture, and agronomy.

Many botanists work in colleges and universities where they teach and conduct research. Some are employed by government agencies. A small number of botanists work for private industry and in museums and botanical gardens.

Although their jobs may differ widely, most botanists are scientists who carry out research at least some of the time. Botanists use scientific equipment and methods in their work, including various types of microscopes and staining processes. They may work alone or as part of a research team. Sometimes biological technicians assist them.

The discoveries of botanists could lead to cures for diseases such as cancer, or to the development of new food sources. *(©LWA-Stephen Welstead/Corbis.)*

The work of botanists is vital to our lives because we depend heavily on plants for food, fiber, wood, energy, and oxygen. In addition, the discoveries of botanists provide treatments for diseases such as cancer and to the development of new food sources.

## Education and Training Requirements

Botanists generally need a doctoral degree. If you want to be a botanist, you should major in botany or biology as an undergraduate. You can receive a master's or doctoral degree in botany or in a more specialized area, such as plant physiology. Although there are some jobs for those with a bachelor's degree, such as technical writer or biological technician, opportunities for advancement are limited. There are some teaching and applied research positions for those who have earned a master's degree in an area of botany. You need a doctoral degree for a teaching and research position at a university or a job as an administrator. It generally takes four years to earn a bachelor's degree and another one or two years for a master's degree. You need to study for an additional two or three years to obtain a doctoral degree. To keep up with new findings in plant science, botanists must continue to study throughout their careers.

## Getting the Job

Your professors and college placement office may help you to find a job as a botanist. You can also apply directly to colleges and universities, private firms, museums, botanical gardens, and government agencies involved with plant science. Sometimes you must pass a civil service test to get a government job. There are job openings listed in newspaper classifieds, Internet job banks, and professional journals.

## Advancement Possibilities and Employment Outlook

There are many advancement possibilities for botanists, especially for those who have a doctoral degree. They can become directors of research at government agencies or in private companies. Those who teach and do research at universities and colleges can advance to the rank of full professor. Many botanists feel that the highest form of advancement is to be recognized as experts in their areas of specialization. Generally botanists get this recognition after publishing significant research findings in professional journals.

The employment outlook for botanists who have advanced degrees is good through 2014; their employment is projected to grow about as fast as average. However, botanists can expect to face considerable competition for research positions. The number of grants awarded by the government to researchers will be limited due to recent budget cuts. In addition, the number of newly trained botanists has continued to increase at a steady rate, creating further competition for grants. The market for teaching jobs in colleges and universities will remain competitive.

## Working Conditions

Working conditions vary widely throughout the field. Some botanists work indoors in clean, well-lighted laboratories. Others spend much of their time outdoors or in greenhouses. Some botanists need to travel from time to time to sites where they can collect plant specimens. Botanists often spend part of their time in offices and classrooms. Their working hours are generally flexible but often total more than forty hours a week. Because some experiments need to be tended around the clock, botanists may sometimes have to work rotating shifts.

Botanists should be curious and patient. They should enjoy working with plants and have the manual dexterity needed to handle delicate specimens and equipment. They should be willing to spend long hours in the laboratory or greenhouse, planning and carrying out experiments. Although botanists often work independently, they must be able to work well with others as members of scientific research teams. They should also be skilled at communicating their ideas to others.

### Earnings and Benefits

The earnings of botanists depend on their education and experience, the location, and the kind of job. In the federal government in 2005, botanists in nonsupervisory, supervisory, and managerial positions earned an average salary of $62,207. Botanists generally receive benefits that include paid holidays and vacations, health insurance, and pension plans.

**Where to Go for More Information**

Society for Ecological Restoration International
285 W. 18th St., Ste. 1
Tucson, AZ 85701
(520) 622-5491
http://www.ser.org

Botanical Society of America
P.O. Box 299
St. Louis, MO 63166-0299
(314) 577-9566
http://www.botany.org

## *Cable Television Engineer*

**Education and Training**
College plus training

**Salary**
Average—$64,416 per year

**Employment Outlook**
Good

### Definition and Nature of the Work

Cable television engineers design, develop, and maintain wired cable television systems. Their main goal is to establish strong cable reception with minimal interference in a given service area. Some of these engineers introduce methods to improve the operation of existing cable systems and develop new ideas and plans for cable equipment.

Many cable television engineers work as part of a cable company's franchising team. They help develop competitive proposals that enable their company to win cable contracts. Cable television is regulated at the federal and local levels and sometimes at the state level. When a community wants a cable system to be installed in its area, it requests bids from cable companies that are interested in constructing the cable system. To develop these bids, cable television engineers supervise extensive topographic studies. These studies determine how difficult the construction phase of the cable system will be. The engineers project what types of electronic and electrical equipment will be needed and also select where the headend, or electronic control center of the cable system, will be located. The headend is the site of the receiving antenna and signal processing equipment that is essential to a properly functioning cable system. Cable television engineers also evaluate whether the receivers used in the cable system are properly aligned.

A cable television engineer typically works for a chief cable television engineer. The chief engineer holds the highest technical position in a cable company. This position requires extensive knowledge in the field of telecommunications. Chief engineers develop specifications and standards for cable equipment and related telecommunications equipment, direct the actual construction of cable plant facilities, and oversee all electrical installations.

Chief cable television engineers may be involved in the development of new cable markets. In this job, they provide counseling concerning franchise acquisitions and give technical updates to local government representatives. Chief cable television engineers also help develop cable system budgets and general cable growth plans.

## Education and Training Requirements

Prospective cable television engineers generally need at least a bachelor's degree in electronics engineering to enter the field. Some engineering programs include work experience along with formal classroom instruction. Courses in business administration may also be helpful. Most employers require candidates to have considerable experience in the operation and maintenance of cable TV facilities, equipment, and systems.

The cable television field is rapidly evolving and changing. Engineers who participate in this area should continually upgrade their studies to keep up with new developments.

## Getting the Job

Prospective cable television engineers may be able to find jobs through their college placement office. The best chances for employment are in areas where cable television has recently been set up or is soon to be franchised. Candidates should also contact local government officials to determine the status of cable in their area.

In addition, other cable systems may have been introduced recently in surrounding areas. To find out about these areas students can review *The Television and Cable Factbook,* published by Warren Communications. Copies of the print edition can be found at most large libraries. Also available online, *The Factbook* is considered the leading source of up-to-date information on cable systems in the United States and Canada. Interested individuals should also refer to trade publications and Internet job sites for job listings. Industries related to cable television, such as cable equipment suppliers, may have job openings as well.

## Advancement Possibilities and Employment Outlook

Cable television engineers generally advance by taking on more responsibility or moving to a larger cable system. Some engineers may eventually become chief engineers or executives of cable companies. Other engineers may start their own cable companies.

According to the U.S. Census Bureau, nearly 250,000 people are employed in the U.S. cable television industry. The employment outlook for cable television engineers is good through the year 2014. Cable television systems already reach approximately 70 percent of American homes, and this figure is expected to continue to increase.

## Working Conditions

Cable television engineers work in a variety of outdoor and indoor surroundings. Engineers who are part of a franchising team may spend most of their time traveling and visiting possible franchise sites nationwide. Sometimes they work outdoors at noisy construction sites where the cable systems are erected. At other times they work in an office.

The standard number of hours worked by cable television engineers is thirty-five to forty per week. However, overtime is often necessary, particularly when installation deadlines must be met. Cable engineers must be able to work well with other cable system team members. Chief cable engineers must be able to speak in front of large groups of people to present the views of the cable company. They provide technical advice and counseling to various members of the company, including the operating managers, and are responsible for overseeing all the activities of the engineering staff.

## Earnings and Benefits

Salaries for cable television engineers vary with experience and are also tied to the size and location of the cable system that employs them. According to the U.S. Bureau of Labor Statistics, the average salary for a cable television engineer is $64,416 per year. Chief cable television engineers earn more. Benefits generally include paid holidays and vacations, health insurance, and retirement plans.

### Where to Go for More Information

Institute of Electrical and Electronics Engineers, Inc.—U.S.A.
1828 L St. NW, Ste. 1202
Washington, DC 20036
(202) 785-0017
http://www.ieeeusa.org

National Cable and Telecommunications Association
1724 Massachusetts Ave. NW
Washington, DC 20036
(202) 775-3550
http://www.ncta.com

Society of Cable Telecommunications Engineers
140 Philips Rd.
Exton, PA 19341-1318
(800) 542-5040
http://www.scte.org

# Ceramic Engineer

**Education and Training**
Bachelor's degree or higher

**Salary**
Median—$67,110 per year

**Employment Outlook**
Good

## Definition and Nature of the Work

Ceramic engineers are specialized materials engineers who work with ceramics, which are nonmetallic, inorganic materials that are processed at high temperatures. Glass, porcelain, brick, and cement are all examples of ceramics. Ceramic engineers develop new ceramic products as well as methods and equipment for processing ceramic materials. They work with a wide variety of products, ranging from glassware and electronic components to nuclear reactors and linings for blast furnaces and jet engines.

Most ceramic engineers are employed in the stone, clay, and glass industries. Others work in industries that use ceramics, such as the aerospace, iron and steel, and chemical industries. Some ceramic engineers teach and do research in universities. Others work for government agencies and research centers.

Ceramic engineers often specialize in one type of work. For example, many are involved in research and development. They develop new ceramic materials synthetically or from minerals found in the earth. Ceramics for superconductivity require rare earth minerals, including yttrium and erbium. Other ceramic engineers advance the technology of existing ceramics, such as improving heat and fire resistance. Ceramic engineers may also explore new uses for ceramic products, such as using ceramics in miniaturized circuits and human bone and teeth replacements. Many ceramic engineers are involved in production. They direct the processing of the natural raw minerals and synthetic materials used to make ceramics. They also design the kilns and other equipment used in manufacturing as well as direct the crews that build the plants and operate the kilns. Other ceramic engineers work in sales and show customers ways to use ceramics to solve their design and production problems. They sometimes oversee the installation and operation of ceramic equipment in customers' plants.

There are also several product fields within the industry. Ceramic engineers usually specialize in one or more of these products. For example, some work with refractories, which are fire- and heat-resistant materials. For example, coatings made of refractory materials are used to protect the metal exteriors of spacecraft. Ceramic engineers who specialize in electrical ceramic materials are called dielectrical engineers. They are concerned with the production of thermal, nuclear, and electrical current containments for power generation. Many engineers specialize in glass and whitewares, which is a broad field that includes china dishes and electric insulators. Other special product fields include abrasives, cements, structural ceramics, superconducting materials, and nonmetallic nuclear fuels.

Ceramics is a materials science, which means that it includes the study of the properties and uses of metals and plastics. Engineers in the ceramics industry often work as part of a team of engineers and technicians. They need to have some knowledge of other engineering fields, especially electrical engineering. They must also understand both open-pit and underground mining methods. Although ceramic engineering is a relatively small field, it is related to many others. In medicine, for example, ceramic carbon fiber patches may be used to help repair ligament damage. Ceramic engineers work with physicists developing superconductors.

## Education and Training Requirements

To enter this field, you need a bachelor's degree, which takes four or five years of study. In some programs, you can combine work experience with classroom study. Some jobs require advanced degrees. You can earn a master's degree in an additional one to two years of full-time study. It usually takes about four years of study after obtaining a bachelor's degree to receive a doctoral degree. Employers usually encourage engineers to continue their education to improve their job performance. Many pay tuition for advanced degrees. Engineers must read and study throughout their careers to keep up with changes in engineering technology.

Engineers who offer their services to the public or whose work affects life, health, or property must be licensed by the state in which they work. In general, they need a degree from an approved engineering college, about four years of work experience as an engineer, and a passing grade on a state examination before they can be licensed as professional engineers.

## Getting the Job

Your college placement office will help you find a job as a ceramic engineer. If you take part in a work-study program in college, you may be able to continue working for your employer after you graduate. You can also check job listings in newspaper classifieds, job banks on the Internet, and trade and professional journals. Attending conferences of the professional associations and looking at company exhibits may give you a better idea of the job opportunities available.

## Advancement Possibilities and Employment Outlook

Ceramic engineers often start as assistants and then advance to positions with more responsibility. They can become junior members of sales or production teams. With more education and experience, they can become project supervisors, department heads, and even executives of large companies.

Materials engineers in general are expected to have employment growth about as fast as the average for all occupations through 2014. Although declining employment is expected in this profession, ceramics engineers still will be needed to develop new materials for electronics and biotechnology. Growth should be particularly strong for engineers working on nanomaterials (microscopic technology).

## Working Conditions

Working conditions depend on the area of employment within the field. Ceramic engineers in research and development often work forty-hour weeks, mostly in modern offices and laboratories. Those involved in production are likely to spend more time at production or construction sites. They may have to work overtime or rotating shifts. Sales engineers must travel extensively. All ceramic engineers spend additional time on the job when deadlines must be met.

Ceramic engineers must be able to solve problems and communicate their ideas to others. They should have skill in science and mathematics. Because they often work as part of a team, ceramic engineers should also be able to cooperate and work well with others.

## Earnings and Benefits

Salaries vary depending on the education and experience of the ceramic engineer, the location, and the type of job. In 2005 the average annual salary for a ceramics engineer working for the federal government was $100,059. In 2004 the median annual earnings of materials engineers in general were $67,110. In 2005 the average starting salary for a materials engineer with a bachelor's degree was $50,982. Benefits generally include paid holidays and vacations, health insurance, and retirement savings plans.

### Where to Go for More Information

The American Ceramic Society
735 Ceramic Place, Ste. 100
Westerville, OH 43081
(614) 890-4700
http://www.ceramics.org

National Society of Professional Engineers
1420 King St.
Alexandria, VA 22314-2794
(703) 684-2800
http://www.nspe.org

# *Chemical Engineer*

**Education and Training**
Bachelor's degree or higher

**Salary**
Median—$76,770 per year

**Employment Outlook**
Good

## Definition and Nature of the Work

Chemical engineers work in the production of chemicals and many other products that require chemical processing. They use the theories and laws of chemistry to develop industrial chemical processes. They generally build on the findings of research chemists, who work with small amounts of materials in laboratories. Chemical engineers are concerned with the design, construction, operation, and marketing of equipment that can reproduce on a large scale the processes or products developed by chemists. Chemical engineers work with industrial chemical processes to help produce a large variety of goods. They are often assisted by chemical technicians.

Chemical engineers need to have knowledge of not only chemistry and physics but also of mechanical and electrical engineering. In some cases they specialize in one area, such as oxidation, pollution control, or the production of plastics. Sometimes a chemical engineer's title reflects his or her area of specialization. For example, some chemical engineers are known as plastics engineers.

Chemical engineers work in many industries, including those that produce chemicals, petroleum, and electronic products. In some cases these products are sold to other industries that use them to make other products ranging from fine textiles to automobile tires. Chemicals are used in the processing and treatment of many of the foods we eat, much of the water we drink, and many of the clothes we wear. Chemical engineers develop the processes and design the factories that make it possible to bring such products to consumers.

The work of chemical engineers may begin after chemists have developed a basic product or process, such as a new kind of paint or a new way of refining coal to make synthetic natural gas. The engineer will then solve the practical problems in the manufacture and use of these products. Chemical engineers consult with chemists at many points during their work. Engineers do experiments and calculate such things as the temperature and pressure to be expected during an industrial process. They help to design buildings and plan what machinery will be needed. They estimate the number of people needed to operate a plant as well as the cost of power and raw materials. They make extensive use of computers in this work. Chemical engineers must also consider the effect of a plant or process on the environment. They cannot build a plant that will release deadly fumes into the air. They cannot pollute lakes or streams or harm wildlife. Chemical engineers often build pilot plants or small-scale models of the actual processing facility. Pilot plants allow the engineers to test their work and to experiment with new processes.

Some chemical engineers supervise the construction of new facilities. They test equipment and teach operators how to use it. Other chemical engineers work in the manufacturing process itself. They solve many of the everyday problems incurred in running a plant. They make sure that standards of quality are met while production costs are kept as low as possible. Some engineers work in sales or management. A small number of chemical engineers work as consultants, offering their services to small businesses that do not need full-time chemical engineers. Still others teach and do research at colleges and universities.

In recent years chemical engineers have entered the field of biotechnology, designing bioreactors for plant cultures or developing models of ecosystem behavior following the spillage of chemicals. Another frontier for chemical engineers has been electronics, where they have researched the chemical synthesis of microelectronic components.

## Education and Training Requirements

You usually need at least a bachelor's degree in chemical engineering to enter this field. Some engineering colleges offer work-study programs that combine work experience with formal study. It generally takes four or five years to earn a bachelor's degree in engineering. Many jobs in chemical engineering also require advanced degrees. You can earn a master's degree in one or two additional years of full-time study. Many chemical engineers find that a master's degree in business administration is useful, especially if they want to become managers. If you want to do research or teach at the university level, you will need a doctoral degree. It usually takes about four years of full-time study beyond the bachelor's degree to earn a doctoral degree. Many engineers continue their education on a part-time basis after they have found jobs in their field. Employers often pay tuition for courses that engineers take to improve their job skills. Chemical engineers must be willing to study throughout their careers so that they can keep up with advances in engineering technology.

Engineers who offer their services to the public or whose work affects life, health, or property must be licensed by the state in which they work. They generally need a degree from an approved engineering college, about four years of work experience as an engineer, and a passing grade on a state examination before being licensed as a professional engineer.

## Getting the Job

If you take part in a work-study program in college, you may be able to work full time for your employer after you graduate. Your college placement office can also help you find a job as a chemical engineer. Newspapers, Internet job banks, and professional journals often list openings for chemical engineers. You can also apply directly to companies that hire chemical engineers.

## Advancement Possibilities and Employment Outlook

Advancement depends on education and experience. Chemical engineers who have bachelor's degrees generally start as assistants to experienced engineers. After they gain experience, they are usually given more responsibility. Many become experts in their special fields. Engineers can become team leaders or technical service and development (TS&D) officers. The TS&D engineer expands the applications for his or her company's products and finds new ones. Some chemical engineers go on to become managers or executives. A few start their own consulting firms or businesses. Others use their background in chemical engineering to advance in marketing or sales careers.

The employment outlook for chemical engineers is good. The number of jobs is expected to increase about as fast as the average for all jobs through the year 2014. Much of the projected growth in employment will be in service industries, such as scientific research and development. Job opportunities for chemical engineers will be better in pharmaceuticals, specialty chemicals, electronics, and plastics materials.

## Working Conditions

Chemical engineers generally work in clean, well-equipped plants, offices, and laboratories. At times they must supervise construction or production lines. Although chemicals can be dangerous, workers follow strict safety regulations and injuries are rare. The basic workweek for chemical engineers is forty hours, but overtime is often necessary. Chemical engineers should have interest and aptitude in math and science as well as strong analytical skills. They must be able to work in teams and to communicate their ideas effectively. Chemical engineers must be creative and imaginative and enjoy the challenge of solving problems.

## Earnings and Benefits

Earnings vary depending on the experience of the chemical engineer, the location, and the type of job. In 2004 chemical engineers earned a median salary of $76,770 per year. In 2005 those with a bachelor's degree earned an average starting salary of $53,813 per year. Chemical engineers with master's degrees earned an average starting salary of $57,260 per year. Those with doctoral degrees earned an average starting salary of $79,591. Benefits usually include paid holidays and vacations, health insurance, and pension plans.

### Where to Go for More Information

American Institute of Chemical Engineers
3 Park Avenue
New York, NY 10016-5991
(800) 242-4363
http://www.aiche.org

National Society of Professional Engineers
1420 King St.
Alexandria, VA 22314-2794
(703) 684-2800
http://www.nspe.org

Society of Plastics Engineers
14 Fairfield Dr.
P.O. Box 403
Brookfield, CT 06804-0403
(203) 775-0471
http://www.4spe.org

# Chemist

**Education and Training**
Master's or doctoral degree

**Salary**
Median—$56,060 per year

**Employment Outlook**
Fair

## Definition and Nature of the Work

Chemists are scientists who study the makeup of substances and the changes that they undergo. They often work in teams with other chemists, chemical engineers, and chemical technicians. Chemists work for private companies in a variety of industries. They are employed in plants that make plastics, textiles, cosmetics, and chemicals. They work in fields such as petroleum refining, mining, food processing, and water and sewage treatment. Government agencies also employ chemists in such areas as agriculture and pollution control. In addition, many chemists work for colleges and universities, hospitals, and independent research institutes. A few have jobs in such fields as printing, medicine, legal chemistry, patent law, and information science. Some chemists spend all or part of their time teaching. Others are involved in sales or marketing. Some serve as consultants to private industry or government agencies.

More than half of all chemists work in research and development. Some chemists are involved in basic research and try to gain knowledge about substances. They also study the ways these substances combine and react with each other. Basic research often leads to the development of new products. For example, research into the formation of larger molecules from the union of smaller ones led to the development of synthetic plastics. Other research chemists work on more practical or domestic problems. For instance, they may work to develop a fabric that will not burn, soil, or wrinkle easily. They must often perform many laboratory tests before they are able to create the desired product.

Many chemists work in production and quality control. They may work with chemical engineers to develop exact instructions for mixing the ingredients needed to produce huge vats of paint in a paint factory. Chemists involved in quality control may supervise the testing of samples of this paint to make sure that it satisfies certain standards.

There are several special fields of chemistry. Organic chemists specialize in compounds that contain the element carbon. These compounds include animal

Most chemists work in research and development, trying to uncover new knowledge about substances or to develop new products. *(© M. Taghi/zefa/Corbis.)*

and vegetable matter, plastics, and other substances. Inorganic chemists work with compounds that do not contain carbon, such as metals, minerals, and other substances. Their work may involve materials to be used in solid-state circuits for electronic equipment. Physical chemists work with the basic theories of chemistry. For example, they study how energy levels are altered when substances undergo chemical changes. The work of physical chemists sometimes leads to the development of new energy sources. Analytical chemists study the composition of substances. They use special laboratory equipment and techniques to determine the exact makeup of a sample, such as a piece of moon rock. These chemists also calculate the amount of a given chemical that is present in each gallon of a city's or town's water supply. Biochemists study the chemistry of living things. There are many other kinds of chemists, including those who specialize in food chemistry or clinical chemistry.

## Education and Training Requirements

You can qualify for some entry-level chemist jobs with a bachelor's degree in chemistry or a related subject. It usually takes four years of study to earn a bachelor's degree. You can start in technical sales or service, as an assistant to an experienced chemist, or in product testing. In many states, a bachelor's degree will give you the qualifications necessary to teach chemistry and other science courses in a high school. You must also meet your state's requirements for certification before you can get most teaching jobs. Those with a bachelor's degree who have completed internships or have had other chemistry-related work experience while in school can usually negotiate higher starting salaries than individuals without those experiences.

Most chemistry jobs require a master's degree or a doctoral degree in a branch of chemistry. You can earn a master's degree in one or two years of study beyond the bachelor's degree. It takes about four years of study after you receive a bachelor's degree to earn a doctoral degree. You usually need a doctoral degree to do basic research, teach in a university, or become an administrator. Some chemists pursue an advanced degree part time while they are working. Many employers encourage chemists to take courses that will improve their job performance. Some employers have their own special training programs for graduates with degrees in chemistry. Many chemists continue to study throughout their careers in order to keep up with new developments.

## Getting the Job

Your college placement office and professors can often provide you with job information. You can apply directly to private companies, institutions, and government agencies that hire chemists. State and private employment agencies may also be able to help you find a job. You should contact your civil service office for information about examinations that may be required for some government jobs. Other openings are often listed in chemical trade and professional journals as well as in newspaper classifieds and Internet job banks.

## Advancement Possibilities and Employment Outlook

Advancement generally depends on education and experience. Many chemists advance by becoming project directors or supervisors. A few gain recognition in their profession for their scholarly research findings and publications. Others move into positions such as sales representative, manager, or even executive for a chemical company. A few receive training in other fields and become scientific librarians or patent attorneys. Since chemistry is such a broad and basic science, it provides many different opportunities for advancement.

The job outlook for chemists is fair through the year 2014. Employment of chemists is expected to grow more slowly than the average rate for all occupations through 2014. Job growth will be concentrated in drug manufacturing, research, development, and testing. Employment in non-drug-related segments of the chemical industry is expected to decline from 2004 through 2014. However, chemists will be needed to develop technologies and processes used to produce chemicals for all purposes and to monitor air and water pollutants to ensure compliance with local, state, and federal regulations. Companies that provide research services for other firms are expected to provide numerous job opportunities.

## Working Conditions

Chemists usually work in pleasant, well-equipped laboratories, plants, offices, or classrooms. They sometimes work with materials that are poisonous or explosive. Because chemical workers must follow strict safety regulations, accidents and injuries are rare. Chemists generally work forty hours per week, although extra time is often needed to complete a project. Chemists working in production must sometimes work night or weekend shifts.

Chemists should have good mathematical aptitude. They must give close attention to details. They must have the patience to carry out long series of tests to develop new products or hypotheses. Since most chemists work as part of a team, they must be able to cooperate and communicate well with others.

### Where to Go for More Information

American Chemical Society
1155 Sixteenth St. NW
Washington, DC 20036
(800) 227-5558
http://www.acs.org

Synthetic Organic Chemical Manufacturers Association
1850 M St. NW, Ste. 700
Washington, DC 20036-5810
(202) 721-4100
http://www.socma.com

## Earnings and Benefits

Salaries vary depending on education, experience, location, and the type of work done. Median annual earnings of chemists in 2004 were $56,060. The American Chemical Society reported that in 2004 the median salary of its members with a bachelor's degree was $62,000, with a master's degree was $72,300, and with a Ph.D. was $91,600. The median salary was highest for those working in private industry and lowest for those in academia. In 2004 inexperienced chemistry graduates with a bachelor's degree earned a median starting salary of $32,500, with a master's degree earned $43,600, and with a Ph.D. earned $65,000. Chemists usually receive benefits that include paid holidays and vacations, health insurance, and retirement plans.

# *Demographer*

**Education and Training**
Master's or doctoral degree

**Salary**
Average—$53,160 per year

**Employment Outlook**
Good

## Definition and Nature of the Work

Demographers study the makeup, distribution, and trends of populations. They also make observations about the causes and effects of population changes, such as increases in birth rates or immigration. Demographers collect statistical data, analyze the data to identify any trends, and then predict future trends. These predictions can help governments, social service agencies, and private companies to plan ahead. Demographers are sometimes called population sociologists. Sociology is a broader field than demography and is concerned with the characteristics of social groups.

Many demographers work for government agencies. For example, the Bureau of Labor Statistics hires demographers to research information such as the number

Government agencies, corporations, and news organizations hire demographers to collect statistical data, analyze data, and predict future trends. This demographer is presenting her findings. *(© Martha Tabor/Working Images Photographs. Reproduced by permission.)*

of women working in a certain industry or the effects that a college education has on employment in a particular field. The Immigration and Naturalization Service needs demographic information to plan effective immigration policies. The Environmental Protection Agency commissions demographic reports on population factors in resource depletion and environmental degradation. The Bureau of the Census also employs demographers to plan and interpret census data.

Corporations and market research organizations may also employ demographers. An electric company considering a major capital investment must first take into account predicted changes in local population and habits of electricity consumption. Demographers provide these projections.

Mapmakers sometimes employ demographers to map population data for certain geographic areas. Demographers use computers for this task. Large news organizations may employ reporters with a background in demography. These reporters may investigate such issues as the future of immigration to the Sun Belt states.

## Education and Training Requirements

Although a master's degree is the minimum requirement for most demographic work, there are a few positions available for those with only a bachelor's degree. Demographers usually have a bachelor's degree in urban planning or sociology with coursework in statistics, psychology, sociological theory, and economics as a foundation before they do their graduate studies. A master's degree requires about two years of graduate study. For an academic or research position in this field, a doctoral degree is required.

## Getting the Job

During their doctoral studies, students may find work as college instructors or interviewers for market research organizations. These jobs provide field experience as well as job contacts. Population associations hold annual conferences where beginning demographers can meet potential employers. These organizations also publish journals with job advertisements.

## Advancement Possibilities and Employment Outlook

College professors can advance to full professor or to a position with high administrative status. Those demographers who have good connections and reputations can set themselves up as demographic consultants.

Employment of sociologists in general will grow more slowly than the average for all occupations through 2014. However, opportunities exist for demographers, particularly in government. The Census Bureau employs demographers, as do many government agencies, such as the National Institutes of Health, that conduct surveys. Demographers are also employed by colleges and universities and by non-profit organizations. Some jobs will be available in business and marketing. Businesses have begun to rely on statistical population information to make decisions about expanding or downsizing. Consumer products and professional services companies often employ demographers in their marketing departments.

## Working Conditions

Entry-level demographers may conduct field work, carrying out interviews or testing census questionnaires. Most of the analysis of demographic statistics is carried out in modern, well-lighted offices. Many demographers spend a lot of time working with computers.

## Earnings and Benefits

In 2005 the average salary for demographers was $53,160 per year. Those employed in business and industry tend to earn more than their counterparts working for government or universities. Most colleges and government agencies offer benefits covering health insurance, paid vacations, and retirement plans. Self-employed demographic consultants must provide these benefits for themselves.

### Where to Go for More Information

Population Association of America
8630 Fenton St., Ste. 722
Silver Spring, MD 20910-3812
(301) 565-6710
http://www.popassoc.org

American Sociological Association
1307 New York Ave. NW, Ste. 700
Washington, DC 20005-4712
(202) 383-9005
http://www.asanet.org

# *Economist*

**Education and Training**
Master's or doctoral degree

**Salary**
Median—$72,780 per year

**Employment Outlook**
Fair

## Definition and Nature of the Work

Economists study the ways that society uses limited resources, such as land, water, raw materials, and human labor, to satisfy their needs and wants. They are social scientists who have expert knowledge about systems that produce, distribute, and use goods and services. Economists are concerned with how individuals, businesses, and governments at all levels obtain, invest, and spend money. They also study the reasons why people follow certain economic courses. They sometimes analyze the relationship between the supply and demand of goods and services.

Since economics is a very broad field, economists often specialize in more focused areas of interest, such as industrial productivity, taxes, farm policies, or international trade. They may develop hypotheses to explain problems such as

Economists use statistics, mathematical analysis, and economic theory to conduct studies concerning such issues as unemployment, inflation, industrial productivity, farm policies, and international trade. *(© Martha Tabor/ Working Images Photographs. Reproduced by permission.)*

unemployment or inflation. They often advise governments or businesses on ways to cope with economic problems. Economists usually study many forms of economic data in their work. Because economic activity is measured numerically, economists must be skilled in using statistics and mathematical analyses as well as economic theory. They often use computerized data in their work.

Approximately one-third of all economists work in private industry or for private research organizations. They provide information about the economy that helps managers make decisions about the marketing and pricing of their company's goods or services. Economists study government policies in such areas as international trade and inform managers of the effect that these policies are likely to have on their businesses. Sometimes economists investigate the advantages and disadvantages of manufacturing a new product or opening new branches of a store, bank, or factory. They prepare forecasts for both the U.S. economy and foreign economies. Economists work for such private organizations as banks, insurance companies, manufacturing companies, and management consulting firms. A few economists have their own consulting businesses.

Another third of all economists are employed by colleges and universities. They teach, do research, and often write books and articles. Sometimes these economists also do consulting for businesses, individuals, or government agencies.

The remaining group of economists is employed by government agencies at the local, state, and federal levels. They serve as economic analysts and policy advisers. Government economists work in areas such as transportation, international trade and development, agriculture, and labor.

## Education and Training Requirements

You need a master's or doctoral degree to become an economist. You should major in economics as an undergraduate and take courses in related areas, such as history, political science, and law. You will also need some training in mathematics, especially in the related fields of statistics and computer science.

There are many jobs open to applicants who have completed a four-year course leading to a bachelor's degree in economics. For example, they can work as management or sales trainees. Those with a master's degree, which takes an additional one or two years of study, will be qualified for many jobs in government or industry as administrators, researchers, or planners. Teaching or research jobs are available in some colleges and universities, but those hired are expected to continue working toward a doctoral degree.

A doctoral degree in economics is required for many jobs in this field, especially positions in colleges and universities. Many students pursuing a doctoral degree specialize in a particular area, such as economic history or public finance. It normally takes about eight years of schooling beyond the high school level to receive a doctoral degree in economics. Economists usually continue reading, studying, and attending seminars throughout their careers so that they can keep up with changes in their field.

## Getting the Job

Your professors or the placement office at your college or university can give you information about getting a job. Openings for economists are often listed in professional journals or in newspaper classifieds. You can also apply directly to colleges and universities, businesses, or government agencies that hire economists. To get a government job, you may need to pass a civil service examination.

## Advancement Possibilities and Employment Outlook

Advancement usually depends on the education, experience, and skill of the individual. Those with advanced degrees often move on to jobs with more responsibility in research or administration. In private industry, economists can become managers or executives. They can play an important role in setting the financial policies of businesses or governments. Economists who work in colleges and universities can advance to the rank of full professor. An important form of advancement for an economist is to become a recognized expert in the field. At times they even achieve broad public fame by writing successful books or newspaper and magazine articles. Some economists advance by starting their own financial consulting firms.

The employment outlook for economists is fair through 2014. Employment of economists is expected to grow more slowly than average for all occupations through 2014. Most jobs are likely to result from the need to replace workers who leave the field. Opportunities should be best in private industry for those with doctoral degrees, especially in research, testing, and consulting. Federal, state, and local government agencies will also need economists to deal with problems in such areas as housing, transportation, and training for employment. Those with doctoral degrees are likely to face keen competition for teaching jobs in colleges and universities.

## Working Conditions

Economists usually work in offices that are pleasant and comfortable. They sometimes have to do some fieldwork or traveling, especially to attend professional meetings. Although the basic workweek is often forty hours long, economists may put in much longer hours. Their work requires a great deal of concentration and can be very detailed. They are often required to do much specialized reading and studying. Although they often work alone, at times economists meet with students, managers, government officials, and other people. They should be able to express their ideas and to get along well with others. Since they often have to prepare reports and articles, economists should be able to write clearly and well.

## Earnings and Benefits

Earnings vary depending on the education and experience of the economist and the type of position. In 2004 the median annual income of economists was $72,780. In 2005 the starting salary for individuals with a bachelor's degree in economics was $24,667, and for those with superior academic records it was $30,567. The starting salary for individuals with a master's degree in economics was $37,390, and for those with a Ph.D. was $45,239.

A number of economists supplement their incomes by writing books and articles or by doing consulting work. Economists who work for federal or state governments, colleges and universities, or private corporations receive benefits, which usually include paid holidays and vacations, health insurance, and retirement plans.

### Where to Go for More Information

American Economic Association
2014 Broadway, Ste. 305
Nashville, TN 37203-2418
(615) 322-2595
http://www.vanderbilt.edu/AEA

National Association of Business Economists
1233 Twentieth St. NW, Ste. 505
Washington, DC 20036-2304
(202) 463-6223
http://www.nabe.com

# *Electrical and Electronics Engineer*

### Education and Training

Bachelor's degree or higher

### Salary

Median—$71,610 to $75,770 per year

### Employment Outlook

Good

## Definition and Nature of the Work

Electrical and electronics engineers are concerned with the production and use of electricity. They are members of the largest branch of engineering. The focus of electrical engineers is on the generation and supply of power, and the focus of electronics engineers is on applications of electricity to control systems or signal processing. Engineers use basic knowledge collected by scientists to solve a wide range of problems.

Electrical and electronics engineers generally specialize in one of the two branches of their profession—either electric power or electronics. Engineers specializing in electric power often are involved with the creation of electricity at generating stations. These generating stations primarily use steam or water power to drive their turbines and change mechanical energy into electricity. Steam-powered plants may use coal, gas, oil, nuclear, or solar energy for fuel. Electrical engineers working in the area of electric power also work with the equipment that transmits electricity from the power plant to the consumer. They are concerned with electric motors and with the lighting and wiring in buildings, automobiles, airplanes, and other places. These engineers generally work with relatively large amounts of electricity.

Engineers specializing in electronics deal with relatively small amounts of electricity. Electronics engineers work with a variety of equipment including radar, telephone systems, and missile guidance systems. They also work with consumer goods, such as televisions and stereo equipment.

In either branch of electrical and electronic engineering, engineers work in a wide range of jobs. Many work in research, development, and design. These engineers come up with the ideas and plans for new equipment and methods or for improvements in existing equipment and methods. Their work may result in a

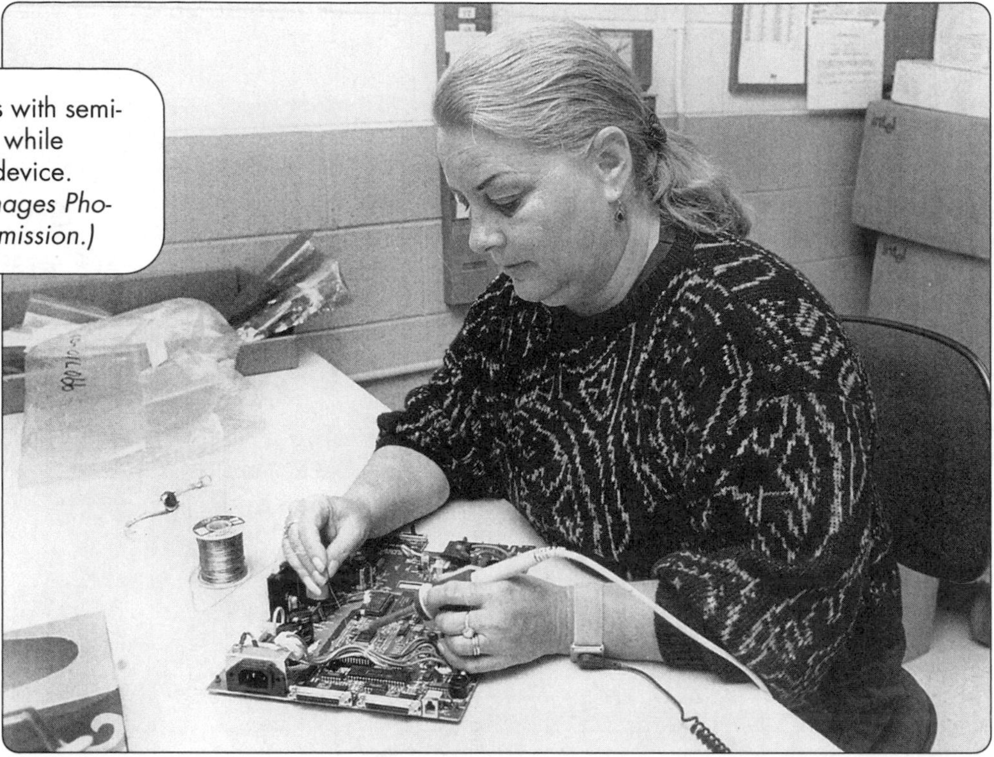

An electronics engineer works with semiconductors on a circuit board while developing a new electronic device. *(© Martha Tabor/Working Images Photographs. Reproduced by permission.)*

more efficient or safer power plant or in the development of a computer program used in hospitals for the care of heart attack victims.

The remaining engineers work in construction or production. These engineers may oversee the construction, installation, and operation of power generating equipment in a power plant. Some may be in charge of certain phases in the manufacturing of circuits to be used in a telephone system. Other electrical and electronics engineers work as managers, executives, or sales representatives in areas related to their field. A few do part-time or full-time consulting work for businesses or individuals for specific projects. Still other electrical engineers have teaching or research jobs at colleges and universities.

Most electrical and electronics engineers work in private industry. Others are employed by state and federal government. Some of these engineers work in military or space programs. Electrical and electronics engineers are also employed by power companies, telephone and telegraph companies, and firms that make electrical and electronic equipment. In addition, some engineers work for colleges and universities or construction or engineering firms.

## Education and Training Requirements

You need at least a bachelor's degree in electrical engineering to enter this field. A few colleges offer training in electronics engineering. It usually takes four or five years to earn a bachelor's degree in engineering. Some colleges offer work-study programs in which students receive on-the-job training while they are still in school. For some jobs, especially those in research or teaching, you need a master's or doctoral degree. Because engineering is a rapidly changing field, engineers must continue to study and keep up with new developments throughout their careers.

Electrical and electronics engineers whose work affects life, health, or property or who offer their services to the public need to be licensed by the state in which they work. They generally need a degree from an accredited engineering school, four years of work experience as an engineer, and a passing grade on a state examination before being licensed as professional engineers.

## Getting the Job

Your college placement office may be able to help you find a job as an electrical and electronics engineer. If you are enrolled in a work-study program during college, you may be able to continue working for a participating employer after graduation. You can check for job openings in the classified ads in newspapers, Internet job banks, and professional journals. You can also apply directly to the many private firms and government agencies that employ electrical and electronics engineers. To get a government job, you may have to pass a civil service examination.

## Advancement Possibilities and Employment Outlook

Electrical and electronics engineers generally advance by taking on more responsibility, for which they earn higher salaries. Some eventually become managers or executives. Other engineers who receive further training can become highly paid specialists. Still other engineers advance by moving into sales engineering or starting their own engineering firms.

The employment outlook for electrical and electronics engineers is good through the year 2014. Employment is expected to increase about as fast as the average for all jobs through 2014. Demand for improved communications systems should create many new jobs. New openings should also result from a rising demand for electrical and electronic consumer goods, but foreign competition will temper that growth. Job growth is expected to be fastest in services industries, since many firms are hiring consulting services for electronic engineering expertise.

## Working Conditions

Electrical and electronics engineers work in a variety of surroundings. Sometimes they work in modern factories, offices, or laboratories. Others work at noisy construction sites or in busy power plants. Engineers usually work at least forty hours a week. Overtime is often necessary, especially when project deadlines must be met.

Engineers must be able to work well as part of a team. They must be able to communicate their ideas to others. Electrical and electronics engineers should have an aptitude for science and mathematics and should enjoy solving problems.

## Earnings and Benefits

Earnings vary depending on the education and experience of the engineer, the location, and the kind of job. Electrical and electronics engineers earn salaries that are close to the average salaries earned by all kinds of engineers. In 2005 beginning electrical and electronics engineers with bachelor's degrees earned an average starting salary of $51,888 per year. Those with master's degrees started at an average of $64,416 per year, and those with doctoral degrees at an average of $80,206. In 2004 the median annual salary for electrical and electronics engineers ranged from $71,610 to $75,770. Benefits generally include paid holidays and vacations, health insurance, and pension plans.

### Where to Go for More Information

Institute of Electrical and Electronics Engineers-USA
1828 L St. NW, Ste. 1202
Washington, DC 20036-5104
(202) 785-0017
http://www.ieeeusa.org

National Society of Professional Engineers
1420 King St.
Alexandria, VA 22314-2794
(703) 684-2800
http://www.nspe.org

# Entomologist

**Education and Training**
Doctoral degree

**Salary**
Median—$51,200 per year

**Employment Outlook**
Good

## Definition and Nature of the Work

Entomologists are biological scientists who study insects. There are nearly a million known species of insects, and thousands of new species are discovered every year. Insects make up over three-quarters of all the species of animals. All insects play roles in ecosystems. Some roles are beneficial and some harmful to humans. Bees, for example, pollinate plants and produce honey. Many other insects help bacteria and fungi break down organic matter and form soil. Some insects damage growing crops and spoil harvests in storage. This causes farms to lose millions of dollars every year in the United States. They can also physically harm humans, pets, livestock, and wildlife. For instance, females of some species of *Anopheles* mosquitoes carry the causative agent of malaria and can transmit it to humans. Beetles can wipe out entire forests. An insect known as the screwworm fly kills thousands of cattle each year.

Some entomologists study insects to learn more about their basic life processes. Others direct their research toward finding ways to control harmful insects and use desirable insects to advantage.

Entomologists are specialized zoologists or animal biologists. Their field is known as entomology. About one-third of all entomologists work for government agencies in fields such as agriculture and food inspection. Others are employed by colleges and universities. Companies that make insecticides, pest control companies, medical centers, and museums also employ entomologists.

Although their jobs vary widely, most entomologists do some research or laboratory work. They may study the life cycles and body processes of insects as well as their group behavior. They use scientific instruments and sometimes collect or observe insects in their natural habitats. They are often assisted by biological technicians or pest control workers.

Entomologists are searching for ways to control or eliminate pests in infested areas without destroying other forms of life. Instead of using deadly poisons, they are developing ways to trap insects or to sterilize them so that they cannot reproduce. They are helping to develop crops that are insect resistant. Entomologists are also experimenting with ways to use birds or harmless insects to control the population of destructive insects. Entomologists must have knowledge of related fields, including horticulture, genetics, physiology, forestry, and microbiology. They often work closely with other scientists, such as plant pathologists, who are experts in plant disease, or with veterinarians.

An entomologist may study insects to find ways to control harmful insects and to use desirable insects to an advantage. *(© Ed Young/Corbis.)*

## Education and Training Requirements

You generally need a doctoral degree to become an entomologist. You can major in entomology, biology, or zoology as an undergraduate and continue with a specialized study of insects in graduate school. Graduates with bachelor's degrees can find jobs as inspectors of food products, advanced biological technicians, or sales representatives for firms that make insecticides. However, their opportunities for advancement are limited. Those who have earned a master's degree in entomology are qualified for some jobs in teaching or applied research. You usually need a doctoral degree for a job as an administrator or for a teaching and research position at a university. It takes about four years to earn a bachelor's degree and another one or two years to earn a master's degree. You must spend about two or three additional years in school to get a doctoral degree. In order to keep up with new developments in your field, you should continue to study throughout your career.

## Getting the Job

Your professors and college placement office may be able to give you information about getting a job as an entomologist. Professional journals, newspaper classifieds, and job banks on the Internet are good sources of job openings. You can also apply directly to colleges and universities, private firms, and government agencies that conduct research concerning insects and insect control. You may have to pass a civil service examination to get a government job.

## Advancement Possibilities and Employment Outlook

There are many advancement opportunities for entomologists, especially for those who have a doctoral degree. They can become directors of research in government agencies or private firms. Those who work in universities can advance to the rank of full professor. Some entomologists start their own consulting or pest control businesses. Others become recognized for important discoveries that result from their research.

Although entomology is a rather small field with a narrow range of issues, there are still many unsolved problems in insect control. Although past research has led to the successful control of insects, more research is necessary as insects and diseases continue to adapt to pesticides and as soil fertility and water quality deteriorate due to the use of harmful chemicals. Both government and private industry are expected to devote funds to research into these issues. The job outlook is good through the year 2014 for entomologists with advanced degrees. Entomologists will also be needed to replace workers who retire or leave the field for other reasons. There will be keen competition for teaching jobs in colleges and universities.

## Working Conditions

Working conditions for entomologists depend on the type of job. Many spend part of their time in offices and classrooms. Research entomologists usually work in well-lighted, well-equipped laboratories. Those who work with dangerous chemicals and insects must follow safety rules. Entomologists who work and consult with farmers spend much of their time on farms. Entomologists may have to inspect grain elevators or the holds of ships. Other entomologists may find themselves in remote lands studying rare insects or looking for new species. Entomologists involved in pest control may face strong odors and other unpleasant conditions at times. Working hours vary and are often flexible. Entomologists may work more than forty hours per week, especially on field trips or when experiments need to be monitored around the clock. In addition, entomologists must spend time reading and studying to keep up with new scientific developments that affect their work.

Entomologists must have an aptitude for science. They must have the patience to carry out carefully designed experiments over long periods of time. They should be creative and curious to explore new areas in the study of insects. Entomolo-

**Where to Go for More Information**

American Entomological Society
1900 Benjamin Franklin Pkwy.
Philadelphia, PA 19103-1195
(215) 561-3978
http://www.acnatsci.org/hosted/aes/

Entomological Society of America
10001 Derekwood Lane, Ste. 100
Lanham, MD 20706-4876
(301) 731-4538
http://www.entsoc.org

gists should be able to work both independently and as part of a scientific team. They also need to be able to clearly express themselves orally and in writing.

## Earnings and Benefits

Earnings depend on the education and experience of the entomologist, the location, and the kind of job. Entomologists are often grouped with plant scientists when looking at earnings. The median annual earnings of plant scientists was $51,200 in 2004. Entomologists generally receive such benefits as paid holidays and vacations, health insurance, and pension plans.

# *Ergonomist*

**Education and Training**
Master's or doctoral degree

**Salary**
$40,000 to $72,000 per year

**Employment Outlook**
Very good

## Definition and Nature of the Work

Ergonomists, also known as human factors engineers, assist in the design of machines, tools, and other equipment to ensure that they can be used easily and correctly. The widespread use of computers has created a large demand for ergonomists to make office and home computer stations more user-friendly. They must take into account human factors, which include difficulty in understanding a machine's functions and discomfort when operating the machine. Such factors can cause vision problems, fatigue, physical pain, or even serious chronic conditions if they are not relieved. Ergonomists are also employed in many other fields, where they work with a variety of equipment and furniture ranging from desk chairs to military aircraft monitors.

Companies hire ergonomists when they are remodeling their work environments to increase the productivity of employees who may be adversely affected by poor lighting, uncomfortable furniture, or other factors. In addition, ergonomists play an important role in marketing new products. They can increase the sales of cameras, computers, and other equipment by making them easier to use.

Many ergonomists are employed full time by large manufacturing companies, such as automakers and computer firms. Others work as consultants for corporations, universities, and government agencies.

## Education and Training Requirements

Because ergonomics draws on expertise from many disciplines, specialists from a variety of fields become ergonomists. Some major in engineering or computer science, while others are trained in psychology, biology, physiology, or anthropology. In the United States, most ergonomist jobs require some graduate study. Some colleges and universities have recently added undergraduate and graduate programs in ergonomics. A list of schools offering bachelor's, master's and doctoral programs in ergonomics and human factors engineering can be found on the Web site of the Human Factors and Ergonomics Society.

## Getting the Job

Your college's placement office may be able to help you find a position in this field. You can also apply directly to manufacturers or other businesses that may

The widespread use of computers has created a large demand for ergonomists to make office and home computer stations more user-friendly. *(© Martha Tabor/Working Images Photographs. Reproduced by permission.)*

need the services of an ergonomist. Trade and professional journals, newspaper classifieds, and Internet job banks may also list job openings in this field.

## Advancement Possibilities and Employment Outlook

Ergonomists generally advance by moving to a larger company with more benefits or by becoming managers of ergonomics groups. Some ergonomists open their own consulting firms.

Employment opportunities are expected to increase at a rate faster than the average for all occupations as their expertise is applied to an increasing number of fields and as manufacturers compete to develop the most user-friendly products. Computer companies and others that use automated systems will need ergonomists to develop a comfortable, safe, and productive work setting.

## Working Conditions

Ergonomists work in comfortable, well-lighted offices and studios. They may have to travel to different locations when work environments or pieces of equipment need to be remodeled. They must be able to communicate effectively with people to determine exactly what type of problems they are having.

## Earnings and Benefits

Salaries differ widely according to an ergonomist's area of specialization and the location of the job. In 2006 the range of average annual salaries for ergonomists was from $40,000 to $72,000. Benefits for ergonomists who work for large institutions include paid holidays and vacations, health insurance, and retirement plans.

### Where to Go for More Information

Human Factors and Ergonomics Society
P.O. Box 1369
Santa Monica, CA 90406-1369
(310) 394-1811
http://www.hfes.org

# Fire Protection Engineer

**Education and Training**
Bachelor's degree or higher

**Salary**
Median—$80,000 to $100,000 per year

**Employment Outlook**
Very good

## Definition and Nature of the Work

Fire protection engineers are experts who save lives and money by preventing fires and reducing the danger when fires do break out. They provide advice that helps people to safely design buildings and products, prevent fires, and extinguish or escape from fires. Many also inspect buildings and homes to determine the amount of fire danger that is present and suggest ways to minimize this danger.

Fire protection engineers are employed in a variety of industries. They work with architects, builders, and owners to design buildings that are safe from fires. They plan changes in older buildings to make them safer. Many industries employ fire protection engineers full time in plants or refineries, particularly where dangerous processes or materials are involved. Fire protection engineers ensure that safety measures are followed at all times. They also teach managers and workers what to do in emergencies. Insurance companies employ many engineers to inspect the buildings that they insure, to give advice to the owners, and to judge the amount of fire danger so that insurance rates can be set. Makers of fire fighting and fire protection equipment use their staff engineers to help design, install, sell, and service their products. Federal, state, and local governments employ fire protection engineers to keep their properties safe from fire and to make sure that the public observes fire protection regulations. Some fire protection engineers teach on the college level. Others work as independent consultants.

## Education and Training Requirements

A bachelor's degree in science or engineering is required to become a fire protection engineer. It generally takes four years to earn a degree in science and four or five years to earn an engineering degree. Some employers prefer applicants who have degrees in fire protection engineering, but only a few schools offer this ma-

A fire protection engineer studies building plans to provide advice on safe design to architects and builders. *(© Martha Tabor/Working Images. Reproduced by permission.)*

jor. Many people enter the field with a background in chemistry or physics or with training in industrial, civil, mechanical, electrical, or chemical engineering. They often take a few courses in fire protection or get this training on the job. Some employers prefer applicants who have a master's degree. It usually takes one or two years of additional full-time study to get a master's degree. Workers who have experience may be eligible for certification by the Society of Fire Protection Engineers. This certification is a mark of recognition within the field.

In some cases engineers need to be licensed by the state in which they work. They generally need a degree from an approved engineering college, about four years of work experience as an engineer, and a passing grade on a state examination before being licensed as a professional engineer.

## Getting the Job

Your college placement office may be able to help you find a job in fire protection engineering. You can apply directly to insurance companies, consulting firms, manufacturers, oil refineries, makers of fire protection equipment, government agencies, and other places that employ fire protection engineers. To get a government job, you may need to take a civil service exam. In some cases employers advertise job openings in newspapers or professional and trade journals.

## Advancement Possibilities and Employment Outlook

Advancement opportunities depend on education, experience, and the industry. In large manufacturing plants, fire protection engineers often begin as trainees. They can advance to such positions as supervising engineer or department manager. Titles vary from company to company. In an insurance organization, fire protection engineers can advance to department head, branch manager, and even executive. Sometimes they start their own consulting firms.

There is a growing need for fire protection engineers. Greater public interest in safety, the growing cost of fires, higher insurance rates, and stricter government fire prevention standards create a need for more trained and experienced professionals. The best jobs will probably go to those with college training in fire protection engineering.

## Working Conditions

Working conditions in the fire protection field vary depending on the employer and the kind of job. Some engineers work mostly in offices on plans, designs, and specifications. Some spend most of their time in industrial plants or facilities. Others travel a great deal to inspect, consult, or do other similar work. The basic workweek for fire protection engineers is generally forty hours long. In some cases longer hours are necessary. Positions in manufacturing plants may require some shift work. Sometimes fire protection engineers are on call to deal with fire emergencies. There is some danger involved in their work, but they take safety precautions to keep this danger to a minimum.

Fire protection engineers must be able to analyze problems and find solutions. They need creativity and the ability to work with and communicate their ideas to others. In addition to having knowledge about the engineering problems involved in fire protection, they should also understand management methods and how to motivate others.

## Earnings and Benefits

Salaries vary depending on the experience and education of the fire protection engineer, as well as on the location and kind of job. A 2003 survey by the Society

### Where to Go for More Information

Society of Fire Protection Engineers
7315 Wisconsin Ave., Ste. 620E
Bethesda, MD 20814
(301) 718-2910
http://www.sfpe.org

of Fire Protection Engineers revealed that the median annual salary for fire protection engineers with doctoral degrees was about $100,000. The median annual salary for those with master's, bachelor's, or technical school degrees was approximately $80,000. Benefits usually include paid holidays and vacations, health insurance, and retirement plans. Fire protection engineers who travel on the job are reimbursed for their expenses.

# Forensic Scientist

**Education and Training**
Bachelor's, master's, or doctoral degree

**Salary**
Varies—see profile

**Employment Outlook**
Good

## Definition and Nature of the Work

Forensic scientists gather and evaluate evidence from the victims, vehicles, and scenes of crimes. They analyze the data scientifically, and their findings may help to convict or prove the innocence of a person accused of a crime. Forensic scientists are sometimes known as crime lab analysts or criminalists. Almost all of the people in this field work for federal, state, or local law enforcement and investigative agencies.

Police may submit clothing to be tested for the presence of drugs. Forensic scientists may be asked to decide whether spent bullets match firearms, or they may test and examine burned debris, footprints, inks, and papers.

The forensic scientist's report may be requested in civil as well as criminal cases. For instance, in a case where a company is held responsible for the pollution of a stream, the forensic scientist may test water samples for traces of waste from the company's plant.

## Education and Training Requirements

High school students interested in a forensic science career should take courses in mathematics, computers, earth sciences, biology, and chemistry. Almost all jobs require at least a bachelor's degree. Several colleges offer both undergraduate and graduate degrees in forensic science. A bachelor's degree with a major in forensic, natural, or physical science from an accredited college prepares job seekers for work in a crime laboratory. However, most employers prefer applicants with a master's or doctoral degree. Employers often pay tuition for courses that forensic scientists take to improve their job skills.

Most crime laboratories offer initial on-the-job training. Some trainees who have served as police officers enter the forensic science field and continue to take college courses while they work. Computer skills are increasingly important as databases are used for retrieval of information on drugs and other substances.

## Getting the Job

Visiting a crime laboratory and talking to employees may be an interesting and helpful introduction to this career. The Federal Bureau of Investigation (FBI), a major employer, can send you an application. College placement offices and state employment offices will also help graduates find jobs in forensic science.

## Advancement Possibilities and Employment Outlook

Forensic scientists may become managers of the crime laboratories in which they work. They can direct the training of new crime lab analysts. They can also establish their own consulting businesses.

Jobs for forensic science technicians (those with a bachelor's degree only) are expected to increase much faster than average. Employment opportunities for forensic scientists are expected to increase at an average rate. Job growth to some extent is directly related to crime rates and the number of civil action cases brought against companies accused of endangering personal or public health. However, crime rates have decreased in many areas, and the federal and state governments are expected to reduce the number and severity of environmental regulations imposed on companies.

## Working Conditions

Although much of their time is spent in clean, well-equipped laboratories, forensic scientists may accompany police into dangerous territory and may observe very unpleasant sights. They may take some risks working with firearms. They may have to examine some weapons that are in poor condition. They may be exposed to fumes and odors from decaying remains. They may also work with poisons. Most forensic scientists work a five-day, forty-hour week. However, situations may arise when they must work beyond their normal hours.

## Earnings and Benefits

Earnings vary widely depending on education, specialty, and location of employment. In 2005 entry-level forensic lab technicians earned about $30,000 per year, and the median salary for forensic technicians was slightly more than $40,000 per year. More experienced forensic scientists with bachelor's or master's degrees earned up to $70,000 per year. Medical doctors who work in the field of forensics, such as pathologists, earned more than $200,000 per year. Benefits include sick leave, medical insurance, and pension plans.

### Where to Go for More Information

American Academy of Forensic Sciences
410 North 21st St.
Colorado Springs, CO 80904-2798
(719) 636-1100
http://www.aafs.org

American Society of Crime Laboratory Directors
139K Technology Dr.
Garner, NC 27529
(919) 773-2044

# *Genetic Engineering Research Scientist*

**Education and Training**
Doctoral degree

**Salary**
Median—$65,110 per year

**Employment Outlook**
Very good

## Definition and Nature of the Work

Genetic engineering research scientists, or biotechnologists, manipulate and modify the genes, or hereditary makeup, of microorganisms, plants, and animals. They are specialists in the field of genetics and conduct research in a broad range of biological sciences including biochemistry, botany, embryology, and microbiology. They have developed techniques with numerous important applications in the fields of medicine, agriculture, and animal husbandry.

By isolating and modifying genetic material, genetic engineering research scientists have developed strains of bacteria that improve the effects of antibiotics and other useful pharmaceutical products. Clinical tests to help diagnose hereditary diseases and to circumvent infertility in humans have also been developed

By isolating and modifying genetic material, genetic engineering research scientists have made medical breakthroughs concerning antibiotics, hereditary diseases, and infertility in humans. *(© Rick Friedman/Corbis.)*

through genetic engineering. In agriculture, this technology is used to develop new crops that are more nutritious, disease-resistant, and able to flourish with less fertilizer. Genetic engineering has also been used to regulate animal breeding. In addition, other work has been directed toward the development of microorganisms that can be used to detoxify industrial waste or to provide alternate fuel sources. The U.S. Patent Office has approved many genetically engineered products including bacteria that consume oil spills and hormones that improve the milk yield of cows.

Genetic engineering research scientists are involved in researching, developing, and testing new methods and products with many potential applications. They are employed in private industry by chemical and pharmaceutical companies and firms that specialize in genetic engineering. Some work in medical facilities, colleges, or universities. Many are engaged in AIDS research.

Most genetic engineering research scientists are microbiologists. They use recombinant DNA (deoxyribonucleic acid) techniques, or gene splicing, to isolate genetic material from one organism and transplant it into another.

Genetically engineered drugs, chemicals, and other products are subjected to numerous forms of laboratory testing, including pyrogen (temperature) testing, microbial limit testing, and sterility testing, among many others. Based on their findings, genetic engineering research scientists must establish protocols, or stringent product standards, for the products they develop. After their development in vitro ("under glass," or in test tubes), these products undergo extensive in vivo ("in life") testing, or testing on a representative sample of the population for which the product is intended. Frequently a biostatistician enters the test data and results into a computer system and analyzes them. After the testing is completed, the scientists must carefully review the results and prepare a comprehensive report detailing the product trials.

## Education and Training Requirements

You generally need a doctoral degree in a biological science to become a genetic engineering research scientist. You should major in biology, botany, chemistry, zoology, or a related field as an undergraduate. Later, in graduate school, you may want to specialize in microbiology, genetics, embryology, biochemistry, or another specialized bioscience or medical science. It usually takes four years to earn a bachelor's degree and another one or two years to earn a master's degree. You need to go to school for an additional three or four years after receiving a bachelor's degree to obtain a doctoral degree. A few genetic engineering research scientists get both a doctor of medicine (M.D.) degree and a doctoral (Ph.D.) degree. Some colleges and universities offer undergraduate and graduate programs in genetic engineering.

## Getting the Job

Your professors and college placement office may help you to find a job as a scientist specializing in genetic engineering research. Biology and genetics department notice boards may advertise summer positions for graduate students. Professional journals, newspaper classifieds, and job banks on the Internet are good sources of job openings. You can also apply directly to genetic engineering firms, chemical companies, and pharmaceutical companies. Medical schools and some research hospitals also may hire genetic engineering research scientists.

## Advancement Possibilities and Employment Outlook

Genetic engineering research scientists can become project leaders or administrators of entire research programs. The publishing of important research findings in professional journals can lead to advancement. Some genetic engineering research scientists may be able to start their own consulting firms or biotechnology laboratories.

The employment outlook for genetic engineering research scientists is very good. Interest in genetic research has rapidly increased in the past few years, with discoveries leading to the possible cures and the treatment of many diseases. Research scientists will be in high demand as more and more applications for genetic engineering are found in medicine, agriculture, and private industry.

## Working Conditions

Most genetic engineering research scientists spend a large proportion of their time in clean, well-equipped laboratories. They generally work thirty-five to forty hours a week. In some cases, they may work extra hours to complete special projects.

Genetic engineering research scientists usually work as part of a team. They must be able to cooperate and communicate with other scientists in their field. They should enjoy working with precise and complex subject matter and be willing to comply with stringent cleanliness and safety standards.

## Earnings and Benefits

Earnings for genetic engineering research scientists vary depending on their education and experience. In 2004 the median salary for scientists working for scientific research and development services was $65,110. Benefits include paid holidays and vacations, health insurance, and pension plans.

### Where to Go for More Information

American Institute for Medical and Biological Engineering
1901 Pennsylvania Avenue NW, Ste. 401
Washington, DC 20006
(202) 496-9660
http://www.aimbe.org

American Society of Human Genetics
9650 Rockville Pike
Bethesda, MD 20814-3998
(866) HUM-GENE
http://www.ashg.org

# Historian

**Education and Training**
Doctoral degree

**Salary**
Median—$44,490 per year

**Employment Outlook**
Fair

## Definition and Nature of the Work

Historians study events, ideas, institutions, and individuals of the past. They may research and interpret events that occurred in the earliest periods of recorded time or ones that people can remember. Unlike archaeologists, who work chiefly with physical objects, historians rely mostly on written records for evidence to support their claims. However, historians sometimes use physical objects, such as photographs, costumes, and tools, to shed light on past lifestyles. Historians often try to relate knowledge of the past to present-day situations or problems.

History is a very broad field, and historians usually specialize in a particular time period, country, or region. For example, a historian may specialize in U.S. history with a more specific focus on the Great Depression. Another historian may focus on medieval history and concentrate on the German-speaking areas of Europe. Historians also specialize in certain kinds of history, such as the history of ideas, the history of immigration, the history of women, or the history of science. Sometimes historians specialize in a particular field, such as economic, social, or political history. Although historians are encouraged to specialize, they also need general knowledge to relate their findings to the broad patterns of change and continuity traced throughout the past.

About 70 percent of all historians are employed by colleges and universities. Although some have administrative duties, they generally teach, write, and do research. Some historians, known as archivists, collect historical documents and other objects for museums, special libraries, historical societies, and other organizations. Archivists prepare exhibits and organize historical materials for people who do historical research. Archivists work in places called archives where records, historic documents, and other materials are collected and preserved. Some historians working for government agencies or historical societies are involved in the preservation of historic buildings. Other historians work for publishing firms where they edit history textbooks, magazines, and other materials. Some historians serve as consultants for radio, television, and film producers,

A historian examines a weathered volume. *(© SETBOUN/Corbis.)*

checking for the accurate depiction of past events, styles, and portrayals of people. A few historians are self-employed researchers who write about historic events or people of the past.

Although their jobs may differ, almost all historians do some historical research. This research involves reading a great deal about a subject. For example, to study the history of a particular city, historians use original resource materials, such as old maps, pictures and photographs, election returns, tax lists, census records, and city directories that list the businesses and residents of a given period. They may read many issues of old newspapers and interview people who lived in the city during the period they are studying. They may listen to tape-recorded interviews of visitors and city residents or view films of city events. They may read letters or diaries of individuals who wrote in or about the city. Their research may involve looking at the records of the city's churches and temples. Historians are trained to analyze this mass of information and sometimes make use of statistical methods and computerized data. Historians piece the information together into a picture of what the city was like during an event or an era of the past. They usually compile their findings in books or articles. They may also present them to students, groups of historians, or other people in the form of lectures.

## Education and Training Requirements

You need an advanced degree to become a historian. If you have a bachelor's degree in history, you may find a job in historical research, but advancement opportunities will be limited. Most graduates with bachelor's degrees in history have jobs that are not directly related to history. Many find that their training in history is a good background for graduate study in journalism, law, business administration, and other fields. If you continue your education for one or two years after receiving a bachelor's degree and earn a master's degree in history, you will be qualified for jobs as a teacher, researcher, or archivist. In some cases you will be expected to continue studying for a doctoral degree. As early as possible, you should take courses in the language and literature of the area and period in which you plan to specialize. You may also want to take courses in statistics.

Most positions in administration and many teaching jobs in universities require a doctoral degree. It usually takes an additional two or three years of study after receiving a master's degree to obtain a doctoral degree. Historians must continue reading and studying throughout their careers so that they can keep up with new scholarship.

## Getting the Job

Your professors and the placement office at your college or university can give you information about getting a job in the field of history. Openings are sometimes listed in professional journals. You can also apply directly to colleges and universities, archives, government agencies, publishing firms, and other employers that are likely to employ historians. To obtain a government job, you may have to apply through a civil service office.

## Advancement Possibilities and Employment Outlook

Historians who have a doctoral degree can become full professors in colleges or universities. They can also move into jobs as administrators in colleges, universities, archives, or government agencies. Most historians advance by increasing their skills and publishing books and articles to win the recognition of other scholars. Some historians write books that have broad appeal to those outside their profession. The authors of such books are often in demand as lecturers.

Historians are social scientists, and employment opportunities for social scientists are expected to increase more slowly than the average for all occupations through the year 2014. Many qualified graduates who have a doctoral degree in history are expected to be seeking jobs. Most openings will be to replace historians who leave the field. Historians will likely face competition for academic positions, but find opportunities with historic preservation societies as public interest in preserving and restoring historical sites increases.

## Working Conditions

Historians spend most of their time in pleasant offices, classrooms, and libraries. While their hours are flexible, they often total more than forty hours per week. At times historians may visit archives or historic sites or buildings as they do research. They sometimes travel to distant cities or countries to examine evidence. They need the patience to work long hours tracking down elusive facts. They must have the ability to arrange many details into a convincing and coherent picture of the past. Historians must be able to work independently and be willing to spend long hours reading and studying. They must also be able to work well with other historians, students, and the public. Historians must have excellent communication skills.

### Where to Go for More Information

American Historical Association
400 A St. SE
Washington, DC 20003-3889
(202) 544-2422
http://www.historians.org

Organization of American Historians
112 North Bryan Ave.
Bloomington, IN 47408-5457
(812) 855-7311
http://www.oah.org

Society of American Archivists
527 South Wells St., 5th Fl.
Chicago, IL 60607-3922
(312) 922-0140
http://www.archivists.org

## Earnings and Benefits

Earnings depend on the education and experience of the historian and the kind of job. In May 2004 the annual median income of historians was $44,490. Those employed by private companies generally earn higher salaries. Many historians add to their income through writing, lecturing, or consulting projects. Benefits include paid holidays and vacations, insurance, and retirement plans.

# *Industrial Hygienist*

**Education and Training**
Bachelor's degree

**Salary**
Median—$69,103 per year

**Employment Outlook**
Good

## Definition and Nature of the Work

Industrial hygienists are occupational health and safety specialists concerned with the maintenance of good health among industrial workers. They attempt to prevent occupational diseases among employees and minimize environmental health hazards in the workplace. They are trained to anticipate, recognize, evaluate, and work to alleviate adverse working conditions that may cause illness or impair the health of workers. Such conditions may include excessive noise or the presence of dust, vapors, chemicals, and other potentially hazardous materials common to some industrial settings. Industrial hygienists frequently collect air or water samples and monitor noise levels to determine if any harmful conditions exist. They may also conduct radiological studies to measure radioactivity levels at job sites. The growth of high-technology and service industries has led to stress-related health problems, which industrial hygienists also examine.

Industrial hygienists are employed by large industrial manufacturers, insurance companies, public health agencies, and consulting firms. Some spend

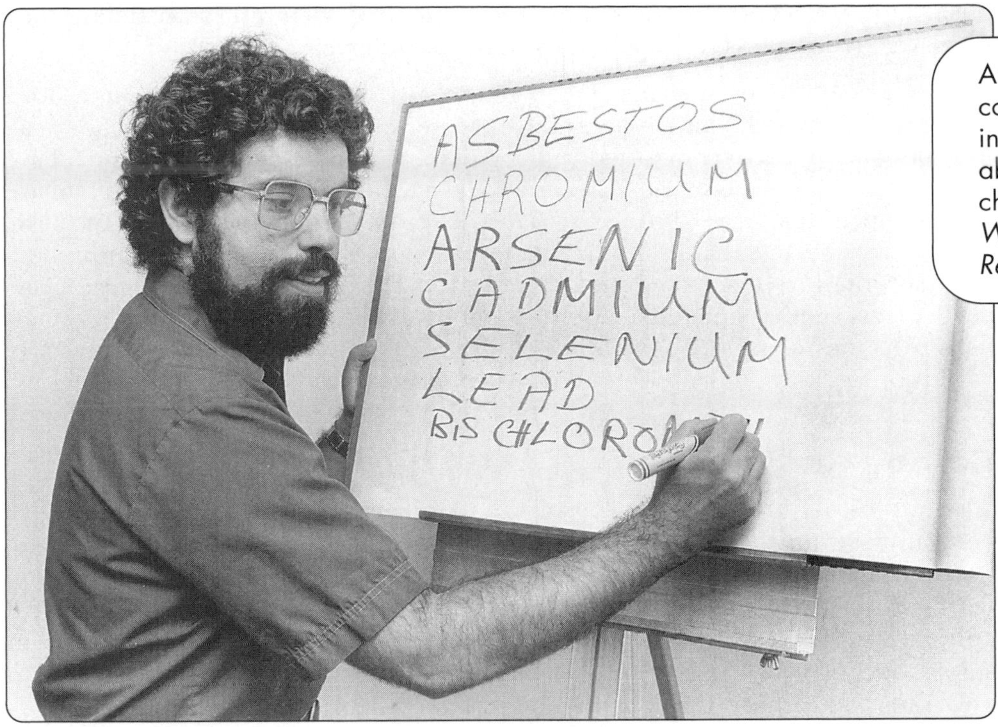

An industrial hygienist conducts a training session in which he informs workers about the dangers of particular chemicals. *(© Martha Tabor/ Working Images Photographs. Reproduced by permission.)*

most of their time in laboratories, where they analyze air samples, determine the effects of exposure to certain chemicals, or run tests on the reliability of health equipment, such as pacemakers and respirators. These professionals are sometimes called industrial hygiene chemists.

Other hygienists work on-site, where they confer with plant management, labor organizations, government officials, and in some cases environmental groups to establish health and safety programs that satisfy the different needs of all these groups. Industrial hygienists who specialize in pollution problems may help devise systems for the safe storage or disposal of toxic wastes from an industrial plant. Those with backgrounds in engineering may conduct detailed plant surveys to locate and correct work hazards. These professionals are called industrial hygiene engineers.

Industrial hygienists keep companies and labor groups informed of federal, state, and local health requirements. They prepare hazard communication sheets and interactive computer software to ensure that workers understand the dangers of the chemicals and equipment they use. Industrial hygienists are sometimes called on to testify at governmental hearings on product safety, working conditions, and environmental pollution. They also may be asked to represent their employers in workers' compensation hearings.

## Education and Training Requirements

High school students interested in careers in industrial hygiene should take biology, chemistry, mathematics, and physics. You generally need at least a bachelor's degree in science or engineering to become an industrial hygienist. Many employers prefer to hire applicants who have graduate-level training. Some colleges and universities offer undergraduate and graduate programs in industrial hygiene. It usually takes a minimum of four years to earn a bachelor's degree and one or two additional years of study to earn a master's degree. A good background in physical or biological sciences is a sound base for entry into this career. Engineers, chemists, physicians, nurses, toxicologists, and statisticians may move from these fields into positions in industrial hygiene.

The American Board of Industrial Hygiene (ABIH) grants certification to practicing hygienists who have a bachelor's degree in chemistry; physics; chemical, mechanical, or sanitary engineering; medicine; or biology. They also must have passed two ABIH examinations: a core examination and either a comprehensive or a chemical practice examination. The core examination covers all of the basic principles and facts that industrial hygienists should know, and the comprehensive examination covers them in greater depth. The chemical practice exam covers subjects such as chemical reactions and analytical procedures and methods used for monitoring the environment. A certified industrial hygienist usually earns considerably more than one who is not certified.

## Getting the Job

Your professors or the placement office at your college or university can give you information about getting a job. Work-study programs offered in college are good springboards for later jobs. Openings for hygienists are often listed in professional journals, newspaper classifieds, and Internet job banks. The annual conference of the American Industrial Hygiene Association has an employment service for job seekers. You can also apply directly to large corporations, insurance companies, consulting firms, and public health agencies.

## Advancement Possibilities and Employment Outlook

Advancement usually depends on the education and experience of the industrial hygienist. In the insurance industry, industrial hygienists can be promoted to the position of department manager in a branch office or to an executive position in the home office. In industrial firms, industrial hygienists can advance to safety and health managerial positions for one or several plants. Industrial hygienists may also become private consultants. Transferring from governmental employment to private industry may also offer promotional opportunities.

Industrial hygienists are occupational health and safety specialists, and employment of occupational health and safety specialists is expected to grow about as fast as the average for all occupations through 2014. This reflects a balance of continuing public demand for a safe and healthy work environment against the desire for smaller government and fewer regulations. The best opportunities will be for graduates of specialized industrial hygiene programs.

## Working Conditions

Industrial hygienists generally spend part of their time at worksites, which may be noisy. They also spend some of their time in offices or laboratories. Some may travel a great deal. For example, industrial hygienists who work for an insurance company may spend about half the time away from the home office while they are inspecting worksites. Most industrial hygienists work thirty-five to forty hours a week during regular business hours. However, industrial hygienists employed in factories that operate continuously may work all or part of a night shift when problems require their services.

Industrial hygienists must have the ability to establish and maintain good working relationships with both manage-

### Where to Go for More Information

American Board of Industrial Hygiene
6015 West St. Joseph, Ste. 102
Lansing, MI 48917-3980
(517) 321-2638
http://www.abih.org

American Conference of Governmental Industrial Hygienists
1330 Kemper Meadow Dr.
Cincinnati, OH 45240
(513) 742-2020
http://www.acgih.org

American Industrial Hygiene Association
2700 Prosperity Avenue, Ste. 250
Fairfax, VA 22031
(703) 849-8888
http://www.aiha.org

ment and workers. In many cases, hygienists are the link between these groups in instituting safe working conditions. They must be able to think and act quickly and be good at solving problems. Good communication skills are essential.

## Earnings and Benefits

Salaries for industrial hygienists vary depending on their experience and education as well as the location and kind of job. In 2006 the median annual income of industrial hygienists with at least four years of experience was $69,103.

# *Linguist*

**Education and Training**
Bachelor's, master's, or doctoral degree

**Salary**
Varies—see profile

**Employment Outlook**
Good

## Definition and Nature of the Work

Linguists study and explore all aspects of ancient and modern languages. They use scientific techniques to work with meanings, sounds, and origins of spoken and written words. Lexicographers compile definitions into dictionaries. Etymologists study the origin and evolution of words. Linguistic anthropologists study the relationships between written and spoken languages and the groups of people who use them, including those from rural cultures in developing nations or modern urban cultures in the West.

Linguists work with language in a variety of ways. Some may develop and promote artificial languages, such as Esperanto, which is an international language based on words common to the major European languages. In private companies, linguists may work with computer scientists to create new computer languages that are more like human languages. Linguists also look for ways to make computers respond to voice commands and give spoken answers, rather than printed responses on a screen or a printout. They develop ways to use computers to translate languages and methods to analyze documents to check the validity of their stated origin. For example, linguists may closely scrutinize a poem claimed to be the work of William Shakespeare. Linguists have also developed and refined American Sign Language (AMESLAN). They are now using it in their research and communication with animals.

## Education and Training Requirements

Linguists work for universities, high-tech companies, research institutions, consulting firms, the government, and the military. Educational requirements for linguists vary depending on the types of jobs they wish to pursue. A bachelor's degree with a major in linguistics, English, or a foreign language is essential for entry-level work. A master's degree incorporating some practical linguistic applications will make you more employable. Those interested in teaching linguistics at the college level or doing advanced research will need a doctoral degree. During doctoral studies, graduates can often work as teaching assistants and gain useful experience while earning a stipend.

## Getting the Job

Check for job openings on English department notice boards in colleges and universities and in the major scholarly journals. Interviews with prospective employers can be arranged at job desks set up during yearly conventions of the Modern Language Association (MLA) and other professional bodies. If your specialization is lexicography or etymology, check with the major dictionary publishers.

## Advancement Possibilities and Employment Outlook

The employment outlook for linguists is good. While the academic market for linguists remains fairly steady, there has been considerable growth in the area of computer-assisted language learning and online dictionaries and thesauruses. Once a linguist's work and publications have been recognized, consulting work may be available.

## Working Conditions

Linguists in colleges and universities split their time between teaching and research. Most work thirty-five to forty hours a week. Etymologists and lexicographers spend most of these hours at their computers or in libraries conducting painstaking and detailed research.

## Earnings and Benefits

Linguists' salaries depend largely on their area of expertise, their experience, and their education. In 2004 linguists with doctoral degrees working in high-tech companies earned starting salaries of about $60,000, and those with master's degrees earned slightly less. Linguists who worked on the development of computer languages earned higher salaries. Researchers and university professors earned lower salaries, as did linguists with only undergraduate degrees. Linguists working in corporate or academic environments usually receive retirement plans, health insurance, and vacation benefits.

Linguists are social scientists. In 2005 social scientists with bachelor's degrees and no experience could start working for the federal government at an annual salary of $24,677 to $30,567, depending on their college records. Those with master's degrees could start at $37,390, and those with doctoral degrees could begin at $45,239.

### Where to Go for More Information

Linguistic Society of America
1325 Eighteenth St. NW, Ste. 211
Washington, DC 20036-6501
(202) 835-1714
http://www.lsadc.org

American Association of Applied Linguistics
3416 Primm Lane
Birmingham, AL 35216
(866) 821-7700
http://www.aaal.org

# Mathematician

## Definition and Nature of the Work

Mathematics is the study of the measurement, properties, and relationships of quantities and sets, using numbers and symbols. Mathematicians use tools such as mathematical theory, well-defined procedures called algorithms, and the latest computer technology to solve economic, scientific, engineering, physics, and business problems. Mathematics is divided into two areas: theoretical, or pure, mathematics, and applied mathematics. However, these two areas often overlap.

Mathematicians working in theoretical mathematics are concerned with expanding and clarifying mathematical theories and laws. They seek to increase basic knowledge about mathematical relationships and formulate new laws of mathematics. Although the few mathematicians in theoretical research do not consider the practical uses of their findings, their work has been essential in many areas of science and engineering. For example, a new kind of geometry developed in the 1850s formed part of the basis for the theory of relativity, which in turn made the development of nuclear energy possible.

Mathematicians doing applied work use the theories and laws developed by theoretical mathematicians. Applied mathematicians solve specific problems in such fields as physical science, social science, business, computer science, government, biology, and engineering. They may work in the electronics industry developing new kinds of computers and software. Applied mathematicians sometimes study numerical information about medical problems, such as the effect of a new drug on a disease. Mathematicians working in the aerospace field may provide calculations that help determine whether the outside surfaces of a spaceship are properly designed to keep it on course.

Although mathematicians work in many different fields and apply their work in a variety of ways, they all use numbers. Mathematicians take abstract ideas or specific problems and put them into numerical form. They use computers regularly, as well as more traditional computational devices such as slide rules and calculators.

**Education and Training**
Master's or doctoral degree

**Salary**
Median—$81,240 per year

**Employment Outlook**
Poor

Mathematicians take abstract ideas or specific problems and put them into numerical form. Some provide calculations used in fields such as medicine, aeronautics and business. *(© Jim Sugar/Corbis.)*

About three-quarters of all mathematicians are employed by colleges and universities. Most of these mathematicians teach, but some also do research. Other mathematicians work for private companies in industries such as aerospace, communications, and electrical equipment manufacturing. Most mathematicians who work for the federal government are involved in space or defense-related projects.

Many workers who are not considered mathematicians use mathematical techniques extensively. Statisticians, actuaries, systems analysts, computer programmers, and mathematics teachers all use mathematics.

## Education and Training Requirements

You generally need a doctoral degree to become a mathematician. As an undergraduate, you can major in mathematics and include courses in related areas, such as statistics and computer science. If you have a bachelor's degree, you may be able to find a job as an assistant to a mathematician. You may also be able to obtain a position in an area related to mathematics in government or private industry. However, your opportunities for advancement as a mathematician will be limited. Many jobs in teaching and applied research are open to those who have a master's degree in mathematics. A job as a theoretical mathematician or a teaching and research position in a university requires a doctoral degree in mathematics. It usually takes four years to earn a bachelor's degree, another one or two years to receive a master's degree, and an additional two or three years for a doctoral degree. A career in mathematics often requires you to continue reading and studying in order to keep up with new developments in the field.

## Getting the Job

Your professors and college placement office may be good sources of information about getting a job in mathematics. You can also apply directly to colleges and universities, private companies, and government agencies that hire mathematicians. You sometimes need to pass a civil service examination to get a job with the government. Professional and trade journals, newspaper classifieds, and Internet job banks may also list openings for mathematicians.

## Advancement Possibilities and Employment Outlook

Advancement opportunities are good for mathematicians who have an advanced degree. They can become supervisors, managers, or directors of research. Mathematicians who have a doctoral degree can become full professors at colleges and universities. Many theoretical and applied mathematicians advance by becoming experts in a special area, such as algebra, geometry, or computing. They may gain the recognition of other mathematicians by publishing their findings in professional journals. Mathematicians who become experts are also often rewarded by higher salaries, especially in private industry.

Employment of mathematicians is expected to decrease through the year 2014. Those holding bachelor's degrees are usually not qualified to be mathematicians. Those with master's degrees will likely face keen competition for jobs in theoretical research. Those with master's and doctoral degrees who have strong backgrounds in mathematics and related disciplines, such as engineering or computer science, should have the best job opportunities.

## Working Conditions

Mathematicians who are employed by private companies or government agencies often work a standard thirty-five to forty-hour week in well-lighted, comfortable offices. At times they may have to work overtime to complete special projects. Although mathematicians working at colleges and universities usually have flexible schedules, they often put in long hours.

Although their work is not strenuous, mathematicians must have the patience to spend long periods of time concentrating on complex problems. They must be able to work independently. They should have good reasoning ability and enjoy working with abstract ideas and solving problems. At times, mathematicians must work with others. They need to be able to listen carefully to specific problems that need to be solved in applied mathematics. They must also be able to present their own ideas clearly.

## Earnings and Benefits

Salaries for mathematicians vary according to the location, kind of job, and education and experience of the individual. Median annual earnings of mathematicians were $81,240 in 2004. In 2005 average annual salaries for mathematicians employed by the federal government were slightly higher, at $88,194. Benefits usually include paid holidays and vacations, health insurance, and retirement plans.

### Where to Go for More Information

American Mathematical Society
201 Charles St.
Providence, RI 02940-2294
(800) 321-4267
http://www.ams.org

The Mathematical Association of America
1529 Eighteenth St. NW
Washington, DC 20036-1358
(800) 741-9415
http://www.maa.org

Society for Industrial and Applied Mathematics
3600 University City Science Center
Philadelphia, PA 19104-2688
(215) 382-9800
http://www.siam.org

# Mechanical Engineer

### Education and Training

Bachelor's degree or higher

### Salary

Median—$66,320 per year

### Employment Outlook

Good

## Definition and Nature of the Work

Mechanical engineers work with many kinds of machines that produce, transmit, or use power. They are concerned with mechanisms and methods that convert natural energy sources into practical uses. Mechanical engineers also design tools that other engineers need. They often work as part of a team that includes scientists who develop new theories and methods, and mechanical engineering technicians who assist engineers with some of their more routine tasks.

Mechanical engineers design and develop machines that produce energy, such as car engines and nuclear reactors. They also design and develop machines that use energy including air conditioners, power saws, elevators, and printing presses. Mechanical engineers work on various types of equipment and machines ranging from tiny mechanisms for delicate instruments to huge gears for bulldozers. The field of mechanical engineering is very broad, and some of the diverse job titles include air pollution control engineer, environmental systems engineer, manufacturing engineer, and automotive engineer.

Mechanical engineers generally specialize in one area of engineering. For example, they may work with aircraft engines or with commercial refrigeration equipment. Other fields of specialty include fluid power, instrumentation, and bioengineering. Some work in a particular industry, such as petroleum or plastics.

Within each branch of mechanical engineering there are specific jobs. Some engineers design products. They must determine the needs of the user, the physical problems of building the equipment, the cost of the equipment, and its effect on the environment. Other mechanical engineers supervise the production and in-

Most mechanical engineers work for manufacturing companies that make primary and fabricated materials, machinery, and electrical and transportation equipment. *(© Martha Tabor/ Working Images Photographs. Reproduced by permission.)*

stallation of equipment or are in charge of its maintenance and operation. Still other mechanical engineers are involved in sales, research and development, or teaching at the university level. Mechanical engineers also work as administrators and as consultants.

Mechanical engineers are employed throughout the United States. Three-fourths of them work in manufacturing—chiefly for companies that make primary and fabricated materials, machinery, and electrical and transportation equipment. Others work for government agencies, colleges and universities, and consulting firms.

## Education and Training Requirements

You generally need at least a bachelor's degree in mechanical engineering to enter this field. It takes four or five years to earn a bachelor's degree in engineering. Some programs include periods of work experience along with formal classes. Many engineers go on to obtain advanced degrees in a specialized field of engineering or business administration. Engineers often continue their education throughout their careers to remain aware of new developments in their field. Most employers encourage engineers to take formal courses that help engineers to improve their job performance. Some even pay the cost of tuition for these courses. In addition, mechanical engineers read and study professional and trade journals.

Engineers whose work affects life, health, or property or who offer their services to the public must be licensed by the state in which they work. They generally need a degree from an approved engineering college, about four years of work experience as an engineer, and a passing grade on a state examination before being licensed as a professional engineer.

## Getting the Job

If you are in a work-study program in college, you may be able to work full time for your employer after you graduate. Your college placement office may be able to help you find a job as a mechanical engineer. You might also look in newspapers, Internet job banks, and professional or trade journals for job openings.

## Advancement Possibilities and Employment Outlook

Mechanical engineers generally begin as assistants to experienced engineers. As they gain experience, they can become supervisors or experts in their field. Some advance to jobs as managers or executives. Mechanical engineers with the necessary education can become research directors. Some engineers start their own consulting or manufacturing companies.

The employment outlook for mechanical engineers is good through the year 2014; they are projected to have a rate of employment growth that is equal to the average for all occupations. There is a continuing need for industrial machinery and tools. Many trained engineers will be needed to develop complex new products, and emerging technologies will create new job opportunities for mechanical engineers. In addition, mechanical engineers have skills that they can apply in other engineering specialties.

## Working Conditions

Mechanical engineers spend part of their time in clean, well-lighted office buildings. At other times they work at construction sites or in noisy factories. Working conditions vary widely since mechanical engineers are employed in so many different kinds of jobs. Their basic workweek is usually forty hours. Overtime is necessary in some jobs, especially when project deadlines must be met.

Mechanical engineers should have aptitude in science and mathematics. They should enjoy working with machinery and using it to solve problems. In addition, mechanical engineers need to be able to cooperate with and communicate their ideas to other people.

## Earnings and Benefits

Earnings depend on the education and experience of the mechanical engineer, the location, and the kind of job. Mechanical engineers earn salaries that are close to the average salaries earned by all kinds of engineers. In 2004 the median annual earnings of mechanical engineers was $66,320. In 2005 beginning mechanical engineers with bachelor's degrees earned an average salary of $50,236 per year. Those with master's degrees started at an average salary of $59,880 per year, and those with doctoral degrees started at an average salary of $68,299 per year. Benefits include paid holidays and vacations, insurance, and retirement plans.

### Where to Go for More Information

American Society for Engineering Education
1818 N St. NW, Ste. 600
Washington, DC 20036-2479
(202) 331-3500
http://www.asee.org

American Society of Mechanical Engineers
Three Park Ave.
New York, NY 10016-5990
(800) 843-2763
http://www.asme.org

# Metallurgical Engineer

**Education and Training**
Bachelor's degree or higher

**Salary**
Median—$67,110 per year

**Employment Outlook**
Fair

## Definition and Nature of the Work

Metallurgical engineers develop ways of processing metals and converting them into useful products. Metallurgy, the science of metals, is one of the materials sciences. Other materials sciences include physical metallurgy, ceramics, and polymer chemistry, or plastics. Metallurgical engineers, a subspecialty of materials engineers, work primarily in industrial areas, particularly in the iron and steel industries. Some work with other metals such as aluminum or copper. Metallurgical engineers are also employed in industries that make machinery and other products using metal, such as automobiles and electrical equipment. Some work for government agencies or colleges and universities.

The work of metallurgical engineers is similar to the work of metallurgical scientists, or metallurgists. Metallurgical engineers use complex equipment, including electron microscopes, X-ray machines, and spectrographs. They use the latest scientific and technological findings in their work. Metallurgical engineers are often assisted by metallurgical technicians.

There are two main branches of metallurgy—extractive metallurgy and physical metallurgy. Extractive metallurgy involves the separation, or extraction, of metals from ores. Ores are mixtures of metals and other substances. Once the ore has been mined, many steps are needed to extract the metal and refine it to a relatively pure form. Metallurgical engineers design and supervise the processes that separate the metals from their ores. They often cooperate with mining engineers in the early steps of the extraction process. After metallic compounds have been separated from the rock and other waste materials, metallurgical engineers can use a number of different processes to refine the metals. These processes

Metallurgical engineers who work in physical metallurgy develop new alloys for products such as electronics equipment and automobiles. *(© Martha Tabor/Working Images Photographs. Reproduced by permission.)*

might involve the use of heat, electric current, or chemicals dissolved in water to produce a pure and usable metal.

Metallurgical engineers involved in extractive metallurgy work in laboratories, ore treatment plants, refineries, and steel mills. They are concerned with finding new and better ways of separating relatively small amounts of metal from huge quantities of waste rock. They must consider the effects that the process has on the environment, the conservation of energy, and the proper disposal of the waste rock.

Physical metallurgy is the study of the structure and physical properties of metals and alloys. It also involves the many processes used to convert a refined metal into a finished product. Most metals are not useful in their pure form. They must be made into alloys, or mixtures of a metal and one or more other elements. Steel is an example of an alloy. It is made from iron and small amounts of carbon and other elements. Copper and zinc are combined to form another alloy, brass. Scientists and metallurgical engineers work in physical metallurgy to develop new alloys to meet many needs. These alloys include radiation shielding for nuclear reactors, lightweight but high-strength steel for automobile bodies, and special metals used in electronic equipment. Physical metallurgical engineers also develop production processes that include melting, casting, alloying, rolling, and welding. They design and supervise the processes that produce such goods as structural steel, wire, or sheets of aluminum. Sometimes they are involved in processes that use these metal goods in the manufacture of other finished products. Physical metallurgists often work in laboratories or in manufacturing plants.

## Education and Training Requirements

You need at least a bachelor's degree to become a metallurgical engineer. You can major in metallurgical engineering, metallurgy, or materials science. It usually takes four or five years to earn a bachelor's degree. Some colleges and universities offer a work-study program, which combines practical work experience with formal study. However, many jobs require an advanced degree. You can earn a master's degree in one or two years of additional full-time study. It usually takes about four years of full time study to receive a doctoral degree once you have earned a bachelor's degree. Many metallurgical engineers continue their education while they are employed. Often their employers cover the cost of tuition for courses that will improve their job performance. Since metallurgy is a changing field, engineers have to continue studying and reading professional journals throughout their careers.

Engineers who offer their services to the public or whose work affects life, health, or property must be licensed by the state in which they work. They generally need a degree from an approved college, about four years of experience as an engineer, and a passing grade on a state examination before they can be licensed as a professional engineer.

## Getting the Job

Your college placement office may be able to help you find a job as a metallurgical engineer. If you take part in a work-study program, you may be able to continue working full time for your employer after you graduate. You can apply directly to companies in the metals industries that hire metallurgical engineers. Sometimes job openings are listed in newspaper classifieds, Internet job banks, and trade and professional journals.

## Advancement Possibilities and Employment Outlook

As they gain experience on the job, metallurgical engineers can advance to positions that have more responsibility. Experienced metallurgical engineers, especially those with an advanced degree, can be promoted to top positions in research and management. They can also teach on the college level and become consultants to industry and government.

While materials engineers in general are expected to have employment growth about as fast as the average for all occupations through 2014, the employment outlook for metallurgical engineers is only fair. Declines in manufacturing industries such as primary metals, industrial machinery and equipment, and stone, clay, and glass products are expected. However, employment growth is projected in service industries such as research and testing, personnel supply, and engineering and architectural services.

## Working Conditions

Working conditions for metallurgical engineers vary with their jobs. Most engineers spend some time in offices and laboratories where they work with other engineers and metallurgical technicians. They also do some of their work alone. Some metallurgical engineers meet with supervisors at mines and plants. Production sites can be hot and noisy. In some areas engineers have to wear protective glasses and clothing.

Forty-hour workweeks are standard. Some metallurgical engineers are expected to work rotating shifts. Overtime is also sometimes necessary, especially when project deadlines must be met. Engineers must also devote some time to keeping up with new findings in their field.

Metallurgical engineers should enjoy the challenge of a demanding profession. They should enjoy solving problems and have aptitude in science and mathematics. Because they must often work as part of a team, metallurgical engineers should be able to get along with other people. It is also important for engineers to be able to communicate their ideas to others.

### Where to Go for More Information

American Society for Metals/ASM International
9639 Kinsman Rd.
Materials Park, OH 44073-0002
(440) 338-5151
http://www.asm-intl.org

National Society of Professional Engineers
1420 King St.
Alexandria, VA 22314-2794
(703) 684-2800
http://www.nspe.org

## Earnings and Benefits

Salaries depend on the education and experience of the metallurgical engineer, the location, and the kind of job. In 2004 the median annual income of materials engineers in general was $67,110. In 2005 the average starting salary for a materials engineer with a bachelor's degree was $50,982. Benefits generally include paid holidays and vacations, health insurance, and pension plans.

# Microbiologist

## Definition and Nature of the Work

Microbiologists are biological scientists who study organisms so small that, generally, they can only be seen with a microscope. These microorganisms include bacteria, algae, yeasts, fungi, protozoa, viruses, and other microscopic forms of life. Microbiologists isolate and make cultures of microorganisms, identify their characteristics, and observe their reactions to chemicals and other kinds of stimuli. They also study how microorganisms develop and reproduce as well as their distribution in nature.

**Education and Training**
Doctoral degree

**Salary**
Median—$54,840 per year

**Employment Outlook**
Good

Many microbiologists work for universities, where they teach and do research. Others work at medical centers or in private industry. Some work for government agencies. Although their jobs have different aspects and responsibilities, most microbiologists do some research or laboratory work. They use special equipment to study microorganisms including light microscopes, electron microscopes, centrifuges, glass tubes, slides, and computers. They are often assisted by biological technicians.

Microbiology is a broad field that includes the study of viruses as well as microscopic organisms found in all kingdoms of life: plants, animals, protists, fungi, and bacteria. Some microbiologists specialize in one type of microorganism. For example, bacteriologists concentrate on bacteria and virologists study viruses.

Microbiologists work in several areas. Many do basic research to increase knowledge about the life processes common to microbes. Their work helps to answer basic questions such as those pertaining to the use of food and oxygen in cells. Other microbiologists are employed in medicine. Medical microbiologists study the relationship between microorganisms and disease. They isolate and identify disease-producing organisms and study their distribution. They also study the ways that the organisms enter the bodies of humans and animals, establish themselves, and cause disease. Immunologists, for example, study the body's defensive responses to microorganisms. Other medical microbiologists study the

Microbiologists study microscopic forms of life such as bacteria, algae, yeast, fungi, protozoa, and viruses. *(© CDC/PHIL/Corbis.)*

effects of antibiotics on bacteria. Some are concerned with the role of viruses in cancer. Others help to develop new ways to treat and prevent disease.

Microbiologists are also employed in the related field of public health. They work to combat problems such as outbreaks of epidemics, food poisoning, and the pollution of air and water. For example, public health microbiologists test blood samples sent in by physicians to see whether patients have a communicable disease. They also test drinking water, milk supplies, and other substances that can affect the health of the general public.

Other fields in which microbiologists work include agriculture, marine microbiology, and industry. Agricultural microbiologists study the microorganisms found in soil and their effects on plant growth. Marine microbiologists seek ways to control the growth of harmful bacteria in oceans and rivers. Industrial microbiologists work in a variety of industries, including food processing, chemicals, and drugs. They may work to control the activities of microorganisms in such processes as the tanning of leather and the fermentation of wine.

## Education and Training Requirements

You generally need a doctoral degree to become a microbiologist. You can major in microbiology or any of the other biological sciences as an undergraduate. Although those who have bachelor's degrees can find jobs in the field, they are technicians and their opportunities for advancement are limited. They are usually assigned such tasks as doing diagnostic or quality control testing in laboratories or in industry. Those who have earned master's degrees in microbiology or in related fields such as bacteriology are qualified for many jobs in industry, teaching, and applied research. You need a doctoral degree to obtain most teaching and research positions in universities or to get a job as an administrator. It generally takes four years to earn a bachelor's degree and another one or two years to earn a master's degree. You need to study an additional three or four years to receive a doctoral degree. Some microbiologists have earned the degree of doctor of medicine (M.D.) in addition to a doctoral degree (Ph.D.).

A combination of academic courses and laboratory experience is required for a clinical laboratory license, which is a prerequisite for admission to the certification examinations for some state departments of health. Many employers encourage and assist microbiologists who want to further their education in this field. In order to keep up with new findings in their field, microbiologists must continue studying throughout their careers.

## Getting the Job

Your college instructors or placement office may be able to help you find a job in the field of microbiology. Some companies send recruiters to college job fairs. You may find job openings in newspaper classifieds, job banks on the Internet, or professional journals. You can also apply directly to colleges and universities, medical centers, private firms, and government agencies that hire microbiologists. You may need to pass a civil service examination to get a government job.

## Advancement Possibilities and Employment Outlook

There are many possible avenues of advancement for microbiologists, especially for those with a doctoral degree. Microbiologists can become directors of research in medical centers, private firms, or government agencies. Those who hold a teaching and research position in a university can advance to the rank of full professor. They can also make significant discoveries in their research and gain the recognition of other microbiologists. Many scientists consider this to be the highest form of advancement.

The number of job opportunities for microbiologists will increase at a rate as fast as the average for all occupations through the year 2014. However, the federal government has recently increased its budget and increased the number of grants awarded to researchers. At the same time, the number of advanced degrees awarded has continued to increase. As a result, there will be considerable competition for research positions. Colleges and universities will add only a few positions each year. Nonetheless, increased public awareness in preserving the environment, providing sanitary food production and storage, and finding cures for such diseases as AIDS, cancer, and heart disease are likely to provide the stimulus for increased spending by private companies.

Opportunities for those with bachelor's or master's degrees in microbiology are expected to be better than the opportunities for those with doctoral degrees. These workers can fill jobs in science-related sales and marketing, and can take on technician roles. Some can become high school teachers.

## Working Conditions

Working conditions for microbiologists vary. Most spend at least part of their time in clean, well-lighted laboratories. Some microbiologists have to collect samples of soil, seawater, and other substances that contain microorganisms. Some microbiologists spend part of their time in classrooms and offices. The workweek for many microbiologists in medical centers and private industry is generally forty hours. Those who work in universities and other research centers may have more flexible hours, but their workweeks generally total more than forty hours. Some overtime or shift work may be necessary when a project must be completed or when an experiment must be monitored around the clock. Microbiologists usually spend some time reading and studying to keep up with the newest findings of other scientists.

Microbiologists must take precautions to prevent specimens from being contaminated and to keep harmful microorganisms from reproducing uncontrollably. They should have skill in scientific experimentation and mathematics and be willing to do the precise, detailed work required in microbiology. Microbiologists should be able to work either independently or as part of a team. They must be able to keep careful records and to communicate their ideas and findings to others.

## Earnings and Benefits

The earnings of microbiologists vary widely depending on their education and experience, the location, and the kind of job. The median annual salary of microbiologists was $54,840 in 2004. In 2005 those working for the federal government earned an average of $80,798 per year. Benefits generally include paid holidays and vacations, health insurance, and pension plans.

### Where to Go for More Information

American Institute of Biological Sciences
1444 I St. NW, Ste. 200
Washington, DC 20005
(202) 628-1500
http://www.aibs.org

American Society for Microbiology
1752 N St. NW
Washington, DC 20036
(202) 737-3600
http://www.asm.org

# Microwave Engineer

**Education and Training**
Bachelor's or master's degree

**Salary**
Median—$75,770 per year

**Employment Outlook**
Very good

## Definition and Nature of the Work

Microwave engineers are electronics engineers who specialize in designing, manufacturing, testing, and installing electronic components and systems used to transmit and receive microwave, or short radio wave, signals. A wide variety of devices use microwave signals. These include cellular telephones and radios, portable communications systems such as personal digital assistants, wireless Internet devices, satellites, global positioning systems, aircraft navigation equipment, guidance systems for missiles and other military hardware, and magnetic resonance imaging machines.

A microwave engineer's primary task is to design integrated circuits and other electronic components used in microwave devices. This process may begin by meeting clients to determine the types of products they need and establishing engineering and performance standards for those products. The microwave engineer then works with computer programs to model and lay out potential circuit or component designs for the product. Following the design stage, the engineer tests the model and evaluates its performance against predetermined standards. He or she also ensures that the design meets standards for microwave performance set by the Federal Communications Commission (FCC). This may include preparing and submitting licensing documents or other paperwork to the FCC.

Once a design has been successfully tested, the microwave engineer oversees the engineering and manufacturing staff responsible for creating the final device or component. The engineer meets with marketing personnel to explain the features and advantages of the product so that it can be marketed and sold effectively. In addition, microwave engineers perform follow-up work with customers to make sure the device meets their needs and to troubleshoot any problems the customer may experience.

Sometimes microwave engineers are called on to do fieldwork with existing microwave hardware. This typically involves evaluating microwave towers and transmission equipment and determining the need for improvements and upgrades. The microwave engineer must make sure that any newly designed equipment can operate effectively in existing microwave towers. This evaluation may include analyzing tower clearances and lines of sight to ensure a clear path for microwave signals. The engineer must also determine if existing antennae and support equipment are compatible and function efficiently with any new hardware.

Microwave engineers often have supervisory responsibility for the team that is designing new components and equipment. In this role, the engineer assigns work, establishes and tracks budgets, oversees the work of associate microwave engineers and microwave technicians, and sees that all schedules for the project are followed. As a project manager, the microwave engineer also reports to management personnel on the progress of the work.

## Education and Training Requirements

Microwave engineers must have an extensive background in engineering and electronics. Most positions require a bachelor's degree in electronics engineering or a related field, and many require a master's degree. A thorough knowledge of microwave equipment and support systems is necessary. Experience working with and designing integrated circuits and other electronics components is highly desirable and often required. Because testing and evaluation of designs are a critical part of the job, the microwave engineer should also possess good problem-solving skills. Strong interpersonal and communications skills are important as well for dealing with clients, marketing and sales staff, and management.

## Getting the Job

Becoming a microwave engineer typically requires several years of experience in microwave design and development. Sometimes employees move up from within their own companies. The personnel offices of such companies usually advertise openings within their firms. Employment opportunities for microwave engineers are also advertised in newspaper classified sections, industry magazines, and Internet job banks.

## Advancement Possibilities and Employment Outlook

Microwave engineers who start out as part of a design team may eventually work up to positions as project manager, overseeing the work of an entire team. An experienced project manager may advance to a position in upper management within the company. Microwave engineers who are skillful in communicating complex ideas to clients may take positions in marketing or sales where they can combine their technical knowledge and interpersonal skills.

The use of wireless and microwave communication technology is growing rapidly in the United States and around the world. Because microwave-based systems involve far less cost and trouble to install and maintain than wire-based systems, the wireless communications field should continue to expand for the foreseeable future. Many developing countries that do not already have extensive wire-based communications systems rely heavily on microwave communications technology. Thus, demand for microwave engineers should remain strong not only in the United States but overseas as well.

## Working Conditions

Microwave engineers spend a great deal of their time designing and laying out microwave circuits or components on computers. This usually takes place in a clean and modern office environment. Once the design and layout is complete, the engineer must test it in a laboratory setting. Microwave engineers must also meet with clients to determine their needs and provide product support. Engineers working with towers or other field equipment may spend a fair amount of time outdoors.

## Earnings and Benefits

In 2004 the median annual earnings for electronics engineers in general was $75,770. A microwave engineer with extensive experience who works as a project manager can earn up to $120,000 a year. Most companies that employ microwave engineers also offer benefits that include paid vacation, medical coverage, a retirement package, and perhaps incentive bonuses and profit sharing. Some firms offer a signing bonus to highly desirable applicants.

### Where to Go for More Information

Institute of Electrical and Electronics Engineers-USA
1828 L St. NW, Ste. 1202
Washington, DC 20036-5104
(202) 785-0017
http://www.ieeeusa.org

National Society of Professional Engineers
1420 King St.
Alexandria, VA 22314-2794
(703) 684-2800
http://www.nspe.org

# Nuclear Engineer

**Education and Training**
Bachelor's, master's, or doctoral degree

**Salary**
Median—$84,880 per year

**Employment Outlook**
Fair

## Definition and Nature of the Work

Nuclear engineers use their knowledge about nuclear energy to solve engineering problems. Their work allows for the practical application of many discoveries by nuclear physicists and other scientists. Nuclear engineers have knowledge of the processes that produce nuclear energy and understand the properties of the radiation and radioactive atoms produced in nuclear reactions. They are trained to use this specialized knowledge in design, construction, research, and development.

Many nuclear engineers work in private and governmental research and development laboratories. Some teach in colleges and universities. Other engineers are employed in nuclear power plants and in factories that make nuclear equipment or weapons.

Sometimes nuclear engineers work chiefly in design engineering. They often design and develop new devices used to generate nuclear power, such as nuclear reactors. They also may develop equipment used to process nuclear fuels and dispose of radioactive waste materials. Some nuclear engineers design equipment that makes use of radioactive materials to solve a wide variety of problems in agriculture, medicine, science, and industry. Other engineers work closely with scientists in the development of equipment and methods to be used in nuclear research. Their work may help scientists to gain more knowledge about the structure and dynamics of matter and energy as well as lead to new ways of producing and using nuclear energy.

Sometimes nuclear engineers work in a specific construction project or in on-site engineering. For example, they may work at the construction site of a new nuclear power plant. On-site engineers work closely with other specialists and supervise the part of the construction for which they are responsible. When problems related to the use of nuclear energy arise, nuclear engineers must analyze and solve them quickly. Nuclear engineers may supervise the loading of fuel into a nuclear reactor and the critical steps leading to the generation of nuclear energy.

Other nuclear engineers supervise the operation of nuclear facilities. They may work in nuclear power plants or in plants that make nuclear equipment or fuels. They may be responsible for maintaining safe radiation levels. They may also supervise technicians who use radiation technology in the manufacture of a wide variety of products.

## Education and Training Requirements

You generally need at least a bachelor's degree to become a nuclear engineer. You can earn your bachelor's degree in a science, such as physics, or in engineering. There are some bachelor-level programs in nuclear engineering, but many study for a bachelor's degree in mechanical or chemical engineering instead. A master's degree or a doctoral degree is required for many jobs in nuclear engineering. These advanced degrees can be in nuclear engineering or another branch of engineering. Because nuclear engineering incorporates knowledge from different areas of science and engineering, the field is relatively easy to enter from other fields.

On-the-job training is usually an important part of the education of a nuclear engineer. Nuclear facilities work closely with the federal government to provide opportunities for on-the-job training and college programs for people working in this field. Because nuclear engineering is a rapidly changing field, engineers need to study and update their skills throughout their careers.

All states require licensing for engineers who offer their services to the public or whose work may affect life, health, or property. In general, you need a bachelor's degree from an approved college and four years of experience to become licensed. You must also pass a state licensing examination. Some nuclear engineers work on projects that are restricted because they are vital to national security. These engineers must obtain a security clearance.

## Getting the Job

If you participate in a work-study program in cooperation with a nuclear facility while in undergraduate or graduate school, you may be able to get a full-time job at that facility. Your school placement office may be able to help you find a job as a nuclear engineer. The federal government can give you information about its research programs in the nuclear field. You can also apply directly to power companies, laboratories, or factories that make or use nuclear equipment. In some cases these facilities place classified ads for nuclear engineers in newspapers, Internet job banks, and professional journals.

## Advancement Possibilities and Employment Outlook

Advancement possibilities for nuclear engineers with graduate degrees are very good. Workers who have only a bachelor's degree have less of a chance to advance, but many continue their education on a part-time basis. Since the field of nuclear engineering is changing rapidly, nuclear engineers who want to advance should keep up with new developments by taking additional courses and reading professional journals. Engineers who have the necessary education and experience can become supervisors of other nuclear engineers. They can also move into related fields, such as management, administration, or teaching on the university level.

The employment outlook for nuclear engineers is fair through the year 2014 because employment of nuclear engineers is expected to grow more slowly than average. Due to the high cost of nuclear energy and public concern over its safety, no new commercial reactors have come on line since May 1996. However, the administration of President George W. Bush has been supportive of nuclear expansion, and skilled engineers are needed to operate existing nuclear power plants. In addition, it is likely that there will be new jobs in industries that make use of nuclear energy in ways that are not directly related to generating electricity, such as nuclear medical technology. There should also be new jobs for engineers in the military area.

## Working Conditions

Working conditions for nuclear engineers vary according to the job. Nuclear engineers involved in design usually work in well-lighted offices and often put in a forty-hour workweek. They may have to work overtime to meet deadlines or handle unforeseen problems. Some engineers need to travel from assignment to assignment. Nuclear engineers employed by nuclear power plants or factories that make or use nuclear equipment sometimes have to work weekends and evening shifts.

Nuclear engineers need to follow special safety measures that keep worksites and workers safe from radiation poisoning. Workers are protected by heavy barriers that seal off the radiation produced by nuclear devices and reactors. Because of these shields and other precautions, the nuclear energy field has an excellent safety record.

**Where to Go for More Information**

American Nuclear Society
555 N. Kensington Ave.
La Grange Park, IL 60526
(708) 352-6611
http://www.ans.org

Nuclear Energy Institute
1776 I St. NW, Ste. 400
Washington, DC 20006-3708
(202) 739-8000
http://www.nei.org

Nuclear engineers must be able to analyze and solve problems. They should be able to work well as part of a team. The nature of their work requires that nuclear engineers be careful and responsible workers.

## Earnings and Benefits

Earnings vary according to the education and experience of the individual, the location, and the type of job. In 2004 nuclear engineers earned median annual salaries of $84,880. In 2005 beginning salaries for those with bachelor's degrees averaged $51,182 and for those with master's degrees averaged $58,814. Benefits generally include paid holidays and vacations, health insurance, and pension plans.

# *Pathologist*

**Education and Training**
Doctoral degree

**Salary**
Varies—see profile

**Employment Outlook**
Very good

## Definition and Nature of the Work

Pathologists are biological or medical scientists who study the nature, causes, and effects of disease in plant and animal life. Pathology is a broad field that concentrates on the changes in organs, tissues, and cells that are caused by disease.

Pathologists work in hospitals, medical laboratories, schools, colleges, and universities. They may teach or do laboratory work or research. They are employed by government agencies associated with agriculture, public health, law enforcement, and many other fields. Private companies that make products such as drugs and insecticides also employ pathologists.

Pathologists concentrate on plant, animal, or human pathology. Although the areas of study of these pathologists are very different, they are all scientists who study disease. Pathology has been called the bridge between basic science and medicine. Pathologists who are concerned with human disease are usually physicians who have received specialized training in pathology. They are sometimes called medical pathologists or are classified according to their subspecialty, such as oral pathology.

Although medical pathologists do not treat patients of their own, they do laboratory tests to diagnose disease in the patients of other physicians. They perform tests on body tissues, secretions, and other specimens to see whether a disease is present and to determine its stage. They evaluate the extent of the disease, estimate the course it is likely to take, and suggest ways to treat the disease. Surgeons may consult pathologists if they find unexpected problems during an operation. Pathologists often stand by during surgery to test specimens taken from a tumor in a patient's body. The patient may remain under anesthesia until the pathologist can evaluate the specimens. Based on the pathologist's expert advice, the surgeon is able to complete the operation in the way best suited to the patient's condition.

Pathologists also do postmortem examinations to determine the cause of death when the cause is unclear. They can evaluate the extent to which treatment had helped a patient. Pathologists' reports help physicians in their care of other patients with similar conditions. Sometimes pathologists serve as medical examiners or coroner's consultants. They determine the cause of death in accidents, poisonings, and suspected murders. Pathologists coordinate and supervise the work of medical laboratory technologists or technicians who prepare specimens or may perform the more routine laboratory tests themselves. Pathologists often specialize in one field, such as hematology (the study of the blood), blood banking, neuropathology (diseases of the nervous system), forensic (or legal) pathology, medical chemistry, medical microbiology, or radioisotopic pathology.

Medical pathologists frequently teach students in schools and colleges that train nurses, physicians, medical laboratory technologists, technicians, and other health care workers. They sometimes conduct seminars for physicians and interns in hospitals. They help train law enforcement officers to use scientific methods of observation when they investigate injuries or deaths. Pathologists also do scientific research into drugs and disease. Laboratories developing new drugs need pathologists to study their safety. Pathologists use microscopes, radioisotopes, and other equipment to study the cause of disease. They also use scientific methods and computerized data as they test theories about disease processes. Cancer, atherosclerosis, allergies, and birth defects are among the many diseases being studied by medical pathologists.

Animal pathologists may be veterinarians or zoologists (animal scientists). Veterinarians specializing in pathology study diseases and disorders in animals. They often specialize in poultry, livestock, or pets. They also help to improve the quality of livestock and poultry used for human food. In addition, their work helps to save human lives since animals can transmit diseases such as rabies and tuberculosis to human beings. Similar to veterinarians and medical pathologists, zoologists specializing in pathology may study the effects of disease, parasites, and insects on the cells, tissues, and organs of animals. Unlike other pathologists, zoologists are often trained to work with a wide variety of animal species. They may study hereditary diseases or disorders in fruit flies in order to increase knowledge about the ways diseases are passed on over a period of many generations. They may study the development of tumors in mice to get clues about the causes and development of cancer in human beings. Animal pathologists often use equipment and methods that are similar to those used by medical pathologists. Zoologists and veterinarians working in animal pathology are employed by colleges and universities, centers for veterinary medicine, zoos, and wildlife refuges as well as government agencies and private industry.

Plant pathologists are botanists (plant scientists) whose special field is sometimes called phytopathology. Sometimes plant pathologists do basic research into the nature of disease in living things. For example, they may study the effect of air pollution on the respiration rate and on the cells and tissues of plants. This study may have applications for medical pathologists who are concerned with the role of industrial pollution in causing lung cancer or emphysema in human beings. On the other hand, many plant pathologists do research that directly relates to plant diseases. They devise ways to control or prevent plant diseases. They help to develop new types of plants that are disease resistant. Their work is useful in improving our food, fiber, and lumber supplies and in preserving the ornamental plants and trees that make our environment more healthful and attractive. Plant pathologists use many of the same kinds of laboratory equipment and scientific methods that medical and animal pathologists use. Plant pathologists teach and do research in colleges and universities. They work for government agencies and private firms involved in agriculture, horticulture, forestry, and related fields.

## Education and Training Requirements

You need advanced training to become a pathologist. As an undergraduate, you should major in premedical studies, a biological science, chemistry, or a related field. Although individuals with bachelor's degrees can find some jobs as medical laboratory technologists or advanced biological technicians, their opportunities for advancement are limited. People who have earned a master's degree in plant or animal pathology or in microbiology, biochemistry, or a related field may be qualified for some jobs in teaching or applied research. It generally takes four years to earn a bachelor's degree and another one or two years to obtain a master's degree.

To be a fully qualified pathologist you need a doctoral degree (Ph.D.). If you want to work with plant diseases, you should obtain a doctoral degree in plant pathology or a related field in botany. If you prefer to work in animal science, you can get a doctoral degree in zoology or pathology or the degree of doctor of veterinary medicine (D.V.M. or V.M.D.). You will need to spend about four additional years in advanced training after you have graduated from a four-year college.

Medical pathologists usually go to medical school for four years after they graduate from college. They receive the degree of doctor of medicine (M.D.). In some cases they spend six years in medical school and earn a doctoral degree in pathology in addition to their medical degree. After medical school, pathologists spend about four more years in a hospital as a resident in pathology. If they choose, they may also take additional training in one of the subspecialties in medical pathology. Medical pathologists need to be licensed by their state to practice medicine and must also be certified by the American Board of Pathology. Medical pathologists are likely to spend a total of at least twelve years in training before they are fully qualified in their profession. Pathologists must spend time reading and studying throughout their careers in order to keep up with new developments in their field.

## Getting the Job

The professors and placement service at your university or medical school are the best sources of information for finding a job in pathology. Openings for pathologists are often listed in professional journals. The conventions of the major pathology associations often have job notice boards and are good places for making job contacts. You can also apply directly to private firms, medical centers, colleges and universities, or government agencies that hire pathologists.

## Advancement Possibilities and Employment Outlook

Pathologists are highly trained professionals who usually advance by improving their skills and becoming experts in their field. They can also advance to become full professors in colleges or universities or directors of research or administrators at universities, medical centers, government agencies, or private companies. Pathologists in the medical field can advance to a position as head of the pathology department in a large hospital. They can also start their own diagnostic laboratories or become consultants to private industry.

The job outlook for pathologists is very good. There is likely to be competition for teaching jobs in universities, but there should be new jobs for pathologists in research and medical laboratory work.

Opportunities for those with bachelor's or master's degrees in pathology are expected to be better than the opportunities for those with doctoral degrees. Jobs will be plentiful in private industry, large hospitals, and medical centers. As a result of increased public interest in preserving the environment, expanding food supplies, and improving health care, private companies are expected to devote funds to research in pathology. There will be a great number of positions in sales, marketing, and research management.

## Working Conditions

Because pathology is a broad field, working conditions vary. However, most pathologists spend some time in scientific or medical research laboratories that are usually well equipped. Depending on their field, pathologists may also spend time in greenhouses, on farms, in hospital wards, or in morgues. Pathologists often work at least part of the time in offices and classrooms. The basic workweek may be forty hours long. Hours are flexible, however, and often total more than forty hours a week. Although pathologists may have to work rotating shifts, their hours are usually more regular than those of physicians who have their own practices.

Pathologists of all kinds are likely to spend time planning projects, attending meetings, and studying the findings of other scientists. They should have the ability to absorb a great deal of information and the patience to complete lengthy research projects. They must be careful and precise workers, especially when their diagnosis is crucial in setting the direction of patient care. Pathologists should be able to work alone, but they also need to cooperate with other members of a medical or scientific team. Pathologists must be able to express their ideas well orally and in writing.

## Earnings and Benefits

Earnings vary depending on the experience of the pathologist, the location, and the kind of job. In 2003 the median salary range of veterinary pathologists working in industry with up to five years experience was $120,000 to $140,000. The median salary range in academia was $80,000 to $100,000. In 2006 medical pathologists with M.D. degrees earned a median salary of $210,984. Salaried pathologists usually receive benefits that include paid holidays and vacations, health insurance, and retirement plans. Self-employed pathologists do not receive benefits.

### Where to Go for More Information

American College of Veterinary Pathologists
2810 Crossroads Dr., Ste. 3800
Madison, WI 53718
(608) 443-2466
http://www.acvp.org

The American Pathology Foundation
1202 Allanson Rd.
Mundelein, IL 60060
(877) 993-9935
http://www.americanpathologyfoundation.org

College of American Pathologists
325 Waukegan Rd.
Northfield, IL 60093-2750
(800) 323-4040
http://www.cap.org

American Phytopathological Society
3340 Pilot Knob Rd.
St. Paul, MN 55121-2097
(651) 454-7250
http://www.apsnet.org

# Photonics Engineer

**Education and Training**
Bachelor's degree or higher

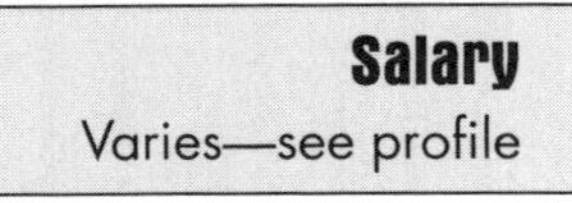

**Salary**
Varies—see profile

**Employment Outlook**
Excellent

## Definition and Nature of the Work

Photonics engineers work in the design, production, and use of laser and fiber optics technology. The job title comes from the word "photon," which is a unit of light. Photonics is the science of using light to generate energy, detect information, or transmit information. Fiber optics technology involves the transmission of light and images through hair-thin strands of plastic-coated glass fiber. The light in these fibers may be generated by beam-like devices known as lasers.

Engineers working in the laser and fiber optics field may design and modify laser equipment or components and may direct the testing of laser systems. They may also use lasers for a variety of useful applications in fields such as telecommunications, medicine, and defense as well as in the manufacturing and construction industries. Because large amounts of information can be transmitted quickly and reliably through optical fiber cables, this technology is replacing telecommunications systems that use metal wiring. In the medical field, lasers are used in numerous diagnostic and treatment procedures, and to perform delicate surgery on the eye and other parts of the body. Lasers are used in industry for aligning, marking, and drilling metals, plastics, and many other substances. In the military, lasers are used in navigation and to provide range information for weaponry and missile targets.

Most photonics engineers work for large telecommunications firms and optical fiber producers. They often specialize in solving problems relating to the light sources used in fiber optics. Photonics engineers are concerned with modulating light sources and controlling the light's wavelength, intensity, and duration. To measure light effectively, photonics engineers often use a spectrometer, a highly sensitive instrument that measures characteristics of light.

Some photonics engineers are primarily concerned with refining the purity of optical fibers. Innovations in this area are very important because impurities in optical fibers can contribute to energy loss. Other specialists create designs of optical fibers with exact dimensions and chemical compositions. Sometimes called optical designers, crystal growers, or optical materials scientists, these specialists generally must have a doctoral degree in chemistry, physics, or materials science. Still other photonics engineers develop methods to reduce production costs for making the fiber optics material.

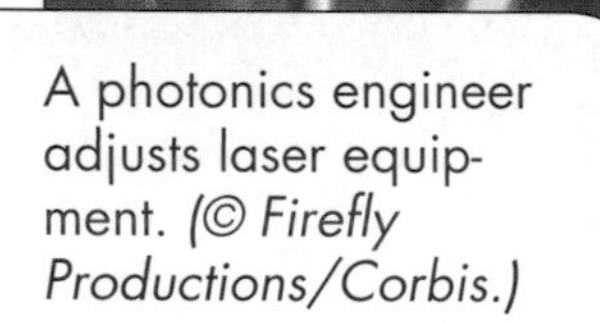

A photonics engineer adjusts laser equipment. *(© Firefly Productions/Corbis.)*

Other photonics engineers work primarily with lasers, applying optics and laser technologies to many different industries. They work with either gas or semiconductor laser systems. Semiconductor laser systems are used primarily in telecommunications equipment, telephones, and computers. Engineers who work with gas-type laser systems design and apply systems that are used by the robotics and materials processing and medical industries. Many photonics engineers are employed by the Defense Department and by companies that manufacture lasers for the department under contract.

## Education and Training Requirements

You generally need at least a bachelor's degree in one of several engineering specialties to enter this field. These degrees include electrical engineering, mechanical engineering, engineering science, or engineering physics. Some colleges and universities offer degrees in optics technology or photonics. It usually takes four to five years to earn a bachelor's degree in engineering. Some colleges offer work-study programs that combine work experience with formal classroom study. Certain positions in the laser and fiber optics area, such as optical designer, require an advanced degree. You can obtain a master's degree in one or two years of additional full-time study. It generally takes about four years of study after earning a bachelor's degree to receive a doctoral degree. All engineers should learn how to use computer-assisted design and drafting, and manufacturing (CADD/CAM) systems. The laser and fiber optics field is advancing rapidly, and engineers in this field must continually update their knowledge to maintain their expertise.

## Getting the Job

Your college placement office may be able to help you find a job. If you are enrolled in a work-study program, you may be able to continue working for a participating employer after graduation. You can also apply directly to companies that hire photonics engineers. Jobs are listed in professional trade journals, newspaper classifieds, and Internet job banks.

## Advancement Possibilities and Employment Outlook

Advancement depends on ability, education, and experience. Most photonics engineers begin as assistants to experienced engineers. As they gain experience, they may become supervisors or specialize in a particular aspect of laser or fiber optics technology. Some engineers advance to management positions. A few engineers with the necessary education can become research directors or principal engineers. Engineers may also advance by starting their own consulting or manufacturing companies.

The employment outlook for photonics engineers is excellent. Currently there is a shortage, and the demand for trained personnel in this field is expected to remain high.

## Working Conditions

Working conditions for photonics engineers vary. They usually work thirty-five to forty hours a week. Overtime may be necessary in some jobs, especially when project deadlines must be met. Research engineers generally work in clean, modern buildings. Laser engineers may work at manufacturing plants. They may also travel to locations where lasers need to be installed and maintained.

Photonics engineers should have a high degree of aptitude in physics and mathematics. They should work well with a team and be able to share information and ideas. They should also be meticulous and detail-oriented and enjoy solving problems.

## Earnings and Benefits

Earnings and benefits vary depending on the education and experience of the engineer and the type of job. Photonics engineers generally earn higher salaries than do engineers in other specialties. In 2004 median annual earnings for engineers across all major specialties of engineering ranged from $56,520 to $88,500. Benefits include paid holidays and vacations, health insurance, and retirement plans.

### Where to Go for More Information

Laser Institute of America
13501 Ingenuity Dr., Ste. 128
Orlando, FL 33826
(800) 345-2737
http://www.laserinstitute.org

Optical Society of America
2010 Massachusetts Avenue NW
Washington, DC 20036
(202) 223-8130
http://www.osa.org

Photonics.com
Laurin Publishing Co., Inc.
Berkshire Common
P.O. Box 4949
Pittsfield, MA 01202-4949
(413) 499-0514
http://www.photonics.com

# Physicist

**Education and Training**
Doctoral degree

**Salary**
Median—$87,450 per year

**Employment Outlook**
Fair

## Definition and Nature of the Work

Physicists are scientists who investigate motion and gravity, the behavior of gases, the structure and behavior of matter, the generation and transfer of energy, and the interaction between matter and energy. They identify basic forces and laws of nature. Theoretical physicists investigate these areas without thought to practical application, concerning themselves with concepts such as the nature of time and the origin of the universe. Other physicists apply their knowledge of physics to practical matters, such as the development of computers, transistors, laser beams, microwave appliances, communications satellites, and a wide variety of other devices. They solve problems in industry, medicine, defense, and other fields.

Physicists work at colleges and universities, independent research centers, hospitals, and government agencies. Many work in private industry, especially for companies that make chemicals, electrical equipment, missiles, and aircraft. Some physicists spend most of their time doing research. Others teach physics and related science courses.

Physics is a very broad science. Many physicists specialize in one branch. For example, nuclear physicists study the structure of atomic nuclei and the way that they interact with one another. Nuclear physicists sometimes use particle accelerators to smash nuclei as an aid to their research. Their work has led to the development of nuclear power plants and the use of radioactive substances that help medical doctors diagnose illness.

Solid-state physicists study the structure and properties of such materials as metals and alloys. They may grow synthetic crystals in a laboratory. The work of solid-state physicists led to the development of the transistor. Health physicists devise equipment to detect harmful radiation. They design and supervise radiation protection programs for nuclear power plants, hospitals, and industries that use radioactive materials. Astrophysicists develop instruments for observation and experimentation in space. Optical physicists are interested in how to control light. Their research on lasers has already been applied to everything from eye surgery to cutting tools. Elementary particle physicists study atomic and subatomic particles. Fluid and plasma physicists investigate the properties of liquids and gases. Plasma physicists are interested in electrically charged fluids, while fluid physicists are interested in uncharged fluids. Plasma physicists help in such areas as reentry of space vehicles into the atmosphere. Acoustical physicists study shock, vibration, underwater sound, and noise. Biophysicists research the medical application of physics. They are responsible for the development of the betatron for radiation therapy.

Physicists are responsible for the theories and discoveries that have led to the development of computers, transistor radios, laser beams, microwave appliances, and communications satellites. *(© Martha Tabor/ Working Images Photographs. Reproduced by permission.)*

## Education and Training Requirements

Graduate training in physics is generally needed for most jobs in this field. It takes about four years to earn a bachelor's degree and another one or two years to earn a master's degree. With these degrees you may qualify for a job in applied research in either the federal government or private industry. Depending on the courses you take, these degrees could also qualify you for a job teaching either in a high school or in a two-year college. Many teaching jobs also require you to be certified to teach in your state. Research assistantships at four-year colleges or universities are often open to those with a bachelor's or master's degree. Many physicists hold such jobs while they study for a doctoral degree. Most jobs in research require a doctoral degree. It takes about four years of full-time study after receiving a bachelor's degree to get a doctoral degree. During graduate school, students narrow their studies to a specialized physical science area. In addition to formal course work, they complete research in their specialty and prepare written reports of their studies.

## Getting the Job

The four major areas in which physics majors can find jobs are industry, government, laboratories, and colleges and universities. Your best sources for job openings are likely to be your college professors and advisers. Your college placement office may also be able to help you find a job as a physicist. In addition, you can apply directly to private companies and government agencies. Other good sources of job openings are professional associations and scientific journals.

## Advancement Possibilities and Employment Outlook

Advancement opportunities are good for physicists with doctoral degrees. Those in teaching positions can advance by moving through the ranks from assistant professor to full professor. Physicists in research centers and in industry can advance by taking on more responsibility and heading project teams. Some become administrators. Those who develop new products sometimes form their own companies. Many physicists consider recognition as an expert in one particular area of physics to be the highest form of achievement in their field. Physicists can generally reach this point only after doing a great deal of research and having the results of their research published in scientific journals.

Persons with bachelor's or master's degrees in physics have less chance to advance than those with doctoral degrees. Their best opportunities are found in teaching physics or other science courses in high school. They can also advance in jobs related to physics in the fields of engineering and computer science.

Employment of physicists is expected to grow more slowly than average for all occupations through 2014. Most job openings for those with doctoral degrees will be to replace physicists who retire. However, there will be some demand in the applied sciences, such as information technology and semiconductor technology. In addition, opportunities should be available for those with master's degrees in applied research and development, product design, and manufacturing. Persons with only a bachelor's degree in physics may qualify for non-research positions related to engineering, mathematics, computer science, and environmental science. Those who meet certification requirements can become high school physics teachers.

## Working Conditions

Most physicists work indoors in clean, well-lighted laboratories and classrooms. Some types of physicists may spend a great deal of time outdoors. Others may work some of the time in hospitals or factories. Physicists generally work at least forty hours per week. Overtime is often necessary for special projects. Most physicists employed as college teachers spend six to eight hours a week in the classroom and the remainder of the workweek preparing lesson materials, advising students, conducting research, and writing. Physicists engaged in research frequently work irregular hours while conducting experiments.

Physicists must be patient and hardworking. They must be willing to devote many hours to research. Physicists must be able to work both independently and as part of a team. They need to have the ability to communicate their ideas to others both orally and in writing.

### Where to Go for More Information

American Institute of Physics
One Physics Ellipse
College Park, MD 20740-3843
(301) 209-3100
http://www.aip.org

American Physical Society
One Physics Ellipse
College Park, MD 20740-3843
(301) 209-3200
http://www.aps.org

## Earnings and Benefits

Salaries vary according to education, location, and job. The median annual income of physicists was $87,450 in 2004. The average annual salary for physicists employed by the federal government was $104,917 in 2005. Physicists at colleges and universities can usually supplement their salaries by doing research and consulting work. Benefits generally include paid holidays and vacations, health insurance, and pension plans.

# *Political Scientist*

**Education and Training**
Master's or doctoral degree

**Salary**
Median—$86,750 per year

**Employment Outlook**
Fair

## Definition and Nature of the Work

Political scientists are social scientists who study government and politics. They analyze many areas of political behavior, including voting, public opinion, taxation, and public administration. Knowledgeable in different forms of government that have existed throughout history, such as democracies, republics, and monarchies, political scientists also examine the ideas and theories behind these political systems. They analyze the structure and operation of governments at all levels, and the effects that these governments have on the people who live under them. Political scientists also study the patterns, sources, and psychology of political power. They collect large amounts of information and then try to organize it into a theory or system that will explain some area of politics or government. Political scientists often make use of computerized data in the course of their work.

About 75 percent of all political scientists are employed by colleges and universities. They do research and teach political science. Sometimes they also teach related subjects, such as economics or history, especially in smaller colleges. Other political scientists work for government agencies. Many are employed by the federal government in Washington, D.C. Some work in state capitals or overseas. The remainder of political scientists work either as consultants or full-time staff members for political or research organizations, civic associations, labor unions, large private companies, management consulting firms, radio and television stations, newspapers, or magazines.

Many political scientists are specialists in one area of their field. They may concentrate on foreign affairs, for example, or on the governments of specific countries. Some are experts on political theories of a historical period, such as the time of the American Revolution. Although their jobs and specialties may differ, nearly all political scientists do some research. They may read books, look up facts in libraries, study voting records, survey public opinion, analyze proposed legislation or laws already passed, interview public officials, and observe political meetings. They usually write reports, articles, or books on their findings. They may also give lectures and oral reports to legislative staffs or committees.

## Education and Training Requirements

You need an advanced degree to become a political scientist. In college you should major in political science or a related field, such as history. People with a bachelor's degree in political science can get jobs as management trainees or research assistants, but they are not usually considered political scientists. College graduates with a major in political science often find that their college training is a good background for further education in such fields as journalism or public administration. Those who go on to get a master's degree in political science are qualified for many research or administrative jobs in government, industry, and nonprofit organizations. For a teaching and research position at most colleges and universities, a doctoral degree is required. A doctoral degree is also necessary for advancement to many top nonacademic positions in research and administration. Most jobs as a professional political scientist require a doctoral degree. People who study for a doctoral degree usually specialize in one area, such as American politics, international politics, political theory, or urban affairs. Their programs of study often include foreign languages and statistical methods. It usually takes from six to eight years of full-time study beyond high school to earn a doctoral degree in political science. Many political scientists get full- or part-time jobs while they are studying for their doctoral degrees. Political scientists must continue to read and study throughout their careers so that they can keep up with new developments in their field.

## Getting the Job

Your professors or the placement office at your college or university will be able to give you information about getting a job as a political scientist. Professional journals often list openings in this field. You may want to apply directly to organizations, businesses, universities, or government agencies that hire political scientists. In some cases you may have to pass a civil service examination to get a government job.

## Advancement Possibilities and Employment Outlook

Political scientists can advance to the rank of full professor in a college or university if they have doctoral degrees. In other organizations and in government agencies they can become administrators or directors of research. Most political scientists advance by becoming experts in their special field. Some win the recognition of other scholars. Others play important roles in advising government officials and helping to set policy or draft laws. Some write books and magazine or newspaper articles that influence other political scientists or inform the public about politics or government.

The employment outlook for political scientists through 2014 is fair. Employment of political scientists will grow more slowly than average, mainly because these workers enjoy fewer opportunities outside of government and academic settings. Most openings are expected to arise due to the need to replace political scientists who leave the field. Many qualified people with doctoral degrees in political science are expected to be seeking jobs. There will also be fewer openings on the faculties of colleges and universities and in political and research organizations and private firms. Competition for jobs in all of these areas will be keen, and there will be many more applicants than job openings.

## Working Conditions

Political scientists spend much of their time in offices, libraries, and classrooms. They usually work in pleasant and comfortable surroundings. Their hours may be flexible but often total more than forty hours a week. Political scientists meet with students, other scholars, government officials, and the general public in certain phases of their work. They should be able to express their ideas clearly and work well with people. Much of the work of political scientists is very detailed and must be done independently. Political scientists have to concentrate on details without losing sight of the broad view of politics that they are trying to explain. They should also be able to write clearly about their findings and hypotheses.

## Earnings and Benefits

The earnings of political scientists depend on their education and experience as well as on the location and kind of position. In 2004 political scientists had median annual earnings of $86,750. Political scientists employed by colleges and universities are usually given opportunities to add to their income by writing books, teaching summer school courses, or doing consulting work. Benefits generally include paid holidays and vacations, health insurance, and retirement plans.

### Where to Go for More Information

The American Political Science Association
1527 New Hampshire Ave. NW
Washington, DC 20036-1206
(202) 483-2512
http://www.apsanet.org

# *Robotics Engineer*

**Education and Training**
Master's or doctoral degree

**Salary**
$50,000 to $60,000 per year

**Employment Outlook**
Very good

## Definition and Nature of the Work

Robotics engineers work in the science of robotics, or flexible automation. Most robots are "manipulators"—machines devised to function in place of a human. Some robots function as "walking" machines, or teleoperators, using remote control or sensory manipulators. Microprocessors, which are very small computers, direct most robots in their tasks.

Robotics engineers are responsible for designing, testing, and building robots that are productive and safe to operate as well as economical to purchase and maintain. These engineers use computer-aided design and drafting, and computer-aided manufacturing (CADD/CAM) systems to perform their tasks. Robotics research engineers design robotic systems and research methods to manufacture them economically. Robotics engineers who work for robot manufacturers are sometimes called robotics test engineers or automation system engineers. These engineers apply the robotic system to a particular use on a manufacturing assembly line. They also create an integrated environment between people and machinery.

Robotics applications vary widely. Robots are used in the automotive, aerospace, metals, nuclear, mining, textile, and computer industries, among others. The robotics engineer must determine the particular needs of each application and customize the robot accordingly. To do this, robotics engineers must plan the

A robotics research engineer tests a racing robot. *(© Gene Blevins/Reuters/Corbis.)*

computer programs suitable for the robot installation. They must also prepare specifications for the robot's capabilities as they relate to the work environment. In addition, robotics engineers are responsible for developing cost proposals, efficiency studies, and quality control reports.

Most robotics engineers are employed by private robot manufacturers or robot users. Some engineers work in military and space programs. Others work for colleges and universities or vocational and trade schools.

## Education and Training Requirements

You generally need at least a bachelor's degree in engineering to enter this field. Because robotics technology draws on the expertise of many different engineering disciplines, engineers who specialize in robotics often have degrees in mechanical, manufacturing, electrical, electronic, or industrial engineering. Some colleges and universities now offer robotics engineering degrees. Robotics courses typically include training in hydraulics and pneumatics, CADD/CAM systems, numerically controlled systems, microprocessors, integrated systems, and logic. It usually takes four to five years to earn a bachelor's degree in engineering. Some colleges offer work-study programs in which students receive on-the-job training while still in school. Most universities that offer robotics courses have well-equipped labs with lasers and CADD/CAM equipment. For most positions and to advance in the field you need a master's or doctoral degree. Robotics engineers must continually upgrade their technical knowledge to keep abreast of new developments in this rapidly changing field.

Like engineers in other disciplines, robotics engineers must be able to work well as team members. They must be able to communicate their ideas effectively. Those entering this field should have an aptitude for mathematics, physics, chemistry, and electronics. They should also be skilled in using computers.

## Getting the Job

Your college placement office may be able to help you find a job as a robotics engineer. If you are enrolled in a work-study program during college, you may be able to continue working for a participating employer after graduation. Check the classifieds in newspapers and professional trade journals for possible job openings. You can also apply directly to robot manufacturers or to firms in industries that use robots. A number of computer firms are entering the robot manufacturing market, so be sure to check this source. Conventions of the American Association of Artificial Intelligence and computer science organizations may also be a good job marketplace.

## Advancement Possibilities and Employment Outlook

Robotics engineers can advance to management positions and become robotics managers or directors of automation. Some robotics engineers advance by moving into robot sales or by starting their own robotics consulting firms.

The employment outlook for robotics engineers is very good. Increasing use of robots is expected in many different manufacturing industries. The military will also operate more robots in the future. The Bureau of Labor Statistics has forecast a need for more than eight hundred thousand people in this high-growth field to design, maintain, and operate robots.

## Working Conditions

Most robotics engineers are employed in offices, manufacturing plants, or laboratories. Manufacturing plants may be noisy, depending on the industry. Robotics engineers usually work forty hours per week. They may also have to work overtime, especially when project deadlines must be met.

## Earnings and Benefits

Earnings vary depending on the experience of the robotics engineer, the location, and the kind of job. In 2006 robotics engineers earned from $50,000 to $60,000 per year. Benefits usually include paid holidays and vacations, health insurance, and retirement plans.

### Where to Go for More Information

Robotics International of the Society of Manufacturing Engineers
P.O. Box 930
One SME Dr.
Dearborn, MI 48121-0930
(800) 733-4763
http://www.sme.org/ri

Robotics Industries Association
900 Victors Way
P.O. Box 3724
Ann Arbor, MI 48106
(734) 994-6088
http://www.robotics.org

# *Safety Engineer*

**Education and Training**
Bachelor's degree

**Salary**
Median—$63,730 per year

**Employment Outlook**
Good

## Definition and Nature of the Work

Safety engineers are responsible for keeping people free from danger, risk, or injury in the workplace. They develop safety programs to minimize losses due to injuries and property damage. They try to eliminate unsafe practices and conditions in industrial plants, mines, and stores as well as on construction sites and throughout transportation systems. Safety engineers work for a wide variety of industrial and commercial companies. Many work for insurance companies. Others are employed by government agencies or safety organizations. Still others teach in colleges and universities or work as independent consultants.

Safety engineers work in many different types of industrial and commercial companies to ensure safety in the workplace as well as in the products the companies make. *(© Martha Tabor/Working Images Photographs. Reproduced by permission.)*

Safety engineers often have other titles, such as director of safety, safety manager, or safety coordinator. Sometimes technicians assist them. The duties of safety engineers vary depending on where they work. Engineers employed in large manufacturing plants often develop broad safety programs. They study the buildings, equipment, procedures, and records of accidents in their plant and point out safety hazards. They may suggest ways to fix unsafe structures or recommend changes in the layout of the plant. Sometimes they draw up plans for the regular maintenance of machinery or teach safe work habits to managers and workers.

Other safety engineers work with designers to make sure that their company's products are safe. They may be responsible for seeing that a new automobile model meets safety standards. Or they may check the design and production of children's toys.

Safety engineers who work for insurance companies usually provide consulting services to their clients. They are experts who can spot hazards and recommend ways to eliminate them. For example, they may review plans for a shopping center that is to be insured by their company and point out dangerous traffic patterns. Once the center is built, they inspect it and check that the elevators have been installed properly so that there will not be accidents. They also study maintenance procedures and may recommend that floors be cleaned when customers are not present. The shopping center owners may be able to lower their insurance rates by following the safety engineer's suggestions.

In the trucking industry, safety engineers review patterns of traffic accidents. They study routes, schedules, loads, and speeds to determine how these factors affect accidents. They also inspect trucks for safety hazards. Safety engineers in the mining industry must check to see that underground or open-pit mines meet the requirements set by state and federal laws. They also design equipment, such as lamps that are used underground. During mining emergencies they may be in charge of rescue teams.

## Education and Training Requirements

You generally need a bachelor's degree in science or engineering to become a safety engineer. It usually takes a minimum of four years to get this formal training. Some employers prefer to hire graduates with special degrees in safety management or occupational safety and health. Others look for people who have a master's degree or some work experience in a related field. In some cases graduates of two-year college programs can become safety engineers after some years of experience as technicians in this field. Undergraduate courses should include behavioral, medical, and social sciences. A list of colleges offering degrees in occupational safety and health is available from the American Society of Safety Engineers. Many companies provide additional training for their employees. Safety engineers continue to study new developments in their field throughout their careers.

In some cases engineers need to be licensed by the state in which they work. They generally need a degree from an approved engineering college, about four years of work experience as an engineer, and a passing grade on a state examination before being licensed as professional engineers.

## Getting the Job

Your college placement office and department notice boards may be able to help you find a job in safety engineering. You can also apply directly to places that hire safety engineers. Your state employment agency may have job information. Other good sources for job leads are the classifieds in trade and professional journals, newspapers, and Internet job banks.

## Advancement Possibilities and Employment Outlook

Advancement depends on education, experience, and the industry. In large manufacturing companies, for example, safety engineers can become managers in charge of safety for a large department, an entire plant, or a group of plants. In an insurance company, safety engineers can advance to department head, branch manager, and eventually executive. Some start their own consulting firms.

Health and safety engineers, except mining safety engineers and inspectors, are projected to experience average employment growth through 2014. Although there is a growing concern for the safety of workers and consumers, there has also been a demand for less government intervention and regulation. Much of the employment growth is expected to be in private industrial firms. This growth will be due to the continuing self-enforcement of government requirements, the rising costs of insurance, and the insistence of unions. Insurance companies should also employ more safety engineers. The best jobs will go to graduates of college programs that are related to safety.

## Working Conditions

Safety engineers spend much of their time reviewing and inspecting on-site safety conditions and investigating accidents. They also have an office in which they analyze data and write reports. They may have to do some traveling to worksites, conferences, and seminars. Safety engineers generally work forty hours per week. In many cases, longer hours are necessary. Manufacturing plants may require some shift work. Sometimes safety engineers have to answer unexpected emergency calls. There may be some danger involved in their work, but safety precautions minimize this danger.

Safety engineers often meet with clients, workers, and managers. They must be able to convince these people of the need for safety measures. In addition to knowledge of the engineering problems involved in keeping work areas and other public places free from hazards, safety engineers need to have a good knowledge of management methods, safety laws, and industrial psychology. They should be good at solving problems.

## Earnings and Benefits

Salaries vary depending on the safety engineer's experience and education as well as the location and the kind of job. In 2004 the median annual income of safety engineers was $63,730. Benefits include paid holidays and vacations, health insurance, and pension plans.

### Where to Go for More Information

American Society of Safety Engineers
1800 E. Oakton St.
Des Plaines, IL 60018-2187
(847) 699-2929
http://www.asse.org

National Safety Council
1121 Spring Lake Dr.
Itasca, IL 60143-3201
(630) 285-1121
http://www.nsc.org

# *Sociologist*

### Education and Training

Doctoral degree

### Salary

Median—$57,870 per year

### Employment Outlook

Fair

## Definition and Nature of the Work

Sociologists are social scientists who study groups of people. These groups range from families and tribes to entire communities and even whole nations. Sociologists analyze ethnic and religious groups and political and business organizations. They also focus on the behavior of group members and on the ways that groups interact with one another. They often trace the origin and development of groups. Sociologists study specific groups with the ultimate goal of establishing general laws and theories that can explain human social behavior.

Sociology is a very broad field. Sociologists generally specialize in one or more areas within the field. For example, some sociologists study how people choose their leaders and organize themselves into social groups based on such factors as income, education, and prestige. Other sociologists concentrate on how groups train their young people and deal with the problems of adolescence. Some sociologists specialize in the sociology of cities or rural areas. Others are experts in medical sociology who study the social factors affecting mental and public health.

More than half of all sociologists are employed by colleges and universities. They usually teach and do research, although some have administrative duties as well. When they do research, sociologists use a variety of sources. They collect information by using books and periodicals, interviews, tests, laboratory experiments, case studies, and statistical surveys. They also often make use of computerized data in their work. For example, sociologists who want to study one aspect of crime begin their research by reading books about how other societies deal with the problem or what other experts have to say about it. Then they may interview police officers or criminals or test the attitudes of a group of criminals and a group of law-abiding citizens to see how the two groups differ in their attitudes toward authority. Next they might study the life histories of a group of criminals to see how their experiences differ from those of a law-abiding group. They may also study statistics that show when and where certain crimes occurred in the past. After collecting and analyzing information carefully, the sociologists may write up a report offering some conclusions on the specific crime problem. They may also draw conclusions about crime and perhaps even about social behavior in general. The conclusions of sociologists are sometimes used by lawmakers, educators, government officials, psychologists, physicians, social workers, and other experts who deal with social problems in their work.

Some sociologists work for government agencies or private social service agencies. They often perform services in family counseling, public relations, community planning, public opinion analysis, or other areas related to their particular fields. They may also deal with such problems as poverty, welfare, and the rehabilitation of drug addicts. Small numbers of sociologists work for private industry, research organizations, or management consulting firms where they may do full- or part-time consulting work. The work of sociologists is related to that done by other professionals in such fields as social work, recreational therapy, and public health. These professions also require some training in sociology.

## Education and Training Requirements

You need doctoral degree in sociology to become a sociologist. Those who complete a four-year college program and obtain a bachelor's degree in sociology are sometimes able to get related jobs as interviewers, research assistants, or counselors. If you study for one or two additional years to obtain a master's degree in sociology, you may qualify for a position in social work, or as a researcher or instructor at a college or university. In many cases you will be expected to continue studying toward your doctoral degree, which is required for most teaching jobs in colleges and universities. Directing major research projects and doing administrative or consulting work also require a doctoral degree. It usually takes two or three years of study beyond the master's level to obtain a doctoral degree in sociology. Sociologists must continue reading and studying throughout their careers to keep up with new developments in their field.

## Getting the Job

Your professors and the placement office at your college or university can give you information about finding a job in the field of sociology. Openings are sometimes listed in professional journals, newspaper classifieds, and job banks on the Internet. You can apply directly to colleges and universities, research organizations, private firms, and government agencies that are likely to hire sociologists. To get a government job, you may have to apply through a civil service office.

## Advancement Possibilities and Employment Outlook

Advancement depends on skill, education, and experience. Sociologists with master's degrees and several years of experience sometimes advance to such positions as supervisor in a government or private agency. Sociologists with a doctoral degree can become full professors in colleges or universities or advance to director of research or administrator. Many sociologists advance by becoming experts in their areas of specialization. They often write up the results of their research in the form of books or articles that may win them the recognition of other sociologists. A few sociologists write books that become best sellers and bring them public acclaim.

The employment outlook for sociologists is fair, with slower than average growth predicted through 2014. Most openings will be to replace workers who leave the field. A few new openings may occur in colleges and universities because of the trend of including sociology courses in the professional training required for degrees in law, medicine, education, and business administration. There are expected to be many qualified graduates with doctoral degrees in sociology, however, and the competition for teaching jobs should be keen. There will be some openings for sociologists in criminology, mental health, social welfare programs, and related areas. Many qualified sociologists will probably have to seek employment in other fields, however. The best opportunities will be found in the areas of research methods and statistics.

### Working Conditions

Sociologists usually spend a large part of their day in pleasant offices, libraries, and classrooms. They spend a good deal of time reading to keep up with the rapid growth of their field. At times, however, sociologists are likely to do some fieldwork that may involve traveling to remote areas or interviewing people from many different backgrounds. Therefore, sociologists should be able to work independently and also know how to interact with the wide variety of people that they are likely to meet in their work. Sometimes sociologists need to cooperate with other social scientists on large-scale research projects. Although hours are often flexible, they normally work more than forty hours a week. The ability to express ideas well, both orally and in writing, is essential for sociologists.

### Earnings and Benefits

The earnings of sociologists depend on the education and experience of the individual, as well as on the location and kind of job. In 2004 the median annual salary for sociologists was $57,870. Many sociologists, especially those employed by colleges and universities, add to their income by doing consulting work, teaching in the summer, or writing books. Benefits usually include paid holidays and vacations, health insurance, and retirement plans.

**Where to Go for More Information**

American Sociological Association
307 New York Avenue NW, Ste. 700
Washington, DC 20005-4701
(202) 383-9005
http://www.asanet.org

## *Systems Engineer*

**Education and Training**
Bachelor's or master's degree

**Salary**
Mean—$74,140 per year

**Employment Outlook**
Good

### Definition and Nature of the Work

Systems engineers design and coordinate large and complex projects known as systems. There are many kinds of systems, and although all are large, they vary in their complexity. A system has many parts that all interact extensively with one another. Often small systems can be part of larger systems. For example, a jet airliner can be a system. So, too, can all of the airplanes owned by one airline. All of the airplanes in a country make up a more extensive system. An even larger and more complex system includes all of a nation's transportation facilities. Systems engineers can work at various levels in the design and coordination of these systems.

Some other examples of systems are water and food distribution networks, experimental manned space flights, and military defense programs. Systems engineers also work on telephone systems, electric power systems, and sewage systems.

Systems engineers are responsible for coordinating the work of many engineers, each of whom is an expert in one part of a system. For instance, in the building of a jet airliner, electronics specialists are responsible for the guidance and control systems. Structural engineers design the body of the plane. Other experts decide on a power source for the jet. Still others design landing and takeoff methods. Each specialist concentrates on one area. The systems engineer coordinates all of these specialized efforts in order to produce the jet airliner.

Systems engineers work at various levels in the design and coordination of large and complex projects known as systems. *(© Martha Tabor/ Working Images Photographs. Reproduced by permission.)*

Both government and private industry employ systems engineers to solve complex scientific and engineering problems, such as the development of new transportation systems, the design of rockets, or the improvement of communications systems. Systems engineers first gather all the necessary information about what is needed in a system. They select several possible ways of designing the system. Then they use a problem-solving method called systems analysis to break down the possible solutions into smaller parts.

Systems engineers use systems analysis to make a diagram of all the parts of a system. They use computers and such mathematical methods as algebra, probability theory, and statistics to convert their diagrams into mathematical equations. They develop theoretical models that will help them choose the best way to design a system. They can use a computer to test these models. For example, systems engineers may want to know whether a mass-transit system will meet future needs. They can feed information on population growth and other data into a computer. The computer will process the data and provide the engineers with information about the usefulness of the system.

Systems engineers can also test a possible system by using small-scale models or actual-size models of parts of a system. Once a system has been designed, further testing is done. Systems engineers generally stay with a system and coordinate all parts of it until it is working smoothly. They coordinate the work of many specialists during the development of a system. Sometimes systems engineers are called on to make improvements in existing systems.

Systems engineers work for government agencies, computer companies, and many industries that need to solve large and complex engineering problems. Large research projects sponsored by government, industry, or universities also employ teams of scientists and engineers, including systems engineers. Sometimes these researchers develop new theories that can be used as the basis for systems and analysis. Workers who use systems analysis to solve business problems rather than engineering problems are usually called systems analysts. These workers are often experts in business rather than in engineering.

## Education and Training Requirements

Most systems engineers are former mechanical, electrical, or aerospace engineers who advance into systems engineering. You generally need a bachelor's or a master's degree to become a systems engineer. You can expect to spend from four to six years getting this formal training. Some colleges and universities offer courses in systems engineering, but it is a relatively new field. Educational requirements still vary widely from job to job. A broad background is important in this field, since systems engineers must take into account many factors, such as the possible legal, social, and psychological effects of a system. Systems engineers must also have a good understanding of computer programming and engineering fields other than their own. They also need to understand modern management techniques. Many engineers receive additional formal training in a second field. Others are able to broaden their knowledge through years of job experience. Some employers will help engineers who are interested in systems engineering to get the kind of broad experience that this field requires.

Engineers who offer their services to the public or whose work affects life, health, or property need to be licensed by the state in which they work. They generally need a degree from an approved engineering college, about four years of work experience as an engineer, and a passing grade on a state examination before being licensed as professional engineers.

## Getting the Job

To become a systems engineer, you should plan your engineering career so that you have the opportunity to learn about many fields of engineering. Your college placement office can help you find a job. You can read trade or professional journals to learn about openings for systems engineers. Newspaper classifieds and job banks on the Internet are also good sources of job information. You should have work experience in one or more fields of engineering when you apply for a job as a systems engineer.

## Advancement Possibilities and Employment Outlook

Systems engineers have already advanced from a specific job in another field of engineering into a systems engineering career. However, as they gain more experience in putting systems together and working with people, they can advance to more difficult and challenging problems.

The job outlook for systems engineers is very good. Systems engineers are likely to be needed for many projects—from designing more practical sewage systems to coordinating space flights.

## Working Conditions

Systems engineers work in many settings—from a computer company's urban offices to a testing center for jet airplanes. The basic workweek is usually forty hours long. Systems engineers generally spend additional hours, however, working to meet deadlines or studying new methods and equipment.

Systems engineers often work in small teams. Although they do much of their work independently, they must talk to a wide variety of other specialists when planning a system. They should be able to get along with these people and to communicate their ideas clearly. They sometimes have to present their plans in the form of oral or written reports. Like all engineers, they should be good at science and mathematics and at problem solving.

## Earnings and Benefits

Salaries vary widely depending on the education and experience of the systems engineer and the location and nature of the job. In 2000 new graduates with master's degrees in systems engineering earned an average starting salary of $56,750. A survey by the *Washington Post* showed that in 1999, the average salary for systems engineers was $69,070. A Massachusetts Institute of Technology (MIT) salary survey revealed that in 2004 the average annual earnings of a systems engineer was $74,140. Systems engineers usually receive benefits that include paid holidays and vacations, health insurance, and pension plans.

### Where to Go for More Information

American Society for Engineering Education
1818 N St. NW, Ste. 600
Washington, DC 20036-2479
(202) 331-3500
http://www.asee.org

International Council on Systems Engineering
(800) 366-1164
http://www.incose.org

# Telecommunications Consultant

**Education and Training**
College

**Salary**
Median—$65,130 per year

**Employment Outlook**
Excellent

## Definition and Nature of the Work

The boom in telecommunications technology has created a strong demand for specialists in the field to help companies choose the telephone, video, and data communications equipment best suited to their needs. Telecommunications consultants, also referred to as telecommunications specialists when employed full time by a telecommunications company, are responsible not only for creating efficient, cost-effective telecommunications systems but also for updating systems as newer and better equipment becomes available.

A small firm might require only short-term assistance with buying and installing its telecommunications equipment. A large company might hire a consultant to assemble a complicated network of telephones, computers, facsimile (fax) equipment, and video terminals that will rapidly transmit voices and paperwork around the world. In every case, however, the consultant must determine what services the company wants and what equipment can best deliver those services.

Professionals who select telecommunications systems may be employed full time by large insurance, banking, or manufacturing companies, among others. They may also work for consulting firms, for the government, or as freelancers, meaning they are self-employed. Some telecommunications specialists, especially those who work for the large telephone companies or for large telecommunications firms, work in research or product and system development and design. Others work in sales and marketing.

With the recent emergence of the wireless Internet, known as WiFi, there are new opportunities for telecommunications consultants and specialists. The proliferation of new technologies has resulted in a need for information technology professionals who can help organizations utilize technology to better communicate with employees, clients, and consumers.

## Education and Training Requirements

Telecommunications consultants who have bachelor's degrees in electrical engineering or computer science are highly sought after by employers. Those who combine a technical degree with a master's degree in business administration have the best opportunities for advancement to management positions. Some colleges are now offering telecommunications management programs.

Employers are also looking for candidates who have bachelor's or master's degrees in business along with courses in computer science, statistics, and math. Companies hire very few liberal arts graduates, but those with master's degrees in business administration do stand a chance of entering the field.

Consultants must continue to take courses throughout their careers to keep up with this ever-changing field.

## Getting the Job

Candidates with technical training often have their choice of assignments and job offers because competent consultants are currently in short supply. Many engineering and computer science majors are recruited directly out of college. Another way to enter the field is to get sales and marketing experience in a related industry.

## Advancement Possibilities and Employment Outlook

Qualified individuals in research or product design can move up to become department or project heads, or they can move into management. Those in sales or marketing can advance to management positions. Some telecommunications specialists open their own consulting firms.

The employment outlook is exceptionally good for telecommunications consultants and specialists because the industry is growing quickly and should have ample room for competent technicians. Experts project that the industry will grow by 25 percent each year through 2010.

## Working Conditions

Telecommunications consultants and specialists usually work in pleasant offices or at home but typically put in more than forty hours per week. Those employed by smaller companies that are striving for a piece of the telecommunications market may work even longer hours and may have to relocate from time to time.

Telecommunications consultants and specialists must have good communications skills. Those who work with system users must be able to explain complex information to people who may not understand the technical aspects of the system. Often specialists who have jobs in research or design work in teams, so they must be able to get along with other people.

## Earnings and Benefits

According to *Computerworld*'s 2005 salary survey, experienced telecommunications specialists earn a median salary of $65,130 per year. Senior specialists can earn more, depending on the size of the firm that employs them. Full-time employees receive paid vacations and holidays and medical insurance. Self-employed consultants must provide their own benefits.

### Where to Go for More Information

International Communications Association
1730 Rhode Island Ave. NW, Ste. 300
Washington, DC 20036
(202) 530-9855
http://www.icahdq.org

Society of Telecommunications Consultants
13275 State Hwy. 89
P.O. Box 70
Old Station, CA 96071
(800) STC-7670
http://www.stcconsultants.org

# *Telecommunications Design Engineer*

### Education and Training

Varies—see profile

### Salary

Median—$50,846 per year

### Employment Outlook

Fair

## Definition and Nature of the Work

Telecommunications design engineers solve technical telecommunications problems. Their understanding of telecommunications equipment allows them to analyze quickly where and why service is interrupted. Once these engineers know what the trouble is, repair workers can be sent out to fix it. Sometimes there are no simple cures for service troubles. The engineers may have to design new tools or equipment to handle new problems. Their job is to make sure that service remains trouble-free and that the equipment does the job it was designed to do.

Design engineers work to anticipate breakdowns in service. They try to spot and fix equipment problems before telecommunications service is affected. Engineers must come up with permanent solutions to problems that occur and plan for improved equipment. Often they write reports for the chief managers. Design engineers work in and visit many central offices. They meet with other engineers from all parts of the country to exchange new ideas.

These telecommunications design engineers are analyzing telephone equipment to suggest improvements. *(© Terry Wild Studio. Reproduced by permission.)*

## Education and Training Requirements

Design engineers must know a great deal about electronics and problem analysis. Some hold degrees in engineering; others may work their way up through other jobs with telecommunications companies, taking company upgrading courses, and going to technical school on their own time. Although engineering skills are required, a degree in engineering is not necessary.

Interested high school students should take courses in mathematics and the sciences, especially physics. Mechanical drawing and shop are also helpful. Postsecondary educational routes include a technical school or college. Candidates with the most formal education generally have greater opportunities to advance.

## Getting the Job

Most design engineers start in other jobs with telecommunications companies and have at least two years of experience in another position such as an installer. It is not unusual for installers and repair workers to become supervisors or engineers.

## Advancement Possibilities and Employment Outlook

Design engineers hold management-level jobs. Some advance even further to become engineering supervisors in charge of the work of other engineers.

The job outlook for design engineers is fair through the year 2014. Although advances in technology have reduced the need for repairs, new equipment requires constant analysis by engineers to prevent recurring problems. Also, those who are involved in designing new products may have a job advantage.

## Working Conditions

Design engineers generally work in pleasant, air-conditioned offices. During breakdowns or other emergencies they may have to put in many extra hours. Their assignments cover different central offices. At times they travel to engineering conferences and meetings with other telecommunications engineers. This work requires continual learning in order to keep up with changing technology.

### Earnings and Benefits

According to the U.S. Bureau of Labor Statistics, design engineers working for the larger telecommunications companies earn a median salary of $50,846 per year. Experienced design engineers earn more. Benefits include paid vacations and holidays, health and life insurance, and retirement provisions.

**Where to Go for More Information**

National Association of Radio and Telecommunications Engineers
167 Village St.
Medway, MA 02053
(800) 89-NARTE
http://www.narte.org

## *Zoologist*

**Education and Training**
Doctoral degree

**Salary**
Median—$50,330 per year

**Employment Outlook**
Good

### Definition and Nature of the Work

Zoologists are biological scientists who study animals. They observe animals both in their natural habitats and in the laboratory in order to learn as much as possible about animal life. Zoologists study the origin and development of animal species, the habits and behavior of animals, and the interaction between animals and their environment. They also do research to learn how animal diseases develop and how traits are passed from generation to generation.

Zoologists are sometimes known as animal scientists or animal biologists. Their field is zoology, or animal biology. Like botany and microbiology, zoology is a major division of biology. Zoology is a broad field. It includes the study of animals as varied as elephants, kangaroos, and killer sharks. Zoologists work in all areas of animal life, studying both simple and complex processes. For example, a zoologist might examine the overall structure of a cat or just the microscopic cells in its brain. Zoologists study the life functions of a single animal, such as an insect, as well as the behavior of whole colonies of ants, flocks of birds, or bands of gorillas.

Most zoologists are employed by colleges and universities where they teach and do research. Large numbers of zoologists work for government agencies in such areas as wildlife management, conservation, and agriculture. A few work for private companies, such as pharmaceutical companies or biological supply houses that sell animal specimens to laboratories. Some zoologists are employed by museums and zoos.

Although their jobs may differ widely, most zoologists spend at least part of their time doing research or laboratory work. They dissect and examine animal specimens. They prepare slides so that they can observe such things as diseased tissue and chemical reactions under light or electron microscopes. Since they often perform experiments with animals, many zoologists keep laboratory animals, such as mice, fruit flies, and guinea pigs. They may breed these animals, raise their offspring under controlled conditions, or test the effects of drugs on them. Some zoologists observe animals in their natural habitats. These zoologists study mating practices, aggression, life histories, and the group behavior of animals. Zoologists may make use of computerized information as well as a wide variety of special laboratory equipment and scientific methods. They are sometimes assisted by biological technicians.

Some zoologists work in zoos, where they engage in scientific studies of animal diseases and animal behavior. *(© Dave G. Houser/Corbis.)*

Zoologists often specialize in the study of one group of animals. For example, ichthyologists concentrate on the fish family. Some ichthyologists provide basic knowledge about fish. They classify fish according to species and study their distribution, size, and growth. They also study the behavior of fish, including migration patterns and feeding habits. Some specialize in one group of fish, such as sharks. Others work with one aspect of fish, such as their anatomy. Ichthyologists serve as fish experts on museum staffs or sometimes write books on the identification of fish. Most teach and do research in colleges and universities. Other zoologists working with fish concentrate on fish that have economic or recreational uses. These scientists are often called fishery biologists. They may work with trout in state fish hatcheries or do research on fish that have commercial uses, such as tuna, cod, or salmon. Zoologists also specialize in other groups of animals. Herpetologists, for example, are experts on reptiles, frogs, and salamanders. Entomologists study insects.

Some zoologists specialize in one area of animal life that may cover many species. Animal taxonomists, for example, identify and classify the many different species of animals. Animal physiologists examine the life processes of animals. They do research on their growth, movement, reproduction, respiration, circulation, and other functions. They also study how the environment of animals affects their life processes and functions. Embryologists focus on the early growth of animals from their beginning as a fertilized cell to their birth or hatching. There are many other kinds of zoologists.

## Education and Training Requirements

You generally need a doctoral degree to become a zoologist. You should major in zoology or biology as an undergraduate. In graduate school, you may want to specialize in genetics, embryology, or another area in animal science. Graduates with a bachelor's degree can get some jobs, such as advanced biological technician, but their opportunities for advancement are limited. People who have earned a master's degree in zoology or a related field are qualified for some jobs as teachers or research assistants. You usually need a doctoral degree, however, to get a job teaching and doing research at a university or working as an administrator. It usually takes four years to earn a bachelor's degree and another one or two years to earn a master's degree. You need to go to school for an additional two or three years to receive a doctoral degree. In order to keep up with new developments in animal science, you should continue to study throughout your career.

## Getting the Job

Your professors or college placement office may be able to help you find a job in zoology. You can apply directly to colleges and universities, zoos, and museums or private companies. You can also check with government agencies about getting work in research, conservation, inspection, management, or another special area. You sometimes need to pass a civil service examination to get a government job. Other sources of job openings include the classified ads in newspapers and professional journals.

## Advancement Possibilities and Employment Outlook

Advancement opportunities are good, especially for zoologists who have a doctoral degree. Zoologists can become project leaders or research directors. Those who work in zoos and museums can become administrators or head curators. Zoologists working for the government can advance to such positions as head of a state fishery or national wildlife refuge. Zoologists employed in colleges and universities can advance to the rank of full professor. Another way that a zoologist can advance is by becoming recognized as an authority in one area of animal science. This kind of recognition generally comes to zoologists who have done important research and have published their findings in professional journals.

Employment of biological scientists in general is projected to grow about as fast as average for all occupations through 2014. There will continue to be demand for zoologists, but opportunities will be limited because of the small size of this field. However, due to public interest in preserving the environment and protecting many species of animals, federal and state governments are devoting more funds to research in animal science. The work of zoologists is also important in finding cures for diseases and improving food supplies. There will probably be openings for trained experts who can contribute to the solution of such problems. Competition for jobs teaching in universities, however, is expected to be keen.

## Working Conditions

The working conditions of zoologists vary widely. Some zoologists spend much of their time in clean, well-lighted, well-equipped laboratories. Others work outdoors, observing wildlife and perhaps making do with improvised equipment. Many zoologists spend some of their time in offices and classrooms. Their working hours are generally flexible but often total more than forty hours per week. Some experiments and projects need to be observed around the clock. Therefore, zoologists may work rotating shifts. Zoologists often spend extra time attending meetings, writing up their findings, or reading to learn about the findings of other scientists.

Zoologists sometimes work independently. At other times they work as part of a scientific team. They must be able to cooperate with and communicate their ideas to other people. They should also be interested in animals and willing to spend many hours working with them or doing research on them. They need to use careful, precise methods in their work.

## Earnings and Benefits

Earnings for zoologists depend on their education and experience, as well as the location and the kind of job. In 2004 the median annual income of zoologists was $50,330. In 2005 zoologists who worked for the federal government in nonsupervisory, supervisory, and managerial positions earned an average salary of $101,601. Benefits generally include paid holidays and vacations, insurance, and retirement plans.

### Where to Go for More Information

American Institute of Biological Sciences
1444 I St. NW, Ste. 200
Washington, DC 20005
(202) 628-1500
http://www.aibs.org

Society for Integrative and Comparative Biology
1313 Dolley Madison Blvd., Ste. 402
McLean, VA 22101
(800) 955-1236
http://www.sicb.org

# Resources General Career Information

## Books

### Exploring the Working World

*American Salaries and Wages Survey*, 8th ed., Helen S. Fisher. Farmington Hills, MI: Thomson Gale, 2005.

*America's Fastest Growing Jobs: Detailed Information on the 140 Fastest Growing Jobs in Our Economy*, 8th ed., Michael Farr. Indianapolis, IN: JIST Publishing, 2004.

*America's Top 101 Jobs for College Graduates*, 6th ed., Michael Farr. Indianapolis, IN: JIST Publishing, 2005.

*America's Top 101 Jobs for People without a Four-Year Degree*, 7th ed., Michael Farr. Indianapolis, IN: JIST Publishing, 2004.

*America's Top 300 Jobs*, 9th ed., U.S. Department of Labor. Indianapolis, IN: JIST Publishing, 2004.

*Best Career and Education Web Sites: A Quick Guide to Online Job Search*, 4th ed., Rachel Singer Gordon and Anne Wolfinger. Indianapolis, IN: JIST Publishing, 2004.

*Best Entry-Level Jobs*, Ron Lieber and Tom Meltzer. New York: Princeton Review, 2006.

*Best Jobs for the 21st Century*, 4th ed., Michael Farr and Laurence Shatkin. Indianapolis, IN: JIST Publishing, 2006.

*Big Book of Jobs, 2003–2004*, U.S. Department of Labor. New York: McGraw-Hill, 2003.

*Career Discovery Encyclopedia*, 5th ed., 8 vols. Chicago: Ferguson, 2003.

*Enhanced Occupational Outlook Handbook*, 5th ed., Indianapolis, IN: JIST Publishing, 2005.

*Job Hunter's Sourcebook: A Thomson Gale Career Information Guide*. Farmington Hills, MI: Thomson Gale, biennial.

*Jobs Rated Almanac*, 6th ed., Les Krantz. Fort Lee, NJ: Barricade, 2002.

*The National JobBank, 2006*. Avon, MA: Adams Media, 2006.

*Occupational Outlook Handbook* series. Washington, DC: United States Government Printing Office, biennial. Briefs, separately published.

*Occupational Outlook Quarterly*. Washington, DC: United States Government Printing Office. Quarterly publication.

*Professional Careers Sourcebook*, 7th ed. Farmington Hills, MI: Thomson Gale, 2002.

*200 Best Jobs for College Graduates*, 3rd ed., Michael Farr and Laurence Shatkin. Indianapolis, IN: JIST Publishing, 2006.

**Recommended**

*Best Jobs for the 21st Century*, 4th ed., Michael Farr and Laurence Shatkin. Indianapolis, IN: JIST Publishing, 2006. Lists five hundred jobs and categorizes them into sixty-five "Best Jobs for..." lists. Organizes jobs by category, education required, best growth potential.

*Jobs Rated Almanac*, 6th ed., Les Krantz. Fort Lee, NJ: Barricade, 2002. Rates 250 jobs and sorts into "best for" and "worst for" rankings. Factors include salary, benefits, and stress level.

*300 Best Jobs without a Four-Year Degree*, 2nd ed., Michael Farr and Laurence Shatkin. Indianapolis, IN: JIST Publishing, 2006.

*VGM's Career Encyclopedia*, 5th ed., New York: McGraw-Hill, 2002.

*Vocational Careers Sourcebook*, 5th ed., Farmington Hills, MI: Thomson Gale, 2002.

## Education and Training Opportunities

*Acing the College Application: How to Maximize Your Chances for Admission to the College of Your Choice*, Michele Hernandez. New York: Ballantine, 2002.

*Admission Matters: What Students and Parents Need to Know about Getting Into College*, Sally P. Springer and Marion R. Franck. San Francisco: Jossey-Bass, 2005.

*Barron's Guide to Graduate Business Schools*, Eugene Miller and Neuman F. Pollack. Hauppauge, NY: Barron's Educational Series, revised regularly.

*Barron's Guide to Law Schools*. Hauppauge, NY: Barron's Educational Series, revised regularly.

*Barron's Guide to Medical and Dental Schools*, Sol Wischnitzer and Edith Wischnitzer. Hauppauge, NY: Barron's Educational Series, revised regularly.

*Barron's Profiles of American Colleges*. Hauppauge, NY: Barron's Educational Series, annual.

*Bear's Guide to College Degrees by Mail and Internet*, 10th ed., John Bear. Berkeley, CA: Ten Speed Press, 2005.

*Best 109 Internships*, 9th ed., Mark Oldman and Samer Hamadah. New York: Princeton Review, 2003.

*The Best 361 Colleges*. New York: Princeton Review, annual.

*Chronicle Vocational School Manual*. Moravia, NY: Chronicle Guidance Publications, annual.

*The College Application Essay*, Sarah Myers McGinty. New York: The College Board, 2004.

*The College Board Book of Majors*, 2nd ed. New York: The College Board, 2006.

*The College Board Scholarship Handbook*. New York: The College Board, annual.

*The College Cost and Financial Aid Handbook*. New York: The College Board, annual.

*College Financial Aid: How to Get Your Fair Share*, 6th ed., Peter V. Laurenzo. Albany, NY: Hudson Financial Press, 2002.

*The College Handbook*. New York: The College Board, annual.

*College Majors Handbook with Real Career Paths and Payoffs*, 2nd ed., Neeta P. Fogg. Indianapolis, IN: JIST Publishing, 2004.

*College Planning for Gifted Students*, 3rd ed., Sandra L. Berger. Waco, TX: Prufrock Press, 2006.

*College Success Guide: Top 12 Secrets for Student Success*, Karine Blackett and Patricia Weiss. Indianapolis, IN: JIST Publishing, 2005.

*Complete Book of Colleges*. New York: Princeton Review, annual.

### Recommended

*Acing the College Application: How to Maximize Your Chances for Admission to the College of Your Choice*, Michele Hernandez. New York: Ballantine, 2002. Written by former Dartmouth College admissions officer. Frank but reassuring advice on application, essay, and personal interview.

*The Insider's Guide to Colleges*. New York: St. Martin's Griffin, annual. Surveys students at 320 U.S. and Canadian schools on dorm life, class size, and other campus-related topics.

*Vault Guide to Top Internships*, Samer Hamadah. New York: Vault, 2005. Provides information on internships offered by 700-plus companies, including Fortune 500 corporations. Nonprofit and government programs also listed.

*Fiske Guide to Colleges*, Edmund Fiske. Naperville, IL: Sourcebooks, annual.

*The Gourman Report: A Rating of Undergraduate Programs in American and International Universities*, Jack Gourman. Los Angeles: National Educational Standards, revised regularly.

*Guide to College Majors*. New York: Princeton Review, 2006.

*Guide to the Most Competitive Colleges*. Hauppauge, NY: Barron's Educational Series, revised regularly.

*How to Choose a College Major*, Linda Landis Andrews. New York: McGraw-Hill, 2006.

*How to Write Your College Application Essay*, Kenneth Nourse. New York: McGraw-Hill, 2001.

*The Insider's Guide to Colleges*. New York: St. Martin's Griffin, annual.

*The Internship Bible*, 10th ed. New York: Princeton Review, 2005.

*The National Guide to Educational Credit for Training Programs*. Washington, DC: American Council on Education, revised regularly.

*100 Successful College Application Essays*, 2nd ed. New York: New American Library, 2002.

*Peterson's Best College Admission Essays*, 3rd ed. Princeton, NJ: Thomson Peterson's, 2004.

*Peterson's College Money Handbook*. Princeton, NJ: Thomson Peterson's, annual.

*Peterson's College and University Almanac*. Princeton, NJ: Thomson Peterson's, annual.

*Peterson's Competitive Colleges*. Princeton, NJ: Thomson Peterson's, annual.

*Peterson's Financial Aid Answer Book*. Princeton, NJ: Thomson Peterson's, annual.

*Peterson's Guide to Four-Year Colleges*. Princeton, NJ: Thomson Peterson's, annual.

*Peterson's Guide to Two-Year Colleges*. Princeton, NJ: Thomson Peterson's, annual.

*Peterson's Internships*. Princeton, NJ: Thomson Peterson's, annual.

*Quick Guide to College Majors and Careers*, Laurence Shatkin. Indianapolis, IN: JIST Publishing, 2002.

*Rugg's Recommendations on the Colleges*, Frederick Rugg. Fallbrook, CA: Rugg's Recommendations, annual.

*Students' Guide to Colleges: The Definitive Guide to America's Top 100 Schools Written by the Real Experts—the Students Who Attend Them*, Jordan Goldman and Colleen Buyers. New York: Penguin, 2005.

*The Truth about Getting In: A Top College Advisor Tells You Everything You Need to Know*, Katherine Cohen. New York: Hyperion, 2002.

*US News Ultimate College Guide*. Naperville, IL: Sourcebooks, annual.

*Vault Guide to Top Internships*, Samer Hamadah. New York, Vault, 2005.

## Career Goals

*The Career Adventure: Your Guide to Personal Assessment, Career Exploration, and Decision Making*, 4th ed., Susan M. Johnston. Upper Saddle, NJ: Prentice-Hall, 2005.

*Career Guide to America's Top Industries*, 6th ed., U.S. Department of Labor. Indianapolis, IN: JIST Publishing, 2004.

*Career Warfare: 10 Rules for Building a Successful Personal Brand and Fighting to Keep It*, David F. D'Alessandro and Michele Owens. New York: McGraw-Hill, 2003.

*College Majors and Careers: A Resource Guide for Effective Life Planning*, 5th ed., Paul Phifer. Chicago: Ferguson, 2003.

*Cool Careers for Dummies*, Marty Nemko, Paul Edwards, and Sarah Edwards. Foster City, CA: IDG Books, 2001.

*Customize Your Career*, Roz Usheroff. New York: McGraw-Hill, 2004.

*Do What You Are: Discover the Perfect Career for You through the Secrets of Personality Type*, 3rd ed., Paul D. Tieger and Barbara Barron-Tieger. New York: Little, Brown, 2001.

*50 Best Jobs for Your Personality*, Michael Farr and Laurence Shatkin. Indianapolis, IN: JIST Publishing, 2005.

*Finding a Career That Works for You: A Step-by-Step Guide to Choosing a Career and Finding a Job*, Wilma Fellman. Plantation, FL: Specialty Press, 2000.

*Finding Your Perfect Work: The New Career Guide to Making a Living, Creating a Life*, 2nd ed., Paul Edwards and Susan Edwards. New York: Penguin, 2003.

*The 5 Patterns of Extraordinary Careers: The Guide for Achieving Success and Satisfaction*, James M. Citrin and Richard Smith. New York: Crown Business, 2003.

*The Global Citizen: A Guide to Creating an International Life and Career*, Elizabeth Kruempelmann. Berkeley, CA: Ten Speed Press, 2002.

*Guide to Your Career*, 5th ed., Alan B. Bernstein. New York: Princeton Review, 2004.

*How Hard Are You Knocking? The Job Seeker's Guide to Opening Career Doors*, Timothy J. Augustine and Rona Curcio. Winchester, VA: Oakhill Press, 2005.

*Job Search and Career Checklists: 101 Proven Time-Saving Checklists to Organize and Plan Your Career Search*, Arlene S. Hirsch. Indianapolis, IN: JIST Publishing, 2005.

*Monster Careers: How to Land the Job of Your Life*, Jeffrey Taylor and Douglas Hardy. New York: Penguin, 2004.

*New Guide for Occupational Exploration: Linking Interests, Learning and Careers*, 4th ed., Michael Farr and Laurence Shatkin. Indianapolis, IN: JIST Publishing, 2006.

*The Play of Your Life: Your Program for Finding the Career of Your Dreams—And a Step-by-Step Guide to Making It a Reality*, Colleen A. Sabatino. New York: Rodale, 2004.

*What Color Is Your Parachute? A Practical Manual for Job-Hunters and Career-Changers*, Richard Nelson Bolles. Berkeley, CA: Ten Speed Press, revised annually.

*What Should I Do with My Life? The True Story of People Who Answered the Ultimate Question*, Po Brosnan. New York: Random House, 2002.

*Where's My Oasis? The Essential Handbook for Everyone Wanting the Perfect Job*, Rowan Manahan. New York: Vermillion, 2004.

**Recommended**

*Finding Your Perfect Work: The New Career Guide to Making a Living, Creating a Life*, 2nd ed., Paul Edwards and Susan Edwards. New York: Penguin, 2003. Lists types of careers, with emphasis on self-employment opportunities.

*What Color Is Your Parachute? A Practical Manual for Job-Hunters and Career-Changers*, Richard Nelson Bolles. Berkeley, CA: Ten Speed Press, revised annually. The classic in the genre, and the top-selling career-advice book consistently since the mid-1970s. Updated to reflect twenty-first-century concerns.

## Getting the Job and Getting Ahead

*Almanac of American Employers*, Jack W. Plunkett. Galveston, TX: Plunkett Research Ltd., biennial.

*e-Resumes: A Guide to Successful Online Job Hunting*, Pat Criscito. Hauppauge, NY: Barron's Educational Series, 2004.

*Guide to Internet Job Searching*, Margaret Riley Dikel. New York: McGraw-Hill, 2004.

*How to Earn What You're Worth: Leveraging Your Goals and Talents to Land Your Dream Job*, Sunny Bates. New York: McGraw-Hill, 2004.

*How to Get Any Job with Any Major: Career Launch & Re-launch for Everyone Under 30 (or How to Avoid Living in Your Parents' Basement)*, Donald Asher. Berkeley, CA: Ten Speed Press, 2004.

*How to Get Your First Job and Keep It*, 2nd ed., Deborah Perlmutter Bloch. New York: McGraw-Hill, 2002.

*Insider's Guide to Finding a Job: Expert Advice from America's Top Employers and Recruiters*, Wendy S. Enelow and Shelly Goldman. Indianapolis, IN: JIST Publishing, 2004.

*International Job Finder: Where the Jobs Are Worldwide*, Daniel Lauber and Kraig Rice. River Forest, IL: Planning/Communications, 2002.

*International Jobs: Where They Are and How to Get Them*, 6th ed., Nina Segal and Eric Kocher. New York: Basic Books, 2003.

*Job-Hunting on the Internet*, 4th ed., Richard Nelson Bolles and Mark Emery Bolles. Berkeley, CA: Ten Speed Press, 2005.

*Job Savvy: How to Be a Success at Work*, 3rd ed., LaVerne L. Ludden. Indianapolis, IN: JIST Publishing, 2002.

*Job Search Magic: Insider Secrets from America's Career and Life Coach*, Susan Britton Whitcomb. Indianapolis, IN: JIST Publishing, 2006.

*The Job Search Solution: The Ultimate System for Finding a Great Job Now!*, Tony Bashara. New York: AMACOM, 2005.

*Job Seeker's Online Goldmine: A Step-by-Step Guidebook to Government and No-Cost Web Tools*, Janet E. Wall. Indianapolis, IN: JIST Publishing, 2006.

*Knock 'Em Dead 2006: The Ultimate Job Seekers Guide*, Martin Yate. Avon, MA: Adams Media, 2006.

*National Job Hotline Directory: The Job Finder's Hot List*, 3rd ed., Sue Cubbage and Marcia Williams. River Forest, IL: Planning/Communications, 2003.

*1000 Best Job Hunting Secrets*, Diane Stafford and Moritza Day. Naperville, IL: Sourcebooks, 2004.

*Super Job Search: The Complete Manual for Job-Seekers & Career-Changers*, 3rd ed., Peter Studner. Los Angeles: Jamenair Ltd., 2003.

*10 Insider Secrets to a Winning Job Search: Everything You Need to Get the Job You Want in 24 Hours—Or Less*, Todd Bermont. Franklin Lakes, NJ: Career Press, 2004.

*Very Quick Job Search: Get a Better Job in Half the Time*, 3rd ed., Michael Farr. Indianapolis, IN: JIST Publishing, 2003.

**Recommended**

*How to Get Any Job with Any Major: Career Launch & Re-launch for Everyone Under 30 (or How to Avoid Living in Your Parents' Basement)*, Donald Asher. Berkeley, CA: Ten Speed Press, 2004. Counsels liberal arts degree-holders on how to package their education and strengths to land a high-paying position.

*Knock 'Em Dead 2006: The Ultimate Job Seekers Guide*, Martin Yate. Avon, MA: Adams Media, 2006. Offers range of advice for job-hunters at all levels, including resume-building, interview strategies, and salary negotiation tips.

## Resumes and Interviews

*Adams Job Interview Almanac*, 2nd ed., Richard Wallace. Avon, MA: Adams Media Corp., 2005.

*Adams Resume Almanac*, 2nd ed., Richard Wallace. Avon, MA: Adams Media Corp., 2005.

*Amazing Resumes: What Employers Want to See—and How to Say It*, Jim Bright and Joanne Earl. Indianapolis, IN: JIST Publishing, 2005.

*Competency-Based Resumes: How to Bring Your Resume to the Top of the Pile*, Robin Kessler and Linda A. Strasburg. Franklin Lakes, NJ: Career Press, 2004.

*Cover Letter Magic*, 2nd ed., Wendy S. Enelow and Louise Kursmark. Indianapolis, IN: JIST Publishing, 2004.

*Cover Letters That Knock 'Em Dead*, 6th ed., Martin Yate. Avon, MA: Adams Media, 2004.

*The Elements of Resume Style: Essential Rules and Eye-opening Advice for Writing Resumes and Cover Letters That Work*, Scott Bennett. New York: AMACOM, 2005.

*Expert Resumes for Career Changers*, Wendy S. Enelow and Louise M. Kursmark. Indianapolis, IN: JIST Publishing, 2005.

*Fearless Interviewing: How to Win the Job by Communicating with Confidence*, Marky Stein. New York: McGraw-Hill, 2002.

*Ferguson Guide to Resumes and Job-Hunting Skills*, Maurene J. Hinds. Chicago: Ferguson, 2005.

*Gallery of Best Resumes: A Collection of Quality Resumes by Professional Resume Writers*, 3rd ed., David F. Noble, Ph.D. Indianapolis, IN: JIST Publishing, 2004.

*Get the Interview Every Time: Fortune 500 Hiring Professionals' Tips for Writing Winning Resumes and Cover Letters*, Brenda Greene. Chicago: Dearborn Trade Publishing, 2004.

*How to Interview Like a Top MBA: Job-Winning Strategies from Headhunters, Fortune 100 Recruiters, and Career Counselors*, Shel Leanne. New York: McGraw-Hill, 2003.

*How to Turn an Interview into a Job*, Jeffrey G. Allen. New York: Simon and Schuster, 2004.

*McGraw-Hill's Big Red Book of Resumes*. New York: McGraw-Hill, 2002.

*Monster Careers: Interviewing—Master the Moment That Gets You the Job*, Jeffrey Taylor and Doug Hardy. New York: Penguin Books, 2005.

*The Resume.com Guide to Writing Unbeatable Resumes*, Warren Simons and Rose Curtis. New York: McGraw-Hill, 2004.

*The Resume Handbook: How to Write Outstanding Resumes & Cover Letters for Every Situation*, 4th ed., Arthur D. Rosenberg and David V. Hizer. Avon, MA: Adams Media, 2003.

*Resume Magic: Trade Secrets of a Professional Resume Writer*, 2nd ed., Susan Britton Whitcomb. Indianapolis, IN: JIST Publishing, 2003.

*Resumes for Dummies*, 4th ed., Joyce Lain Kennedy. Indianapolis, IN: Wiley, 2003.

*Resumes That Knock 'Em Dead*, 6th ed., Martin Yate. Avon, MA: Adams Media, 2004.

*301 Smart Answers to Tough Interview Questions*, Vicky Oliver. Naperville, IL: Sourcebooks, 2005.

*201 Best Questions to Ask on Your Interview*, John Kador. New York: McGraw-Hill, 2002.

*Winning the Interview Game: Everything You Need to Know to Land the Job*, Alan H. Nierenberg. New York: AMACOM, 2005.

## Recommended

*Resume Magic: Trade Secrets of a Professional Resume Writer*, 2nd ed., Susan Britton Whitcomb. Indianapolis, IN: JIST Publishing, 2003. Before and after resume samples provide a how-to on crafting the perfect resume. Includes tips on e-resumes and tricks for scannable-text submissions.

*301 Smart Answers to Tough Interview Questions*, Vicky Oliver. Naperville, IL: Sourcebooks, 2005. Advice on how to handle the questions designed to unsettle, from explaining gaps in work history to acing arcane trivia volleys.

## Mid-Career Options

*Change Your Job, Change Your Life: Careering and Re-Careering in the New Boom/Bust Economy*, 9th ed., Ron Krannich. Manassas Park, VA: Impact, 2004.

*Fearless Career Change*, Marky Stein. New York: McGraw-Hill, 2005.

*Fire Your Boss*, Stephen M. Pollan and Mark Levine. New York: HarperCollins, 2004.

*I Don't Know What I Want, But I Know It's Not This: A Step-by-Step Guide to Finding Gratifying Work*, Julie Jansen. New York: Penguin Books, 2003.

*Over-40 Job Search Guide: 10 Strategies for Making Your Age an Advantage in Your Career*, Gail Geary. Indianapolis, IN: JIST Publishing, 2004.

*Radical Careering: 100 Truths to Jumpstart Your Job, Your Career, and Your Life*, Sally Hogshead. New York: Gotham, 2005.

*Second Acts: Creating the Life You Really Want, Building the Career You Truly Desire*, Stephen M. Pollan and Mark Levine. New York: HarperCollins, 2003.

*Working Identity: Unconventional Strategies for Reinventing Your Career*, Hermania Ibarra. Boston: Harvard Business School Press, 2003.

### Recommended

*I Don't Know What I Want, But I Know It's Not This: A Step-by-Step Guide to Finding Gratifying Work*, Julie Jansen. New York: Penguin Books, 2003. Experienced career coach identifies the top six reasons people are dissatisfied with their jobs and provides a step-by-step process for finding a career that suits every personality.

*Working Identity: Unconventional Strategies for Reinventing Your Career*, Hermania Ibarra. Boston: Harvard Business School Press, 2003. Help for those considering a mid-life career change.

## Equality of Opportunity

*Dancing on the Glass Ceiling*, Nancy Frederick and Candy Deemer. New York: McGraw-Hill, 2004.

*Job-Hunting for the So-Called Handicapped or People Who Have Disabilities*, 2nd ed., Richard Nelson Bolles and Dale Susan Brown. Berkeley, CA: Ten Speed Press, 2001.

*Job Search Handbook for People with Disabilities*, 2nd ed., Daniel J. Ryan. Indianapolis, IN: JIST Publishing, 2004.

*Lavender Road to Success: The Career Guide for the Gay Community*, Kirk Snyder. Berkeley, CA: Ten Speed Press, 2003.

*Resources for People with Disabilities*, 2nd ed., Shawn Woodyard. Chicago: Ferguson, 2001.

### Recommended

*Dancing on the Glass Ceiling*, Nancy Frederick and Candy Deemer. New York: McGraw-Hill, 2004. A former advertising executive teams with a professional executive coach to provide practical as well as inspirational advice for women in the workplace.

*Job-Hunting for the So-Called Handicapped or People Who Have Disabilities*, 2nd ed., Richard Nelson Bolles and Dale Susan Brown. Berkeley, CA: Ten Speed Press, 2001. From the author of *What Color Is Your Parachute?* Advice for the physically or mentally challenged on finding a career niche.

## Lists and Indexes of Career and Vocational Information

*Encyclopedia of Careers and Vocational Guidance*, 13th ed., 5 vols. Chicago: Ferguson, 2006.

*O*Net Dictionary of Occupational Titles*, 3rd ed. Indianapolis, IN: JIST Publishing, 2004.

# Internet Sites

## Sites with Extensive Links

*About.com*
http://careerplanning.about.com

*Beyond.com*
http://www.beyond.com

*Jobweb.com*
http://www.jobweb.com

*JIST Publishing*
http://www.jist.com

*Job Hunt: Online Job Search Guide and Resource Directory*
http://www.job-hunt.org

*Vault.com*
http://www.vault.com

*Vocational Information Center*
http://www.khake.com

## Career Development Resources

*Career Magazine*
http://www.careermag.com

*Career Resource Homepage*
http://www.careerresource.net

*Job Hunters Bible*
http://www.jobhuntersbible.com

*Princeton Review*
http://www.princetonreview.com

*Quintessential Careers*
http://www.quintcareers.com

## Online Information and References

*AT&T Toll-Free Internet Directory*
http://www.tollfree.att.net

*The Best Jobs in the USA Today*
http://www.bestjobsusa.com

*Careers.org*
http://www.careers.org

*Federal Jobs Digest*
http://www.fedworld.gov/jobs/jobsearch.html

*Job Finders Online*
http://www.planningcommunications.com/jf

*Job Safari*
http://www.jobsafari.com

*Monster Career Center*
http://content.monster.com

*Occupational Outlook Handbook*
http://www.bls.gov/oco

*SpherionExchange*
http://employee.spherionexchange.com/start.cfm

*U.S. Bureau of Labor Statistics Homepage*
http://www.bls.gov/home.htm

*US News and World Report Career Center*
http://www.usnews.com/usnews/biztech/career/career_home.htm

*Wall Street Journal Career Journal*
http://www.careerjournal.com

*Yahoo! Business and Economy*
http://dir.yahoo.com/Business_and_Economy

## Job Databases and Resume Posting

*After College*
http://www.aftercollege.com

*America's Job Bank*
http://www.ajb.org

*Career Builder*
http://www.careerbuilder.com

*Career Mart*
http://www.careermart.com

*Employment Guide*
http://www.employmentguide.com

*Yahoo! Hot Jobs*
http://hotjobs.yahoo.com

*Idealist Nonprofit Career Center*
http://www.idealist.org

*Job.com*
http://www.job.com

*JobBank USA*
http://www.jobbankusa.com

*Job Web*
http://www.jobweb.org

*Monster Jobs*
http://www.monster.com

*Monstertrak*
http://www.monstertrak.monster.com

*NationJob.com*
http://www.nationjob.com

*Now Hiring*
http://www.nowhiring.com

# Audiovisual Materials

The following titles include, where possible, the developer's name and location or else the name and location of a distributor. Audiovisual titles may be available through several distributors.

## Exploring the Working World

*Career Advantage: Strategies for Success* series. Video, guide. Princeton, NJ: Films Media Group.

*Career Clusters* series. Video. Charleston, WV: Cambridge Educational.

*Career Exploration* series. Video. South Charleston, WV: Meridian Education Corp.

*Career Guidance Videos* series. Video. South Charleston, WV: Meridian Education Corp.

*Career S.E.L.F. Assessment: Finding a Career That Works for You*. Video. Charleston, WV: Cambridge Educational.

*Careers, Careers, Careers!* Video, guide. Princeton, NJ: Films Media Group.

*Careers for the 21st Century* series. Video, guide. South Charleston, WV: Meridian Education Corp.

*Careers without College*. Video. Charleston, WV: Cambridge Educational.

*The Changing Workplace: Technology and Globalization*. Video. Princeton, NJ: Films Media Group.

*Choices Today for Career Satisfaction Tomorrow*. Video, guide. Charleston, WV: Cambridge Educational.

*Complete Job Search System*. Video. Charleston, WV: Cambridge Educational.

*Connect on the Net: Finding a Job on the Internet*. Video. Charleston, WV: Cambridge Educational.

*Educational Planning for Your Career*. Video. South Charleston, WV: Meridian Education Corp.

*The 50 Best Jobs for the 21st Century* series. Video. Indianapolis, IN: JIST Publishing.

*The JIST Video Guide for Occupational Exploration* series. Video. Indianapolis, IN: JIST Publishing.

*Internet Careers: College Not Required*. Video. Charleston, WV: Cambridge Educational.

*Introduction to Career and Educational Exploration*. Video. Princeton, NJ: Films Media Group.

*JIST TV Series: The Job Search Channel*. Video. Indianapolis, IN: JIST Publishing.

*Jobs for the 21st Century*. Video. Mt. Kisco, NY: Guidance Associates.

*Learning for Earning*. Video, guide. South Charleston, WV: Meridian Education Corp.

*Log On for Success: Using Internet Job Sites*. Video, guide. Charleston, WV: Cambridge Educational.

*Researching Career Options: New Technologies and Current Techniques*. Video. Princeton, NJ: Films Media Group.

*School-to-Work Transition*. Video. South Charleston, WV: Meridian Education Corp.

*Ten Fastest Growing Careers: Jobs for the Future*. Video. Mt. Kisco, NY: Guidance Associates.

*What Would I Be Good At?* Video. Mt. Kisco, NY: Guidance Associates.

*What's Out There: How the World of Work is Organized*. Video. Princeton, NJ: Films Media Group.

*Your Career Search: Taking the First Step*. Video. Mt. Kisco, NY: Guidance Associates.

*Your Future: Planning Through Career Exploration*. Video. South Charleston, WV: Meridian Education Corp.

## Getting the Job and Getting Ahead

*Career Evaluation*. Video. Charleston, WV: Cambridge Educational.

*Common Mistakes People Make in Interviews*. Video, guide. Charleston, WV: Cambridge Educational.

*Exceptional Employee: A Guide to Success on the Job*. Video. Charleston, WV: Cambridge Educational.

*Exceptional Interviewing Tips: A View from the Inside*. Video, workbook. Charleston, WV: Cambridge Educational.

*Extraordinary Answers to Common Interview Questions*. Video. Charleston, WV: Cambridge Educational.

*Finding a Job*. Video. Charleston, WV: Cambridge Educational.

*First Impressions: Etiquette and Work Habits for New Employees*. Video, guide. Charleston, WV: Cambridge Educational.

*From Pinkslip to Paycheck: The Road to Reemployment* series. Video. Indianapolis, IN: JIST Publishing.

*Getting Good Answers to Tough Interview Questions*. Video. Indianapolis, IN: JIST Publishing.

*Getting the Job You Really Want* series. Video, workbook, guide. Indianapolis, IN: JIST Publishing.

*How to Find a Job on the Internet*. Video. Indianapolis, IN: JIST Publishing.

*How to Be a Success at Work* series. Video. Indianapolis, IN: JIST Publishing.

*The Ideal Resume*. Video. Charleston, WV: Cambridge Educational.

*If at First: How to Get a Job and Keep It*. Video. Mt. Kisco, NY: Guidance Associates.

*Interview to Win Your First Job*. Video. Indianapolis, IN: JIST Publishing.

*Interviewing for a Job*. Video. Charleston, WV: Cambridge Educational.

*Job Survival Kit*. Video. Charleston, WV: Cambridge Educational.

*On-the-Job Success* series. Video. Indianapolis, IN: JIST Publishing.

*Planning Your Career*. Video. Charleston, WV: Cambridge Educational.

*The Portfolio Resume* series. Video. Charleston, WV: Cambridge Educational.

*"Quick" Job Search* series. Video. Indianapolis, IN: JIST Publishing.

*Succeeding on the Job*. Video. Charleston, WV: Cambridge Educational.

*Success in the Job World* series. Video. Indianapolis, IN: JIST Publishing.

*Staying on Track in Your Work Search*. Video. Princeton, NJ: Films Media Group.

*Power Interviewing Skills: Strategies for the Interviewee*. Video. Charleston, WV: Cambridge Educational.

*Take This Job and Love It: Keys to Surviving Your New Job*. Video. Charleston, WV: Cambridge Educational.

*Ten Commandments of Resumes*. Video. Charleston, WV: Cambridge Educational.

*Tough Times Job Strategies*. Video, guide. Charleston, WV: Cambridge Educational.

*Understanding and Using the O*NET*. Video, guide. Charleston, WV: Cambridge Educational.

*The Very Quick Job Search Video*. Video. Indianapolis, IN: JIST Publishing.

*The Video Guide to JIST's Self-Directed Job Search* series. Video. Indianapolis, IN: JIST Publishing.

*Web Resumes*. Video. Charleston, WV: Cambridge Educational.

# Computer Software

The following titles include, where possible, the developer's name and location or else the name and location of a distributor. Software titles may be available through several distributors.

*Ace the Interview: The Multimedia Job Interview Guide*. CD-ROM. Charleston, WV: Cambridge Educational.

*Adams Media JobBank FastResume Suite*. CD-ROM for Windows. Avon, MA: Adams Media.

*Barron's Profiles of American Colleges on CD-ROM*. Windows or Macintosh. Hauppauge, NY: Barron's Educational Series.

*Cambridge Career Center*. CD-ROM. Charleston, WV: Cambridge Educational.

*Career Discovery Encyclopedia*. CD-ROM. Chicago, IL: Ferguson.

*Career Explorer*. CD-ROM for Windows. Indianapolis, IN: JIST Publishing.

*Career Finder Plus*. CD-ROM. Indianapolis, IN: JIST Publishing.

*CareerOINKs on the Web*. Network. Indianapolis, IN: JIST Publishing.

*Careers without College*. CD-ROM. Indianapolis, IN: JIST Publishing.

*Complete Resume Designer*. CD-ROM. Charleston, WV: Cambridge Educational.

*Custom Resume Creator*. CD-ROM for Windows. Indianapolis, IN: JIST Publishing.

*Decisions*. CD-ROM. Indianapolis, IN: JIST Publishing.

*Electronic Career Planner*. CD-ROM for Windows. Indianapolis, IN: JIST Publishing.

*Exploring the World of Work*. CD-ROM. New York: McGraw-Hill.

*JIST Presents Interview Mastery*. CD-ROM. Indianapolis, IN: JIST Publishing.

*Job Search* series. CD-ROM. Indianapolis, IN: JIST Publishing.

*Job Survival* series. CD-ROM. Indianapolis, IN: JIST Publishing.

*The Keys to Interviewing Success: Unlocking Your Professional Future*. CD-ROM. Charleston, WV: Cambridge Educational.

*Moving on Up: An Interactive Guide to Finding a Great Job*. CD-ROM for Windows. Charleston, WV: Cambridge Educational.

*Multimedia Career Center*. CD-ROM. Charleston, WV: Cambridge Educational.

*The Multimedia Career Path*. CD-ROM. Charleston, WV: Cambridge Educational.

*The Multimedia Guide to Occupational Exploration*. CD-ROM. Charleston, WV: Cambridge Educational.

*Multimedia Job Search*. CD-ROM for Windows. Charleston, WV: Cambridge Educational.

*Multimedia Take This Job and Love It*. CD-ROM. Charleston, WV: Cambridge Educational.

*OOH Career Center*. CD-ROM. Charleston, WV: Cambridge Educational.

*School-to-Work Career Center*. CD-ROM. Charleston, WV: Cambridge Educational.

*Success in the World of Work: Succeeding on the Job*. CD-ROM. South Charleston, WV: Meridian Education Corp.

*Targeting Success*. CD-ROM. Indianapolis, IN: JIST Publishing.

# General

## Books

*Ace the Technical Interview*, 4th ed., Michael Rothstein. New York: Osborne McGraw-Hill, 2000.

*Advice to Rocket Scientists: A Career Survival Guide to Scientists and Engineers*, Jim Longuski. Reston, VA: American Institute of Aeronautics and Astronautics, Inc., 2004.

*Careers in Engineering*, 2nd ed. Geraldine Garner. New York: McGraw-Hill, 2003.

*Careers in Science*, 4th ed. Thomas Easton. New York: McGraw-Hill, 2004.

*Careers Inside the World of Technology*, rev. ed., Jean W. Spencer. New York: The Rosen Publishing Group, 2000.

*Exploring Tech Careers: Real People Tell You What You Need to Know*, Holli Cosgrove, ed. 2 vols. Chicago: Ferguson, 2001.

*Ferguson's Careers in Focus: Engineering*, 2nd ed. Chicago: Ferguson, 2003.

*Great Jobs for Biology Majors*, 2nd ed., Blythe Camenson. New York: McGraw-Hill, 2004.

*Great Jobs for Engineering Majors*, 2nd ed., Geraldine Garner. New York: McGraw-Hill, 2002.

*Is There an Engineer Inside You?*, Celeste Baine. Belmont, CA: Professional Publications, 2004.

*Job Opportunities in Engineering and Technology*. Princeton, NJ: Petersons, annual.

*Careers in Engineering*, 2nd ed. Geraldine Garner. New York: McGraw-Hill, 2003.

*Opportunities in Biological Science Careers*, Kathleen M. Belikoff. New York: McGraw-Hill, 2004.

*Opportunities in Engineering Careers*, rev. ed., Nicholas Basta. New York: McGraw-Hill, 2003.

*Opportunities in Social Science Careers*, Rosanne J. Marek. New York: McGraw-Hill, 2004.

*Resumes for Engineering Careers*, The Editors of McGraw-Hill. New York: McGraw-Hill, 2005.

*What Can You Do with a Major in Biology? Real People, Real Jobs, Real Rewards*, Bart Astor. Hoboken, NJ: Wiley, 2005.

## Internet Sites

*American Astronomical Society Career Services*
http://www.aas.org/career/index.htm

*American Mathematical Society Careers and Employment*
http://www.ams.org/employment

*Bio.com Career Center*
http://www.bio.com/jobs/index.jhtml

*ChemicalEngineer.com*
http://www.chemicalengineer.com

*EngineeringJobs.com*
http://www.engineeringjobs.com

*EngineeringWeb*
http://www.engineerweb.com

*Institute of Electrical and Electronics Engineers Career Navigator*
http://www.ieeeusa.org/careers/default.asp

*Job Search for Engineers*
http://www.interec.net

*Mathematical Sciences Career Information*
http://www.ams.org/careers

*Mechanical Engineer.com*
http://www.mechanicalengineer.com

*Monster Career Advice*
content.monster.com

*NationJob: Aviation/Aerospace/Defense Jobs Page*
http://www.nationjob.com/aviation

*Physics Today Career Network*
http://www.physicstoday.org/jobs/

*ScienceCareers.org*
sciencecareers.sciencemag.org/

*SolidWorks Job Network*
http://www.swjn.com

*Space Careers*
http://www.space-careers.com/

*Space Jobs*
http://www.spacejobs.com

*Women in Technology International*
http://www.witi.com

## Audiovisual Materials

*Career Options with Math, Science, and Technology*. 12 videos. South Charleston, WV: Meridian Education Corp.

*Careers in Technology*. Video. South Charleston, WV: Meridian Education Corp.

*Exploring Space Technology*. Video. Calhoun, KY: NIMCO.

*Innerview: Research & Development*. Video. Fresno, CA: Edgepoint Productions.

*Innerview: Scientific*. Video. Fresno, CA: Edgepoint Productions.

*Planning and Preparing for a Career in Technology*. Video. South Charleston, WV: Meridian Education Corp.

# *Electronics, Engineering, and Technicians*

## Books

*Becoming an Electronics Technician: Securing Your High-Tech Future*, 4th ed., Ronald A. Reis. Upper Saddle River, NJ: Prentice-Hall, 2002.

*Careers for Computer Buffs and Other Technological Types*, 3rd ed., Marjorie Eberts and Margaret Gisler. New York: McGraw-Hill, 2006.

*The Fantastic Engineer: A Thrillseeker's Guide to Careers in Theme Park Engineering*, 4th ed., Celeste Baine. Belmont, CA: Professional Publications, 2004.

*High Tech Hot Shots: Careers in Sports Engineering*, Celeste Baine. Alexandria, VA: The National Society of Professional Engineers, 2004.

*Ferguson's Careers in Focus: Technicians*, 2nd ed. Chicago: Ferguson, 2004.

*Peterson's Guide to Graduate Programs in Engineering and Applied Sciences*. Princeton, NJ: Petersons, annual.

*Tomorrow's Professor: Preparing for Careers in Science and Engineering*, Richard M. Reis. Piscataway, NJ: Wiley-IEEE Computer Society Press, 2001.

## Audiovisual Materials

*Engineering & Related Occupations*. Video. South Charleston, WV: Meridian Education Corp.

*Innerview: Electronics*. Video. Fresno, CA: Edgepoint Productions.

*Innerview: Engineering*. Video. Fresno, CA: Edgepoint Productions.

*Mechanical Engineering* (*Career Encounters* series). Video. South Charleston, WV: Meridian Education Corps.

*Women in Engineering* (*Career Encounters* series). Video. South Charleston, WV: Meridian Education Corps.

# *The Natural Sciences and Mathematics*

## Books

*2004 Graduate Programs in Physics, Astronomy and Related Fields*. New York: American Institute of Physics, 2003.

*Jobs in the Drug Industry: A Career Guide for Chemists*, Richard J. Friary. San Diego, CA: Academic Press, 2000.

*Opportunities in Aerospace Careers*, 3rd ed., Wallace R. Maples. Lincolnwood, IL: NTC Publishing Group, 2002.

*Opportunities in Biotechnology Careers*, Sheldon S. Brown and Julie Hall. Lincolnwood, IL: NTC Publishing Group, 2000.

*Opportunities in Clinical Laboratory Science Careers*, revised ed., Karen R. Karni. Lincolnwood, IL: VGM Career Books, 2002.

*Opportunities in Forensic Science Careers*, Blythe Camenson. Lincolnwood, IL: VGM Career Books, 2001.

*Put Your Science to Work: The Take Charge Career Guide for Scientists*, Peter S. Fiske. Washington, DC: American Geophysical Union, 2000.

*101 Careers in Mathematics*, 2nd ed., Andre Sterrett, ed. Washington, DC: Mathematical Association of America, 2003.

## Audiovisual Materials

*Innerview: Chemical Production*. Video. Fresno, CA: Edgepoint Production.

*Physical and Life Sciences*. Video. South Charleston, WV: Meridian Education Corp.

# Social Sciences

## Books

*Careers in Anthropology*, W. Richard Stephens. Boston, MA: Allyn & Bacon, 2001.

*Careers in Social Work*, 2nd ed., Leon H. Ginsberg. Upper Saddle River, NJ: Pearson Allyn & Bacon, 2002.

*Great Jobs for Anthropology Majors*, 2nd ed., Blythe Camenson. Lincolnwood, IL: VGM Career Horizons, 2004.

*Great Jobs for History Majors*, 2nd ed., Stephen Lambert and Julie Degalan. Lincolnwood, IL: NTC Publishing Group, 2001.

*Great Jobs for Sociology Majors*, 2nd ed., Stephen Lambert. Lincolnwood, IL: NTC Publishing Group, 2002.

*Guide to Departments of Anthropology*. Washington, DC: American Anthropological Association, periodical.

*Opportunities in Historical Anthropology* (leaflet). Tucson, AZ: Society for Historical Archaeology.

*Opportunities in Social Science Careers*, rev. ed., Rosanne J. Marek. Lincolnwood, IL: NTC Publishing Group, 2004.

## Audiovisual Materials

*Innerview: Historical Sciences*. Video. Fresno, CA: Edgepoint Productions.

*Social Sciences*. Video. Bloomington, IL: Meridian Education Corp.

# Directory Institutions Offering Career Training

The information in this directory was generated from the IPEDS (Integrated Postsecondary Education Data System) database of the U.S. Department of Education. It includes only regionally or nationally accredited institutions offering postsecondary occupational training in engineering, science, technology, and social science. Because college catalogs and directories of colleges and universities are readily available elsewhere, this directory does not include institutions that offer only bachelor's and advanced degrees.

## Chemical Technology

### ILLINOIS

College of Lake County
19351 West Washington St.
**Grayslake 60030-1198**

### IOWA

Eastern Iowa Community College District
306 West River Dr.
**Davenport 52801-1221**

### MICHIGAN

Ferris State University
901 South State St.
**Big Rapids 49307**

Kalamazoo Valley Community College
6767 West O Ave.
**Kalamazoo 49009**

### MISSOURI

Saint Louis Community College, Forest Park
5600 Oakland Ave.
**Saint Louis 63110**

### NEW YORK

Broome Community College
P.O. Box 1017
**Binghamton 13902**

Corning Community College
Spencer Hill
**Corning 14830**

CUNY Bronx Community College
West 181st St. & University Ave.
**Bronx 10453**

CUNY New York City Technical College
300 Jay St.
**Brooklyn 11201**

SUNY College of Technology at Alfred
**Alfred 14802**

### PENNSYLVANIA

Bidwell Training Center, Inc.
1815 Metropolitan St.
**Pittsburgh 15233**

Community College of Philadelphia
1700 Spring Garden St.
**Philadelphia 19130**

### RHODE ISLAND

Community College of Rhode Island
400 East Ave.
**Warwick 02886-1807**

### SOUTH CAROLINA

Aiken Technical College
P.O. Drawer 696
**Aiken 29802**

### TENNESSEE

Northeast State Technical Community College
P.O. Box 246
**Blountville 37617**

### TEXAS

Texas State Technical College, Harlingen Campus
2424 Boxwood
**Harlingen 78550-3697**

Texas State Technical College, Waco Campus
3801 Campus Dr.
**Waco 76705**

### WASHINGTON

Bates Technical College
1101 South Yakima Ave.
**Tacoma 98405**

### WEST VIRGINIA

West Virginia State College
Rte. 25
**Institute 25112**

### WISCONSIN

Milwaukee Area Technical College
700 West State St.
**Milwaukee 53233-1443**

## Drafting and Engineering Graphics

### ALABAMA

Bessemer State Technical College
1100 9th Ave.
**Bessemer 35021**

Bevill State Community College
100 State St.
**Sumiton 35148**

Douglas MacArthur State Technical College
1708 Main St.
**Opp 36467**

George C Wallace State Community College, Hanceville
801 Main St. NW
**Hanceville 35077-2000**

George C Wallace State Community College, Selma
3000 Earl Goodwin Pkwy.
**Selma 36702**

Harry M Ayers State Technical College
1801 Coleman Rd.
**Anniston 36202**

J F Drake State Technical College
3421 Meridian St. N
**Huntsville 35811**

Jefferson State Community College
2601 Carson Rd.
**Birmingham 35215-3098**

John C Calhoun State Community College
Hwy. 31 N
**Decatur 35602**

John M Patterson State Technical College
3920 Troy Hwy.
**Montgomery 36116**

### ALASKA

University of Alaska, Anchorage
3211 Providence Dr.
**Anchorage 99508**

### ARIZONA

Arizona Western College
P.O. Box 929
**Yuma 85366**

Aztech College
941 South Dobson Rd.
**Mesa 85202**

Eastern Arizona College
Church St.
**Thatcher 85552-0769**

Glendale Community College
6000 West Olive Ave.
**Glendale 85302**

High-Technical Institute
1515 East Indian School Rd.
**Phoenix 85014**

ITT Technical Institute
4837 East McDowell Rd.
**Phoenix 85008-4292**

ITT Technical Institute
1840 East Benson Hwy.
**Tucson 85714**

Mesa Community College
1833 West Southern Ave.
**Mesa 85202**

National Education Center, Arizona Auto Institute Campus
6829 North 46th Ave.
**Glendale 85301-3579**

Pima Community College
2202 West Anklam Rd.
**Tucson 85709-0001**

### ARKANSAS

Arkansas State University, Beebe Branch
P.O. Drawer H
**Beebe 72012**

Cotton Boll Technical Institute
155 And Hwy. 148
**Burdette 72321**

Foothills Technical Institute
1800 East Moore St., P.O. Box 909
**Searcy 72143**

Pulaski Technical College
3000 West Scenic Dr.
**North Little Rock 72118**

Westark College
P.O. Box 3649
**Fort Smith 72913**

### CALIFORNIA

American River College
4700 College Oak Dr.
**Sacramento 95841**

Cabrillo College
6500 Soquel Dr.
**Aptos 95003**

Cerritos College
11110 Alondra Blvd.
**Norwalk 90650**

Chabot College
25555 Hesperian Blvd.
**Hayward 94545**

Clovis Adult Education
1452 David East Cook Way
**Clovis 93611**

College of San Mateo
1700 West Hillsdale Blvd.
**San Mateo 94402**

College of the Canyons
26455 Rockwell Canyon Rd.
**Santa Clarita 91355**

De Anza College
21250 Stevens Creek Blvd.
**Cupertino 95014**

East Los Angeles Skill Center
3921 Selig Pl.
**Los Angeles 90031**

El Camino College
16007 Crenshaw Blvd.
**Torrance 90506**

Eldorado College
2204 El Camino Real
**Oceanside 92054**

Evergreen Valley College
3095 Yerba Buena Rd.
**San Jose 95135-1598**

Institute for Business and Technology
2550 Scott Blvd.
**Santa Clara 95050**

ITT Technical Institute
2035 East 223rd
**Carson 90810**

ITT Technical Institute
9700 Goethe Rd.
**Sacramento 95827-5282**

ITT Technical Institute
630 East Brier, Ste. 150
**San Bernardino 92408-2800**

ITT Technical Institute
9680 Granite Ridge Dr.
**San Diego 92123**

Los Angeles ORT Technical Institute
6435 Wilshire Blvd.
**Los Angeles 90048**

Merced College
3600 M St.
**Merced 95348-2898**

Mira Costa College
One Barnard Dr.
**Oceanside 92056-3899**

Mission College
1310 San Fernando Rd.
**San Fernando 91340**

Moorpark College
7075 Campus Rd.
**Moorpark 93021**

MTI College
2011 West Chapman Ave., Ste. 100
**Orange 92668**

MTI College, Colton
760 Via Lata, Ste. 300
**Colton 92324**

Orange Coast College
2701 Fairview Rd.
**Costa Mesa 92626**

Platt College, San Diego
6250 El Cajon Blvd.
**San Diego 92115**

Rio Hondo College
3600 Workman Mill Rd.
**Whittier 90601-1699**

Riverside Community College
4800 Magnolia Ave.
**Riverside 92506-1299**

San Diego City College
1313 12th Ave.
**San Diego 92101**

Santa Barbara City College
721 Cliff Dr.
**Santa Barbara 93109-2394**

Sierra College
5000 Rocklin Rd.
**Rocklin 95677**

Sierra Hi-Tech
7144 Fair Oaks Blvd.
**Carmichael 95608-6409**

Simi Valley Adult School
3192 Los Angeles Ave.
**Simi Valley 93065**

Solano County Community College District
4000 Suisun Valley Rd.
**Suisun 94585-3197**

Westech College
500 West Mission Blvd.
**Pomona 91766**

### COLORADO

Community College of Denver
P.O. Box 173363
**Denver 80217**

Denver Institute of Technology
7350 North Broadway
**Denver 80221**

Front Range Community College
3645 West 112th Ave.
**Westminster 80030**

ITT Technical Institute
2121 South Blackhawk St.
**Aurora 80014**

Red Rocks Community College
13300 West Sixth Ave.
**Lakewood 80228**

Technical Trades Institute
2315 East Pikes Peak Ave.
**Colorado Springs 80909**

### CONNECTICUT

Baran Institute of Technology
611 Day Hill Rd.
**Windsor 06095**

### FLORIDA

Brevard Community College
1519 Clearlake Rd.
**Cocoa 32922**

Florida Technical College
1819 North Semoran Blvd.
**Orlando 32807**

Florida Technical College of Jacksonville, Inc.
8711 Lone Star Rd.
**Jacksonville 32211**

ITT Technical Institute
4809 Memorial Hwy.
**Tampa-7515 33634**

Keiser College
1500 Northwest 49th St.
**Fort Lauderdale 33309**

Manatee Vocational Technical Center
5603 34th St. W
**Bradenton 34210**

North Florida Community College
Turner Davis Dr.
**Madison 32340**

North Technical Education Center
7071 Garden Rd.
**Riviera Beach 33404**

Okaloosa-Walton Community College
100 College Blvd.
**Niceville 32578**

Pinellas Technical Education Center, Clearwater Campus
6100 154th Ave. N
**Clearwater 34620**

Saint Augustine Technical Center
2980 Collins Ave.
**Saint Augustine 32095-1919**

Santa Fe Community College
3000 NW 83rd St.
**Gainesville 32606**

Valencia Community College
P.O. Box 3028
**Orlando 32802**

William T McFatter Vocational Technical Center
6500 Nova Dr.
**Davie 33317**

### GEORGIA

Albany Technical Institute
1021 Lowe Rd.
**Albany 31708**

Athens Area Technical Institute
U.S. Hwy. 29 N
**Athens 30610-0399**

Bainbridge College
2500 East Shotwell St.
**Bainbridge 31717**

Carroll Technical Institute
997 South Hwy. 16
**Carrollton 30117**

Chattahoochee Technical Institute
980 South Cobb Dr.
**Marietta 30060-3398**

Clayton College and State University
5900 Lee St., P.O. Box 285
**Morrow 30260**

Coosa Valley Technical Institute
785 Cedar Ave.
**Rome 30161**

Dalton College
213 North College Dr.
**Dalton 30720**

Dekalb Technical Institute
495 North Indian Creek Dr.
**Clarkston 30021**

Griffin Technical Institute
501 Varsity Rd.
**Griffin 30223**

Gwinnett College of Business
4230 Hwy. 29, Ste. 11
**Lilburn 30047**

Gwinnett Technical Institute
5150 Sugarloaf Pkwy.
**Lawrenceville 30043**

Middle Georgia Technical Institute
1311 Corder Rd.
**Warner Robins 31088**

Moultrie Area Technical Institute
361 Industrial Dr.
**Moultrie 31768**

North Georgia Technical Institute
Georgia Hwy. 197, P.O. Box 65
**Clarkesville 30523**

North Metro Technical Institute
5198 Ross Rd.
**Acworth 30102-3012**

Okefenokee Technical Institute
1701 Carswell Ave.
**Waycross 31501**

Pickens Technical Institute
100 Pickens Tech Dr.
**Jasper 30143**

South Georgia Technical Institute
1583 Souther Field Rd.
**Americus 31709**

Swainsboro Technical Institute
346 Kite Rd.
**Swainsboro 30401**

Thomas Technical Institute
15689 US Hwy. 19 N
**Thomasville 31792**

Valdosta Technical Institute
4089 Valtech Rd.
**Valdosta 31602-9796**

Walker Technical Institute
265 Bicentennial Trail
**Rock Spring 30739**

West Georgia Technical Institute
303 Fort Dr.
**La Grange 30240**

### HAWAII

Hawaii Community College
200 West Kawili St.
**Hilo 96720-4091**

Honolulu Community College
874 Dillingham Blvd.
**Honolulu 96817**

Leeward Community College
96-045 Ala Ike
**Pearl City 96782**

### IDAHO

Boise State University
1910 University Dr.
**Boise 83725**

College of Southern Idaho
P.O. Box 1238
**Twin Falls 83301**

Idaho State University
741 South 7th Ave.
**Pocatello 83209**

ITT Technical Institute
12402 Explorer Dr.
**Boise 83713**

### ILLINOIS

Associated Design Service School of Drafting
11160 Southwest Hwy.
**Palos Hills 60465**

Belleville Area College
2500 Carlyle Rd.
**Belleville 62221**

College of Lake County
19351 West Washington St.
**Grayslake 60030-1198**

John Wood Community College
150 South 48th St.
**Quincy 62301-9147**

Kaskaskia College
27210 College Rd.
**Centralia 62801**

Lewis and Clark Community College
5800 Godfrey Rd.
**Godfrey 62035**

MacMurray College
East College Ave.
**Jacksonville 62650**

Morton College
3801 South Central Ave.
**Cicero 60804**

Richland Community College
One College Park
**Decatur 62521**

Robert Morris College
180 North Lasalle St.
**Chicago 60601**

Rock Valley College
3301 North Mulford Rd.
**Rockford 61114**

Southeastern Illinois College
3575 College Rd.
**Harrisburg 62946**

Zarem Golde ORT Technical Institute
3050 West Touhy
**Chicago 60645**

### INDIANA

Indiana University, Purdue University at Fort Wayne
2101 Coliseum Blvd. E
**Fort Wayne 46805**

Ivy Tech State College, Central Indiana
One West 26th St.
**Indianapolis 46206-1763**

Ivy Tech State College, Columbus
4475 Central Ave.
**Columbus 47203**

Ivy Tech State College, East Central
4301 South Cowan Rd., P.O. Box 3100
**Muncie 47302**

Ivy Tech State College, Kokomo
1815 East Morgan St.
**Kokomo 46901**

Ivy Tech State College, North Central
1534 West Sample St.
**South Bend 46619**

Ivy Tech State College, Northeast
3800 North Anthony Blvd.
**Fort Wayne 46805**

Ivy Tech State College, Northwest
1440 East 35th Ave.
**Gary 46409**

Ivy Tech State College, Southwest
3501 First Ave.
**Evansville 47710**

Ivy Tech State College, Wabash Valley
7999 U.S. Hwy. 41
**Terre Haute 47802-4898**

Purdue University, Main Campus
1076 Freehafer Hall
**West Lafayette 47907-1076**

Vincennes University
1002 North First St.
**Vincennes 47591**

### IOWA

American Institute of Commerce
1801 East Kimberly Rd.
**Davenport 52807**

Des Moines Community College
2006 Ankeny Blvd.
**Ankeny 50021**

Eastern Iowa Community College District
306 West River Dr.
**Davenport 52801-1221**

Hamilton College
2300 Euclid
**Des Moines 50310**

Hamilton Technical College
1011 East 53rd St.
**Davenport 52807**

Indian Hills Community College
525 Grandview
**Ottumwa 52501**

Iowa Central Community College
330 Ave. M
**Fort Dodge 50501**

Southeastern Community College
1015 South Gear Ave., P.O. Drawer F
**West Burlington 52655-0605**

Southwestern Community College
1501 Townline
**Creston 50801**

### KANSAS

Flint Hills Technical College
3301 West 18th St.
**Emporia 66801**

Johnson County Community College
12345 College Blvd.
**Overland Park 66210-1299**

Kansas City Area Vocational Technical School
2220 North 59th St.
**Kansas City 66104**

KAW Area Technical School
5724 Huntoon
**Topeka 66604**

Manhattan Area Technical College
3136 Dickens Ave.
**Manhattan 66503**

Northeast Kansas Area Vocational Technical School
1501 West Riley St., P.O. Box 277
**Atchison 66002**

Northwest Kansas Area Vocational Technical School
P.O. Box 668
**Goodland 67735**

Southeast Kansas Area Vocational Technical School
600 Roosevelt
**Coffeyville 67337**

Wichita Area Technical College
201 North Water
**Wichita 67202-1292**

### KENTUCKY

Kentucky Technical, Bowling Green State Vocational Technical School
845 Loop Dr.
**Bowling Green 42101-3601**

Kentucky Technical, Laurel County State Vocational Technical School
235 South Laurel Rd.
**London 40744**

Kentucky Technical, Madisonville Regional Technology Center
150 School Ave.
**Madisonville 42431**

Louisville Technical Institute
3901 Atkinson Dr.
**Louisville 40218**

Mayo Regional Technology Center
Third St.
**Paintsville 41240**

Northern Kentucky State Vocational Technical School
1025 Amsterdam Rd.
**Covington 41011**

### LOUISIANA

Delgado Community College
501 City Park Ave.
**New Orleans 70119**

Delta School of Business and Technology
517 Broad St.
**Lake Charles 70601**

ITI Technical College
13944 Airline Hwy.
**Baton Rouge 70817**

Louisiana Technical College, Gulf Area Campus
1115 Clover St.
**Abbeville 70510**

Louisiana Technical College, Jefferson Campus
5200 Blair Dr.
**Metairie 70001**

Louisiana Technical College, Ruston Campus
1010 James St.
**Ruston 71273-1070**

Louisiana Technical College, Sabine Valley Campus
1255 Fisher Rd.
**Many 71449**

Louisiana Technical College, Slidell Campus
1000 Canulette Rd., P.O. Box 827
**Slidell 70459**

Louisiana Technical College, South Louisiana Campus
P.O. Box 5033
**Houma 70361-5033**

Louisiana Technical College, Sullivan Campus
1710 Sullivan Dr.
**Bogalusa 70427**

Louisiana Technical College, Teche Area Campus
P.O. Box 11057
**New Iberia 70562-1057**

Louisiana Technical College, West Jefferson Campus
475 Manhattan Blvd.
**Harvey 70058**

Louisiana Technical College, Young Memorial Campus
900 Youngs Rd.
**Morgan City 70380**

### MAINE

Central Maine Technical College
1250 Turner St.
**Auburn 04210**

Northern Maine Technical College
33 Edgemont Dr.
**Presque Isle 04769**

Southern Maine Technical College
Fort Rd.
**South Portland 04106**

### MARYLAND

Charles County Community College
8730 Mitchell Rd.
**La Plata 20646-0910**

Prince Georges Community College
301 Largo Rd.
**Largo 20774-2199**

### MASSACHUSETTS

Computer Processing Institute
615 Massachusetts Ave.
**Cambridge 02139**

Middlesex Community College
Springs Rd.
**Bedford 01730**

North Shore Community College
One Ferncroft Rd.
**Danvers 01923**

Northern Essex Community College
Elliott Way
**Haverhill 01830-2399**

Wentworth Institute of Technology
550 Huntington Ave.
**Boston 02115**

### MICHIGAN

Alpena Community College
666 Johnson St.
**Alpena 49707**

Baker College of Muskegon
1903 Marquette Ave.
**Muskegon 49442**

Bay De Noc Community College
2001 North Lincoln Rd.
**Escanaba 49289**

Ferris State University
901 South State St.
**Big Rapids 49307**

Gogebic Community College
East 4946 Jackson Rd.
**Ironwood 49938**

Grand Rapids Community College
143 Bostwick Ave. NE
**Grand Rapids 49503-3295**

Henry Ford Community College
5101 Evergreen Rd.
**Dearborn 48128**

Jackson Community College
2111 Emmons Rd.
**Jackson 49201-8399**

Kalamazoo Valley Community College
6767 West O Ave.
**Kalamazoo 49009**

Kellogg Community College
450 North Ave.
**Battle Creek 49017**

Kirtland Community College
10775 North Saint Helen Rd.
**Roscommon 48653**

Lake Michigan College
2755 East Napier Ave.
**Benton Harbor 49022-8099**

Lake Superior State University
650 West Easterday Ave.
**Sault Sainte Marie 49783**

Lansing Community College
419 North Capitol Ave.
**Lansing 48901-7210**

Macomb Community College
14500 Twelve Mile Rd.
**Warren 48093-3896**

Monroe County Community College
1555 South Raisinville Rd.
**Monroe 48161**

Mott Community College
1401 East Court St.
**Flint 48503**

North Central Michigan College
1515 Howard St.
**Petoskey 49770**

Northwestern Michigan College
1701 East Front St.
**Traverse City 49686**

Oakland Community College
2100 Opdyke Rd.
**Bloomfield Hills 48304-2266**

Washtenaw Community College
P.O. Drawer 1
**Ann Arbor 48106-1610**

### MINNESOTA

Alexandria Technical College
1601 Jefferson St.
**Alexandria 56308**

Central Lakes College, Staples Technical Campus
1830 Airport Rd.
**Staples 56479**

Hennepin Technical College
9000 Brooklyn Blvd.
**Brooklyn Park 55445**

Hibbing Community College
1515 East 25th St.
**Hibbing 55746**

Lake Superior College
2101 Trinity Rd.
**Duluth 55811**

Minneapolis Drafting School
5700 West Broadway
**Minneapolis 55428-3548**

Northwest Technical College, Moorhead
1900 28th Ave. S
**Moorhead 56560**

Northwest Technical Institute
11995 Singletree Ln.
**Eden Prairie 55344**

Red Wing/Winona Technical College, Winona Campus
1250 Homer Rd., P.O. Box 409
**Winona 55987**

Ridgewater College, A Communication and Technical College
Two Century Ave. SE
**Hutchinson 55350**

Ridgewater College, A Communication and Technical College Wilmar Campus
P.O. Box 1097
**Willmar 56201**

Riverland Community College, Albert Lea
2200 Tech Dr.
**Albert Lea 56007**

Saint Cloud Technical College
1540 Northway Dr.
**Saint Cloud 56303**

South Central Technical College, Faribault Campus
1225 SW Third St.
**Faribault 55021**

South Central Technical College, Mankato
1920 Lee Blvd.
**North Mankato 56003**

### MISSISSIPPI

East Central Community College
**Decatur 39327**

Hinds Community College, Raymond Campus
**Raymond 39154**

Holmes Community College
Hill St.
**Goodman 39079**

Jones County Junior College
900 South Court St.
**Ellisville 39437**

Mississippi Gulf Coast Community College
Central Office, P.O. Box 67
**Perkinston 39573**

Northeast Mississippi Community College
Cunningham Blvd.
**Booneville 38829**

### MISSOURI

East Central College
P.O. Box 529
**Union 63084**

ITT Technical Institute
13505 Lakefront Dr.
**Earth City 63045**

Linn Technical College
One Technology Dr.
**Linn 65051**

Missouri Southern State College
3950 East Newman Rd.
**Joplin 64801-1595**

Rolla Area Technical Institute
1304 East Tenth St.
**Rolla 65401**

Saint Louis Community College, Forest Park
5600 Oakland Ave.
**Saint Louis 63110**

Sikeston Area Vocational Technical School
1002 Virginia St.
**Sikeston 63801**

TAD Technical Institute
7910 Troost Ave.
**Kansas City 64131**

Vatterott College
210 South Main
**Independence 64051**

Vatterott College
1258 East Traffic Way
**Springfield 65802**

Waynesville Technical Academy
810 Roosevelt
**Waynesville 65583**

### MONTANA

Montana State University, College of Technology, Billings
3803 Central Ave.
**Billings 59102**

Montana State University, Northern
300 West 11th St.
**Havre 59501**

### NEBRASKA

Metropolitan Community College Area
5300 North 30th St.
**Omaha 68111**

### NEW HAMPSHIRE

New Hampshire Community College at Nashua
505 Amherst St.
**Nashua 03061-2052**

### NEW JERSEY

Bergen Community College
400 Paramus Rd.
**Paramus 07652**

Brick Computer Science Institute
515 Highway 70
**Brick 08723**

Brookdale Community College
765 Newman Springs Rd.
**Lincroft 07738-1599**

Camden County College
P.O. Box 200
**Blackwood 08012**

County College of Morris
214 Center Grove Rd.
**Randolph 07869**

Lincoln Technical Institute
Rte. 130 North at Haddonfield Rd.
**Pennsauken 08110**

Lincoln Technical Institute
2299 Vauxhall Rd.
**Union 07083**

Pennco Technical
Erial Rd., P.O. Box 1427
**Blackwood 08012**

The Plaza School
Bergen Mall
**Paramus 07652**

### NEW MEXICO

Albuquerque Technical Vocational Institute
525 Buena Vista SE
**Albuquerque 87106**

ITT Technical Institute
5100 Masthead NE
**Albuquerque 87109**

Luna Vocational Technical Institute
P.O. Drawer K
**Las Vegas 87701**

New Mexico Junior College
5317 Lovington Hwy.
**Hobbs 88240**

Northern New Mexico Community College
1002 North Onate St.
**Espanola 87532**

### NEW YORK

CUNY New York City Technical College
300 Jay St.
**Brooklyn 11201**

CUNY Queensborough Community College
56th Ave. & Springfield Blvd.
**New York 11364**

Erie Community College, South Campus
4140 Southwestern Blvd.
**Orchard Park 14127**

Genesee Community College
One College Rd.
**Batavia 14020**

Hudson Valley Community College
80 Vandenburgh Ave.
**Troy 12180**

Island Drafting and Technical Institute
128 Broadway Rte. 110
**Amityville 11701**

Mohawk Valley Community College, Utica Branch
1101 Sherman Dr.
**Utica 13501**

Niagara County Community College
3111 Saunders Settlement Rd.
**Sanborn 14132**

Onondaga Community College
4941 Onondaga Rd.
**Syracuse 13215**

Rochester Institute of Technology
One Lomb Memorial Dr.
**Rochester 14623-5603**

Suffolk County Community College, Ammerman Campus
533 College Rd.
**Selden 11784**

SUNY College of Technology at Alfred
**Alfred 14802**

SUNY College of Technology at Canton
Cornell Drive
**Canton 13617**

SUNY College of Technology at Delhi
**Delhi 13753**

SUNY Ulster County Community College
Cottekill Rd.
**Stone Ridge 12484**

### NORTH CAROLINA

Davidson County Community College
297 Davidson Community College Rd.
**Lexington 27292**

Lenoir Community College
P.O. Box 188
**Kinston 28502-0188**

Mitchell Community College
500 West Broad
**Statesville 28677**

Wake Technical Community College
9101 Fayetteville Rd.
**Raleigh 27603-5696**

### NORTH DAKOTA

North Dakota State College of Science
800 North Sixth St.
**Wahpeton 58076**

### OHIO

Central Ohio Technical College
1179 University Dr.
**Newark 43055-1767**

ETI Technical College
2076 Youngstown Warren Rd.
**Niles 44446-4398**

ETI Technical College
1320 West Maple St. NW
**North Canton 44720**

ITT Technical Institute
1030 North Meridian Rd.
**Youngstown 44509**

North Central Technical College
2441 Kenwood Circle, P.O. Box 698
**Mansfield 44901**

Northwest State Community College
22600 State Rte. 34
**Archbold 43502-9990**

Owens Community College
30335 Oregon Rd.
**Toledo 43699-1947**

Owens Community College, Findlay Campus
300 Davis St.
**Findlay 45840**

Shawnee State University
940 Second St.
**Portsmouth 45662**

Sinclair Community College
444 West Third St.
**Dayton 45402**

Southern State Community College
100 Hobart Dr.
**Hillsboro 45133**

Stark State College of Technology
6200 Frank Ave. NW
**Canton 44720**

Technology Education College
288 South Hamilton Rd.
**Columbus 43213**

Total Technical Institute
6500 Pearl Rd.
**Parma Heights 44130**

University of Toledo
2801 West Bancroft
**Toledo 43606**

Wright State University, Lake Campus
7600 State Rte. 703E
**Celina 45822**

### OKLAHOMA

Central Oklahoma Area Vocational Technical School
3 Court Cir.
**Drumright 74030**

Francis Tuttle Area Vocational Technical Center
12777 North Rockwell Ave.
**Oklahoma City 73142-2789**

Metro Area Vocational Technical School District 22
1900 Springlake Dr.
**Oklahoma City 73111**

Oklahoma City Community College
7777 South May Ave.
**Oklahoma City 73159**

Oklahoma State University, Okmulgee
1801 East Fourth St.
**Okmulgee 74447-3901**

Platt College
309 South Ann Arbor
**Oklahoma City 73128**

Platt College
3801 South Sheridan
**Tulsa 74145**

Pontotoc Area Vocational Technical School
601 West 33rd
**Ada 74820**

Southern Oklahoma Technology Center
2610 Sam Noble Pkwy.
**Ardmore 73401**

Tulsa Community College
6111 East Skelly Dr.
**Tulsa 74135**

### OREGON

Central Oregon Community College
2600 NW College Way
**Bend 97701**

Chemeketa Community College
4000 Lancaster Dr. NE
**Salem 97305**

Clackamas Community College
19600 Molalla Ave.
**Oregon City 97045**

ITT Technical Institute
6035 NE 78th Ct.
**Portland 97218**

Lane Community College
4000 East 30th Ave.
**Eugene 97405**

Linn-Benton Community College
6500 SW Pacific Blvd.
**Albany 97321**

Mount Hood Community College
26000 SE Stark St.
**Gresham 97030**

Portland Community College
P.O. Box 19000
**Portland 97280-0990**

### PENNSYLVANIA

American Center for Technical Arts and Sciences
1616 Orthodox St.
**Philadelphia 19124**

Berks Technical Institute
2205 Ridgewood Rd.
**Wyomissing 19610-1168**

Bucks County Community College
Swamp Rd.
**Newtown 18940**

Butler County Community College
College Dr. Oak Hills
**Butler 16003-1203**

California University of Pennsylvania
250 University Ave.
**California 15419-1394**

Community College of Allegheny County
800 Allegheny Ave.
**Pittsburgh 15233-1895**

Dean Institute of Technology
1501 West Liberty Ave.
**Pittsburgh 15226-9990**

Mercer County Area Vocational Technical School
776 Greenville Rd.
**Mercer 16137-0152**

Pace Institute
606 Court St.
**Reading 19601**

Pennco Technical
3815 Otter St.
**Bristol 19007**

Pennsylvania College of Technology
One College Ave.
**Williamsport 17701**

Triangle Tech, Inc.
1940 Perrysville Ave.
**Pittsburgh 15214**

Triangle Tech Inc., Erie
2000 Liberty St.
**Erie 16502**

Triangle Tech Inc., Greensburg
222 East Pittsburgh St., Ste. A
**Greensburg 15601**

Penn Commercial, Inc.
82 South Main St.
**Washington 15301**

Westmoreland County Community College
**Youngwood 15697-1895**

## RHODE ISLAND

Johnson and Wales University
8 Abbott Park Place
**Providence 02903-3376**

New England Institute of Technology
2500 Post Rd.
**Warwick 02886**

## SOUTH CAROLINA

Central Carolina Technical College
506 North Guignard Dr.
**Sumter 29150**

Greenville Technical College
P.O. Box 5616, Station B
**Greenville 29606-5616**

Midlands Technical College
P.O. Box 2408
**Columbia 29202**

Orangeburg Calhoun Technical College
3250 Saint Matthews Rd.
**Orangeburg 29115**

Piedmont Technical College
P.O. Drawer 1467
**Greenwood 29648**

Spartanburg Technical College
I-85
**Spartanburg 29305**

Technical College of the Lowcountry
921 South Ribaut Rd.
**Beaufort 29901**

Tri-County Technical College
P.O. Box 587
**Pendleton 29670**

Trident Technical College
P.O. Box 118067
**Charleston 29423-8067**

York Technical College
452 South Anderson Rd.
**Rock Hill 29730**

## SOUTH DAKOTA

Lake Area Technical Institute
230 11th St. NE
**Watertown 57201**

## TENNESSEE

Chattanooga State Technical Community College
4501 Amnicola Hwy.
**Chattanooga 37406**

ITT Technical Institute
441 Donelson Pike
**Nashville 37214**

Northeast State Technical Community College
P.O. Box 246
**Blountville 37617**

Pellissippi State Technical Community College
P.O. Box 22990
**Knoxville 37933-0990**

Tennessee Technology Center at Athens
1635 Vo Tech Dr., P.O. Box 848
**Athens 37371-0848**

Tennessee Technology Center at Crump
Hwy. 64 W, P.O. Box 89
**Crump 38327**

Tennessee Technology Center at Hartsville
Hwy. 25, 716 McMurry Blvd.
**Hartsville 37074**

Tennessee Technology Center at Hohenwald
813 West Main
**Hohenwald 38462-2201**

Tennessee Technology Center at Jacksboro
Rte. 1
**Jacksboro 37757**

Tennessee Technology Center at Jackson
2468 Westover Rd.
**Jackson 38301**

Tennessee Technology Center at Knoxville
1100 Liberty St.
**Knoxville 37919**

Tennessee Technology Center at Livingston
740 High Tech Dr.
**Livingston 38570**

Tennessee Technology Center at McKenzie
16940 905 Highland Dr., P.O. Box 427
**McKenzie 38201**

Tennessee Technology Center at McMinnville
241 Vo Tech Dr.
**McMinnville 37110**

Tennessee Technology Center at Memphis
550 Alabama Ave.
**Memphis 38105-3604**

Tennessee Technology Center at Morristown
821 West Louise Ave.
**Morristown 37813**

Tennessee Technology Center at Nashville
100 White Bridge Rd.
**Nashville 37209**

Tennessee Technology Center at Newbern
340 Washington St.
**Newbern 38059**

Tennessee Technology Center at Shelbyville
1405 Madison St.
**Shelbyville 37160**

## TEXAS

Alvin Community College
3110 Mustang Rd.
**Alvin 77511**

Amari Institute, Inc.
4111 Directors Row, Ste. 110
**Houston 77092**

Amarillo College
P.O. Box 447
**Amarillo 79178**

American Commercial College
2007 34th St.
**Lubbock 79411**

American Trades Institute
6627 Maple Ave.
**Dallas 75235**

Angelina College
P.O. Box 1768
**Lufkin 75902-1768**

ATI Career Training Center
2351 West Northwest Hwy., Ste. 1301
**Dallas 75220**

Austin Community College
5930 Middle Fiskville Rd.
**Austin 78752**

Bee County College
3800 Charco Rd.
**Beeville 78102**

Brazosport College
500 College Dr.
**Lake Jackson 77566**

Central Texas College
P.O. Box 1800
**Killeen 76540-1800**

Eastfield College
3737 Motley Dr.
**Mesquite 75150**

El Paso Community College
P.O. Box 20500
**El Paso 79998**

Houston Community College System
22 Waugh Dr., P.O. Box 7849
**Houston 77270-7849**

Lamar University, Beaumont
4400 MLK, P.O. Box 10001
**Beaumont 77710**

Lee College
200 Lee Dr.
**Baytown 77520-4703**

Letourneau University
2100 South Mobberly Ave.
**Longview 75602**

Mountain View College
4849 West Illinois
**Dallas 75211**

North Central Texas College
1525 West California
**Gainesville 76240**

North Harris Montgomery Community College District
250 North Sam Houston Pkwy. E, Ste. 300
**Houston 77060**

Paris Junior College
2400 Clarksville St.
**Paris 75460**

San Antonio College
1300 San Pedro Ave.
**San Antonio 78284**

San Jacinto College, Central Campus
8060 Spencer Hwy.
**Pasadena 77505**

San Jacinto College, North Campus
5800 Uvalde
**Houston 77049**

San Jacinto College, South Campus
13735 Beamer Rd.
**Houston 77089-6009**

South Plains College
1401 College Ave.
**Levelland 79336**

Temple College
2600 South First St.
**Temple 76504-7435**

Texas State Technical College, Harlingen Campus
2424 Boxwood
**Harlingen 78550-3697**

Texas State Technical College, Sweetwater Campus
300 College Dr.
**Sweetwater 79556**

Texas State Technical College, Waco Campus
3801 Campus Dr.
**Waco 76705**

Trinity Valley Community College
500 South Prairieville
**Athens 75751**

Tyler Junior College
1327 South Baxter Ave.
**Tyler 75711**

Wharton County Junior College
911 Boling Hwy.
**Wharton 77488**

## UTAH

Bridgerland Applied Technology Center
1301 North 600 W
**Logan 84321**

Davis Applied Technology Center
550 East 300 S
**Kaysville 84037**

Dixie College
225 South 700 E
**Saint George 84770**

ITT Technical Institute
920 West Levoy Dr.
**Murray 84123**

Odgen-Weber Applied Technology Center
559 East AVC Ln.
**Ogden 84404-6704**

Salt Lake Community College
P.O. Box 30808
**Salt Lake City 84130**

Utah Valley State College
800 West 1200 S
**Orem 84058**

Weber State University
3750 Harrison Blvd.
**Ogden 84408**

## WASHINGTON

Big Bend Community College
7662 Chanute St.
**Moses Lake 98837**

Edmonds Community College
20000 68th Ave. W
**Lynnwood 98036**

Everett Community College
801 Wetmore Ave.
**Everett 98201**

Green River Community College
12401 SE 320th St.
**Auburn 98092**

Highline Community College
P.O. Box 98000
**Des Moines 98198-9800**

ITT Technical Institute
12720 Gateway Dr., Ste. 100
**Seattle 98168**

ITT Technical Institute
North 1050 Argonne Rd.
**Spokane 99212**

Lake Washington Technical College
11605 132nd Ave. NE
**Kirkland 98034**

Seattle Community College, North Campus
9600 College Way N
**Seattle 98103**

Seattle Community College, South Campus
6000 16th Ave. SW
**Seattle 98106**

South Puget Sound Community College
2011 Mottman Rd. SW
**Olympia 98512**

### WEST VIRGINIA

Ben Franklin Career Center
500 28th St.
**Dunbar 25064**

Boone County Career & Technical Center
HC 81, P.O. Box 50B
**Danville 25053**

Cabell County Vocational Technical Center
1035 Norway Ave.
**Huntington 25705**

West Virginia Institute of Technology
**Montgomery 25136**

### WISCONSIN

Chippewa Valley Technical College
620 West Clairemont Ave.
**Eau Claire 54701**

Milwaukee Area Technical College
700 West State St.
**Milwaukee 53233-1443**

Northeast Wisconsin Technical College
2740 West Mason St., P.O. Box 19042
**Green Bay 54307-9042**

Waukesha County Technical College
800 Main St.
**Pewaukee 53072**

Wisconsin Indianhead Technical College
505 Pine Ridge Dr.
**Shell Lake 54871**

### WYOMING

Casper College
125 College Dr.
**Casper 82601**

## Electrical and Electromechanical Technology

### ALABAMA

Community College of the Air Force
130 West Maxwell Blvd.
**Montgomery 36112-6613**

Jefferson State Community College
2601 Carson Rd.
**Birmingham 35215-3098**

J F Drake State Technical College
3421 Meridian St. N
**Huntsville 35811**

John C Calhoun State Community College
Hwy. 31 N
**Decatur 35602**

### ALASKA

University of Alaska, Anchorage
3211 Providence Dr.
**Anchorage 99508**

### ARIZONA

Arizona Western College
P.O. Box 929
**Yuma 85366**

Central Arizona College
8470 North Overfield Rd.
**Coolidge 85228-9778**

Cochise College
4190 West Hwy. 80
**Douglas 85607-9724**

Devry Institute of Technology
2149 West Dunlap Ave.
**Phoenix 85021**

Gateway Community College
108 North 40th St.
**Phoenix 85034**

Glendale Community College
6000 West Olive Ave.
**Glendale 85302**

ITT Technical Institute
4837 East McDowell Rd.
**Phoenix 85008-4292**

ITT Technical Institute
1840 East Benson Hwy.
**Tucson 85714**

Mesa Community College
1833 West Southern Ave.
**Mesa 85202**

Pima Community College
2202 West Anklam Rd.
**Tucson 85709-0001**

Refrigeration School
4210 East Washington
**Phoenix 85034**

### ARKANSAS

Arkansas State University, Beebe Branch
P.O. Drawer H
**Beebe 72012**

Arkansas Valley Technical Institute
P.O. Box 506, Hwy. 23 N
**Ozark 72949**

Foothills Technical Institute
1800 East Moore St.
**Searcy 72143**

Garland County Community College
101 College Dr.
**Hot Springs 71913**

Mississippi County Community College
P.O. Box 1109
**Blytheville 72316-1109**

Northwest Technical Institute
709 South Old Missouri Rd.
**Springdale 72764**

Ouachita Technical College
One College Cir.
**Malvern 72104**

Pulaski Technical College
3000 West Scenic Dr.
**North Little Rock 72118**

Quapaw Technical Institute
200 Mid America Blvd.
**Hot Springs 71913**

Southeast Arkansas Technical College
1900 Hazel
**Pine Bluff 71603**

Southern Arkansas University Technical
SAU Technical Station
**Camden 71701**

Westark Community College
P.O. Box 3649
**Fort Smith 72913**

### CALIFORNIA

Butte College
3536 Butte Campus Dr.
**Oroville 95965**

Cerro Coso Community College
3000 College Heights Blvd.
**Ridgecrest 93555-7777**

Chaffey Community College
5885 Haven Ave.
**Rancho Cucamonga 91737-3002**

City College of San Francisco
50 Phelan Ave.
**San Francisco 94112**

College of San Mateo
1700 West Hillsdale Blvd.
**San Mateo 94402**

College of the Sequoias
915 South Mooney Blvd.
**Visalia 93277**

Contra Costa College
2600 Mission Bell Dr.
**San Pablo 94806**

Cosumnes River College
8401 Center Pkwy.
**Sacramento 95823-5799**

De Anza College
21250 Stevens Creek Blvd.
**Cupertino 95014**

Diablo Valley College
321 Golf Club Rd.
**Pleasant Hill 94523**

East Los Angeles Skill Center
3921 Selig Pl.
**Los Angeles 90031**

El Camino College
16007 Crenshaw Blvd.
**Torrance 90506**

Foothill College
12345 El Monte Rd.
**Los Altos Hills 94022**

Foundation College
3478 Buskirk Ave., Ste. 100
**Pleasant Hill 94523**

Fullerton College
321 East Chapman Ave.
**Fullerton 92832-2095**

Heald College School of Technology, Martinez
2860 Howe Rd.
**Martinez 94553**

ITT Technical Institute
2035 East 223rd
**Carson 90810**

ITT Technical Institute
630 East Brier, Ste. 150
**San Bernardino 92408-2800**

ITT Technical Institute
9680 Granite Ridge Dr.
**San Diego 92123**

Long Beach City College
4901 East Carson St.
**Long Beach 90808**

Los Angeles Trade Technical College
400 West Washington Blvd.
**Los Angeles 90015-4181**

Marin Regional Occupational Program
P.O. Box 4925
**San Rafael 94913**

Orange Coast College
2701 Fairview Rd.
**Costa Mesa 92626**

Pasadena City College
1570 East Colorado Blvd.
**Pasadena 91106**

Rancho Santiago Community College District
1530 West 17th St.
**Santa Ana 92706**

San Diego City College
1313 12th Ave.
**San Diego 92101**

San Diego Mesa College
7250 Mesa College Dr.
**San Diego 92111-4998**

Santa Rosa Junior College
1501 Mendocino Ave.
**Santa Rosa 95401-4395**

Sawyer College, A Corinthian School
8475 Jackson Rd.
**Sacramento 95826**

School of Communications Electronics
184 Second St.
**San Francisco 94105**

Sierra College
5000 Rocklin Rd.
**Rocklin 95677**

Southwestern College
900 Otay Lakes Rd.
**Chula Vista 91910**

Travel and Trade Career Institute
3635 Atlantic Ave.
**Long Beach 90807**

Vallecitos CET, Inc.
597 C St.
**Hayward 94541**

Victor Valley College
18422 Bear Valley Rd.
**Victorville 92392-9699**

### COLORADO

Aims Community College
P.O. Box 69
**Greeley 80632**

Arapahoe Community College
2500 West College Dr.
**Littleton 80160-9002**

Community College of Aurora
16000 East Centre Tech Pkwy.
**Aurora 80011-9036**

Community College of Denver
P.O. Box 173363
**Denver 80217**

Denver Institute of Technology
7350 North Broadway
**Denver 80221**

Denver Technical College
925 South Niagara St.
**Denver 80224**

Denver Technical College at Colorado Springs
225 South Union Blvd.
**Colorado Springs 80910**

Front Range Community College
3645 West 112th Ave.
**Westminster 80030**

ITT Technical Institute
2121 South Blackhawk St., Southeast Commons
**Aurora 80014**

Mesa State College
P.O. Box 2647
**Grand Junction 81502**

Pikes Peak Community College
5675 South Academy Blvd.
**Colorado Springs 80906-5498**

Pueblo Community College
900 West Orman Ave.
**Pueblo 81004**

Red Rocks Community College
13300 West Sixth Ave.
**Lakewood 80228**

T H Pickens Technical Center
500 Airport Blvd.
**Aurora 80011**

Trinidad State Junior College
600 Prospect St.
**Trinidad 81082**

## CONNECTICUT

Porter and Chester Institute
138 Weymouth Rd.
**Enfield 06082**

Porter and Chester Institute
670 Lordship Blvd.
**Stratford 06497**

Porter and Chester Institute
320 Sylvan Lake Rd.
**Watertown 06779-1400**

Porter and Chester Institute
125 Silas Deane Hwy.
**Wethersfield 06109**

## DELAWARE

Delaware Technical and Community College, Terry Campus
1832 North Dupont Pkwy.
**Dover 19901**

Delaware Technical and Community College, Stanton-Wilmington Campus
400 Stanton-Christiana Rd.
**Newark 19702**

## DISTRICT OF COLUMBIA

University of the District of Columbia
4200 Connecticut Ave. NW
**Washington 20008**

## FLORIDA

ATI Career Training Center
2880 NW 62nd St.
**Fort Lauderdale 33309**

Brevard Community College
1519 Clearlake Rd.
**Cocoa 32922**

Central Florida Community College
3001 SW College Rd.
**Ocala 34474**

Chipola Junior College
3094 Indian Cir.
**Marianna 32446**

Edison Community College
8099 College Pkwy. SW
**Fort Myers 33906-6210**

Florida Technical College
1819 North Semoran Blvd.
**Orlando 32807**

Florida Technical College of Jacksonville, Inc.
8711 Lone Star Rd.
**Jacksonville 32211**

Gulf Coast Community College
5230 West Hwy. 98
**Panama City 32401**

Hillsborough Community College
P.O. Box 31127
**Tampa 33631-3127**

Indian River Community College
3209 Virginia Ave.
**Fort Pierce 34981**

ITT Technical Institute
4809 Memorial Hwy.
**Tampa 33634-7515**

Manatee Community College
5840 26th St. W
**Bradenton 34207**

Miami-Dade Community College
300 NE Second Ave.
**Miami 33132**

Okaloosa-Walton Community College
100 College Blvd.
**Niceville 32578**

Palm Beach Community College
4200 Congress Ave.
**Lake Worth 33461**

Pensacola Junior College
1000 College Blvd.
**Pensacola 32504**

Saint Petersburg Junior College
8580 66 St. N
**Pinellas Park 34665**

Santa Fe Community College
3000 NW 83rd St.
**Gainesville 32606**

Seminole Community College
100 Weldon Blvd.
**Sanford 32773-6199**

Southern College
900 Arkadelphia Rd.
**Birmingham 35254**

Valencia Community College
P.O. Box 3028
**Orlando 32802**

Withlacoochee Technical Institute
1201 West Main St.
**Inverness 32650**

## GEORGIA

Augusta Technical Institute
3116 Deans Bridge Rd.
**Augusta 30906**

Bainbridge College
2500 East Shotwell St.
**Bainbridge 31717**

Chattahoochee Technical Institute
980 South Cobb Dr.
**Marietta 30060-3398**

Clayton College and State University
5900 Lee St.
**Morrow 30260**

Dalton College
213 North College Dr.
**Dalton 30720**

Dekalb Technical Institute
495 North Indian Creek Dr.
**Clarkston 30021**

Devry Institute of Technology
250 North Arcadia
**Decatur 30030**

Floyd College
P.O. Box 1864
**Rome 30162-1864**

Savannah Technical Institute
5717 White Bluff Rd.
**Savannah 31405-5594**

## HAWAII

Electronics Institute
1270 Queen Emma St., Rm. 108
**Honolulu 96813**

Honolulu Community College
874 Dillingham Blvd.
**Honolulu 96817**

## IDAHO

Eastern Idaho Technical College
1600 South 2500 E
**Idaho Falls 83404**

Idaho State University
741 South Seventh Ave.
**Pocatello 83209**

ITT Technical Institute
12302 Explorer Dr.
**Boise 83713**

Ricks College
**Rexburg 83460-4107**

## ILLINOIS

Carl Sandburg College
2232 South Lake Storey Rd.
**Galesburg 61401**

College of Du Page
425 22nd St.
**Glen Ellyn 60137-6599**

College of Lake County
19351 West Washington St.
**Grayslake 60030-1198**

Devry Institute of Technology
1221 North Swift Rd.
**Addison 60101**

Devry Institute of Technology
3300 North Campbell Ave.
**Chicago 60618**

Illinois Central College
One College Dr.
**East Peoria 61635-0001**

Illinois Eastern Community Colleges, Olney Central College
305 North West St.
**Olney 62450**

ITT Technical Institute
375 West Higgins Rd.
**Hoffman Estates 60195**

John A Logan College
700 Logan College Rd.
**Carterville 62918**

Joliet Junior College
1215 Houbolt Rd.
**Joliet 60431**

Kankakee Community College
P.O. Box 888
**Kankakee 60901**

Kaskaskia College
27210 College Rd.
**Centralia 62801**

Lake Land College
5001 Lake Land Blvd.
**Mattoon 61938**

Lincoln Land Community College
Shepherd Rd.
**Springfield 62194-9256**

McHenry County College
8900 U.S. Hwy. 14
**Crystal Lake 60012**

Moraine Valley Community College
10900 South 88th Ave.
**Palos Hills 60465-0937**

Oakton Community College
1600 East Golf Rd.
**Des Plaines 60016**

Rock Valley College
3301 North Mulford Rd.
**Rockford 61114**

Sauk Valley Community College
173 Illinois Rte. 2
**Dixon 61021**

South Suburban College
15800 South State St.
**South Holland 60473**

Southern Illinois University, Carbondale
Faner Hall 2179
**Carbondale 62901-4512**

Taylor Business Institute
200 North Michigan Ave., Ste. 301
**Chicago 60601**

Triton College
2000 Fifth Ave.
**River Grove 60171**

Waubonsee Community College
Rte. 47 at Harter Rd.
**Sugar Grove 60554-0901**

William Rainey Harper College
1200 West Algonquin Rd.
**Palatine 60067-7398**

Zarem Golde ORT Technical Institute
3050 West Touhy
**Chicago 60645**

## INDIANA

Indiana University, Purdue University at Fort Wayne
2101 Coliseum Blvd. E
**Fort Wayne 46805**

Indiana University, Purdue University at Indianapolis
355 North Lansing
**Indianapolis 46202**

ITT Technical Institute
4919 Coldwater Rd.
**Fort Wayne 46825**

Ivy Tech State College, Central Indiana
One West 26th St.
**Indianapolis 46206-1763**

Ivy Tech State College, Columbus
4475 Central Ave.
**Columbus 47203**

Ivy Tech State College, East Central
4301 South Cowan Rd., P.O. Box 3100
**Muncie 47302**

Ivy Tech State College, Kokomo
1815 East Morgan St.
**Kokomo 46901**

Ivy Tech State College, Lafayette
3101 South Creasy Ln., P.O. Box 6299
**Lafayette 47903**

Ivy Tech State College, North Central
1534 West Sample St.
**South Bend 46619**

Ivy Tech State College, Northeast
3800 North Anthony Blvd.
**Fort Wayne 46805**

Ivy Tech State College, Northwest
1440 East 35th Ave.
**Gary 46409**

Ivy Tech State College, South Central
8204 Hwy. 311
**Sellersburg 47172**

Ivy Tech State College, Southeast
590 Ivy Tech Dr.
**Madison 47250**

Ivy Tech State College, Southwest
3501 First Ave.
**Evansville 47710**

Ivy Tech State College, Wabash Valley
7999 U.S. Hwy. 41
**Terre Haute 47802-4898**

Purdue University, Calumet Campus
2233 171st St.
**Hammond 46323**

Purdue University, Main Campus
1076 Freehafer Hall
**West Lafayette 47907-1076**

Purdue University, North Central Campus
1401 South U.S. Hwy. 421
**Westville 46391**

Vincennes University
1002 North First St.
**Vincennes 47591**

## IOWA

Des Moines Community College
2006 Ankeny Blvd.
**Ankeny 50021**

Eastern Iowa Community College District
306 West River Dr.
**Davenport 52801-1221**

Hamilton Technical College
1011 East 53rd St.
**Davenport 52807**

Hawkeye Institute of Technology
1501 East Orange Rd.
**Waterloo 50704**

Indian Hills Community College
525 Grandview
**Ottumwa 52501**

Iowa Central Community College
330 Ave. M
**Fort Dodge 50501**

Iowa Western Community College
2700 College Rd., P.O. Box 4C
**Council Bluffs 51502**

Kirkwood Community College
P.O. Box 2068
**Cedar Rapids 52406**

North Iowa Area Community College
500 College Dr.
**Mason City 50401**

Northeast Iowa Community College
Hwy. 150 S, P.O. Box 400
**Calmar 52132-0400**

Northwest Iowa Community College
603 West Park St.
**Sheldon 51201**

Western Iowa Technical Community College
4647 Stone Ave., P.O. Box 5199
**Sioux City 51102-5199**

### KANSAS

Hesston College
Box 3000
**Hesston 67062**

Kansas State University
Anderson Hall
**Manhattan 66506**

Pittsburg State University
1701 South Broadway
**Pittsburg 66762**

Topeka Technical College
1620 Northwest Gage
**Topeka 66618**

Washburn University of Topeka
1700 College Ave.
**Topeka 66621**

Wichita Technical Institute
942 South West St.
**Wichita 67213-1681**

### KENTUCKY

Institute of Electronic Technology
P.O. Box 8252
**Paducah 42001**

Jefferson Community College
109 East Broadway
**Louisville 40202**

Kentucky Advanced Technology Institute
1127 Morgantown Rd.
**Bowling Green 42101-9202**

Kentucky Technical, Hazard Regional Technology Center
101 Vo-Tech Dr.
**Hazard 41701**

Kentucky Technical, Madisonville Regional Technology Center
150 School Ave.
**Madisonville 42431**

Lexington Community College
Cooper Dr.
**Lexington 40506**

Maysville Community College
**Maysville 41056**

Morehead State University
University Blvd.
**Morehead 40351**

University of Louisville
South Third St.
**Louisville 40292-0001**

### LOUISIANA

Delgado Community College
501 City Park Ave.
**New Orleans 70119**

Grantham College of Engineering
34641 Grantham College Rd.
**Slidell 70460**

McNeese State University
4100 Ryan St.
**Lake Charles 70609**

Remington College
303 Rue Louis XIV
**Lafayette 70508**

RETS Training Center
3321 Hessmer Ave.
**Metairie 70002**

### MAINE

Central Maine Technical College
1250 Turner St.
**Auburn 04210**

Eastern Maine Technical College
354 Hogan Rd.
**Bangor 04401**

Kennebec Valley Technical College
92 Western Ave.
**Fairfield 04937-1367**

Northern Maine Technical College
33 Edgemont Dr.
**Presque Isle 04769**

Southern Maine Technical College
Fort Rd.
**South Portland 04106**

### MARYLAND

Allegany College of Maryland
12401 Willowbrook Rd.
**Cumberland 21502**

Anne Arundel Community College
101 College Pkwy.
**Arnold 21012**

Baltimore City Community College
2901 Liberty Heights Ave.
**Baltimore 21215**

Capitol College
11301 Springfield Rd.
**Laurel 20708**

Catonsville Community College
800 South Rolling Rd.
**Catonsville 21228**

Cecil Community College
1000 North East Rd.
**North East 21901-1999**

Essex Community College
7201 Rossville Blvd.
**Baltimore 21237**

Frederick Community College
7932 Opossumtown Pk.
**Frederick 21702**

Hagerstown Junior College
11400 Robinwood Dr.
**Hagerstown 21742-6590**

Harford Community College
401 Thomas Run Rd.
**Bel Air 21015**

Maryland Drafting Institute
2045 University Blvd.
**Langley Park 20783**

Montgomery College of Germantown
20200 Observation Dr.
**Germantown 20874**

Montgomery College of Rockville
51 Mannakee St.
**Rockville 20850**

Prince Georges Community College
301 Largo Rd.
**Largo 20774-2199**

Radio Electronic Television Schools, Inc.
1520 South Caton Ave.
**Baltimore 21227-1063**

Tesst Technology Institute
5122 Baltimore Ave.
**Hyattsville 20781**

### MASSACHUSETTS

Berkshire Community College
1350 West St.
**Pittsfield 01201-5786**

Bristol Community College
777 Elsbree St.
**Fall River 02720**

Bunker Hill Community College
250 New Rutherford Ave.
**Boston 02129**

Franklin Institute of Boston
41 Berkeley St.
**Boston 02116**

ITT Technical Institute
1671 Worcester Rd.
**Framingham 01701-5404**

Massasoit Community College
One Massasoit Blvd.
**Brockton 02402**

Middlesex Community College
Springs Rd.
**Bedford 01730**

Mount Wachusett Community College
444 Green St.
**Gardner 01440**

North Shore Community College
One Ferncroft Rd.
**Danvers 01923**

Northeast Institute of Industrial Technology
41 Phillips St.
**Boston 02114**

Northeastern University
360 Huntington Ave.
**Boston 02115**

Northern Essex Community College
Elliott Way
**Haverhill 01830-2399**

Quinsigamond Community College
670 West Boylston St.
**Worcester 01606**

RETS Electronic School
965 Commonwealth Ave.
**Boston 02215**

Southeastern Technical Institute
250 Foundry St.
**South Easton 02375**

Springfield Technical Community College
1 Armory Square
**Springfield 01105**

University of Massachusetts at Lowell
One University Ave.
**Lowell 01854**

Wentworth Institute of Technology
550 Huntington Ave.
**Boston 02115**

Worcester Technical Institute
251 Belmont St.
**Worcester 01605**

### MICHIGAN

Baker College of Flint
G1050 West Bristol Rd.
**Flint 48507**

Delta College
**University Center 48710**

Ferris State University
901 South State St.
**Big Rapids 49307**

Glen Oaks Community College
62249 Shimmel Rd.
**Centreville 49032**

Grand Rapids Community College
143 Bostwick Ave. NE
**Grand Rapids 49503-3295**

Great Lakes Junior College of Business
310 South Washington Ave.
**Saginaw 48607**

Henry Ford Community College
5101 Evergreen Rd.
**Dearborn 48128**

ITT Technical Institute
1522 East Big Beaver Rd.
**Troy 48083**

Jackson Community College
2111 Emmons Rd.
**Jackson 49201-8399**

Kalamazoo Valley Community College
6767 West O Ave.
**Kalamazoo 49009**

Kellogg Community College
450 North Ave.
**Battle Creek 49017**

Lake Michigan College
2755 East Napier Ave.
**Benton Harbor 49022-8099**

Lake Superior State University
650 West Easterday Ave.
**Sault Sainte Marie 49783**

Lansing Community College
419 North Capitol Ave.
**Lansing 48901-7210**

Lawrence Technological University
21000 West Ten Mile Rd.
**Southfield 48075-1058**

Macomb Community College
14500 Twelve Mile Rd.
**Warren 48093-3896**

Michigan Technological University
1400 Townsend Dr.
**Houghton 49931-1295**

Monroe County Community College
1555 South Raisinville Rd.
**Monroe 48161**

Mott Community College
1401 East Court St.
**Flint 48503**

Muskegon Community College
221 South Quarterline Rd.
**Muskegon 49442**

Northwestern Michigan College
1701 East Front St.
**Traverse City 49686**

Oakland Community College
2480 Opdyke Rd.
**Bloomfield Hills 48304-2266**

Schoolcraft College
18600 Haggerty Rd.
**Livonia 48152**

Siena Heights College
1247 Siena Heights Dr.
**Adrian 49221**

Washtenaw Community College
P.O. Drawer 1
**Ann Arbor 48106-1610**

Wayne County Community College
801 West Fort St.
**Detroit 48226**

West Shore Community College
3000 North Stiles Rd.
**Scottville 49454**

### MINNESOTA

Hennepin Technical College
9000 Brooklyn Blvd.
**Brooklyn Park 55445**

NEI College of Technology
825 41st Ave. NE
**Columbia Heights 55421-9990**

Red Wing/Winona Technical College, Winona Campus
1250 Homer Rd., P.O. Box 409
**Winona 55987**

Ridgewater College, A Communication and Technical College, Wilmar
P.O. Box 1097
**Willmar 56201**

## MISSISSIPPI

East Central Community College
**Decatur 39327**

East Mississippi Community College
P.O. Box 158
**Scooba 39358**

Hinds Community College, Raymond Campus
**Raymond 39154**

Itawamba Community College
602 West Hill St.
**Fulton 38843**

Meridian Community College
910 Hwy. 19 N
**Meridian 39307**

Mississippi Gulf Coast Community College
Central Office, P.O. Box 67
**Perkinston 39573**

Northeast Mississippi Community College
Cunningham Blvd.
**Booneville 38829**

Pearl River Community College
Station A
**Poplarville 39470**

## MISSOURI

Devry Institute of Technology
11224 Holmes Rd.
**Kansas City 64131**

Drury College
900 North Benton Ave.
**Springfield 65802**

Electronics Institute
15329 Kensington Ave.
**Kansas City 64147**

ITT Technical Institute
13505 Lakefront Dr.
**Earth City 63045**

Jefferson College
1000 Viking Dr.
**Hillsboro 63050**

Linn Technical College
One Technology Dr.
**Linn 65051**

Longview Community College
500 Longview Rd.
**Lees Summit 64081**

Maple Woods Community College
2601 NE Barry Rd.
**Kansas City 64156**

Penn Valley Community College
3201 SW Trafficway
**Kansas City 64111**

Saint Louis Community College, Forest Park
5600 Oakland Ave.
**Saint Louis 63110**

Vatterott College
3925 Industrial Dr.
**Saint Ann 63074**

## MONTANA

May Technical College
1306 Central Ave.
**Billings 59103**

May Technical College, Great Falls
1807 Third St. NW
**Great Falls 59404**

Miles Community College
2715 Dickinson
**Miles City 59301**

## NEBRASKA

Metropolitan Community College Area
5300 North 30th St.
**Omaha 68111**

## NEVADA

Community College of Southern Nevada
3200 East Cheyenne Ave.
**Las Vegas 89030**

Western Nevada Community College
2201 West College Pkwy.
**Carson City 89703**

## NEW HAMPSHIRE

New Hampshire Community Technical College at Nashua
505 Amherst St.
**Nashua 03061-2052**

New Hampshire Technical Institute
11 Institute Dr.
**Concord 03301**

## NEW JERSEY

Atlantic Community College
5100 Black Horse Pike
**Mays Landing 08330-2699**

Brookdale Community College
765 Newman Springs Rd.
**Lincroft 07738-1599**

Burlington County College
Rte. 530
**Pemberton 08068**

Camden County College
P.O. Box 200
**Blackwood 08012**

County College of Morris
214 Center Grove Rd.
**Randolph 07869**

Devry Technical Institute
479 Green St.
**Woodbridge 07095**

Essex County College
303 University Ave.
**Newark 07102**

Mercer County Community College
1200 Old Trenton Rd.
**Trenton 08690**

Metropolitan Technical Institute
11 Daniel Rd.
**Fairfield 07004**

Middlesex County College
155 Mill Rd.
**Edison 08818-3050**

Ocean County College
College Dr.
**Toms River 08753**

Pennco Technical
P.O. Box 1427, Erial Rd.
**Blackwood 08012**

RETS Institute
103 Park Ave.
**Nutley 07110**

Salem Community College
460 Hollywood Ave.
**Carneys Point 08069**

Star Technical Institute
1386 South Delsea Dr.
**Vineland 08360**

Thomas A Edison State College
101 West State St.
**Trenton 08608-1176**

Union County College
1033 Springfield Ave.
**Cranford 07016**

## NEW MEXICO

Albuquerque Technical Vocational Institute
525 Buena Vista SE
**Albuquerque 87106**

Clovis Community College
417 Schepps Blvd.
**Clovis 88101**

Eastern New Mexico University, Roswell Campus
52 University Blvd., Admin. Center
**Roswell 88202**

ITT Technical Institute
5100 Masthead NE
**Albuquerque 87109**

Luna Vocational Technical Institute
P.O. Drawer K
**Las Vegas 87701**

Northern New Mexico Community College
1002 North Onate St.
**Espanola 87532**

## NEW YORK

Broome Community College
P.O. Box 1017
**Binghamton 13902**

Bryant and Stratton Business Institute, Buffalo
1028 Main St.
**Buffalo 14202**

Bryant and Stratton Business Institute, Rochester
82 Saint Paul St.
**Rochester 14604**

Bryant and Stratton Business Institute, Syracuse
953 James St.
**Syracuse 13203**

Cayuga County Community College
Franklin St.
**Auburn 13021**

Corning Community College
Spencer Hill
**Corning 14830**

CUNY Bronx Community College
West 181st St. & University Ave.
**Bronx 10453**

CUNY New York City Technical College
300 Jay St.
**Brooklyn 11201**

CUNY Queensborough Community College
56th Ave. & Springfield Blvd.
**New York 11364**

Dutchess Community College
53 Pendell Rd.
**Poughkeepsie 12601**

Erie Community College, North Campus
Main St. and Youngs Rd.
**Williamsville 14221**

Hudson Valley Community College
80 Vandenburgh Ave.
**Troy 12180**

Island Drafting and Technical Institute
128 Broadway Rte. 110
**Amityville 11701**

Jamestown Community College
525 Falconer St.
**Jamestown 14701**

Mohawk Valley Community College, Utica Branch
1101 Sherman Dr.
**Utica 13501**

Monroe Community College
1000 East Henrietta Rd.
**Rochester 14623**

Nassau Community College
One Education Dr.
**Garden City 11530**

New York Institute of Technology, Old Westbury Campus
P.O. Box 8000
**Old Westbury 11568-8000**

Niagara County Community College
3111 Saunders Settlement Rd.
**Sanborn 14132**

Onondaga Community College
4941 Onondaga Rd.
**Syracuse 13215**

Orange County Community College
115 South St.
**Middletown 10940**

Rochester Institute of Technology
One Lamb Memorial Dr.
**Rochester 14623-5603**

Rockland Community College
145 College Rd.
**Suffern 10901**

Schenectady County Community College
Washington Ave.
**Schenectady 12305**

Suburban Technical School
175 Fulton Ave.
**Hempstead 11550**

Suffolk County Community College, Ammerman Campus
533 College Rd.
**Selden 11784**

SUNY College of Technology & Agriculture at Morrisville
**Morrisville 13408**

SUNY College of Technology at Alfred
**Alfred 14802**

SUNY College of Technology at Canton
Cornell Drive
**Canton 13617**

SUNY College of Technology at Delhi
**Delhi 13753**

SUNY College of Technology at Farmingdale
Melville Rd.
**Farmingdale 11735-1021**

SUNY Westchester Commmunity College
75 Grasslands Rd.
**Valhalla 10595**

Technical Career Institutes
320 West 31st St.
**New York 10001**

Tompkins-Cortland Community College
170 North St.
**Dryden 13053**

## NORTH CAROLINA

Alamance Community College
P.O. Box 8000
**Graham 27253**

Asheville Buncombe Technical Community College
340 Victoria Rd.
**Asheville 28801**

Beaufort County Community College
P.O. Box 1069
**Washington 27889**

Blue Ridge Community College
College Dr.
**Flat Rock 28731-9624**

Brunswick Community College
P.O. Box 30
**Supply 28462**

Cape Fear Community College
411 North Front St.
**Wilmington 28401**

Catawba Valley Community College
2550 Hwy. 70 SE
**Hickory 28602-0699**

Central Carolina Community College
1105 Kelly Dr.
**Sanford 27330**

Central Piedmont Community College
P.O. Box 35009
**Charlotte 28235-5009**

Cleveland Community College
137 South Post Rd.
**Shelby 28152**

Craven Community College
800 College Ct.
**New Bern 28562**

Davidson County Community College
297 Davidson Community College Rd.
**Lexington 27292**

Durham Technical Community College
1637 Lawson St.
**Durham 27703**

Fayetteville Technical Community College
2201 Hull Rd.
**Fayetteville 28303-0236**

Forsyth Technical Community College
2100 Silas Creek Pkwy.
**Winston Salem 27103**

Guilford Technical Community College
Box 309
**Jamestown 27282**

Halifax Community College
P.O. Drawer 809
**Weldon 27890**

Haywood Community College
Freedlander Dr.
**Clyde 28721**

Isothermal Community College
P.O. Box 804
**Spindale 28160**

Johnston Community College
P.O. Box 2350
**Smithfield 27577-2350**

Lenoir Community College
P.O. Box 188
**Kinston 28502-0188**

Mayland Community College
P.O. Box 547
**Spruce Pine 28777**

Mitchell Community College
500 West Broad
**Statesville 28677**

Pitt Community College
Hwy. 11 South, P.O. Drawer 7007
**Greenville 27835-7007**

Rockingham Community College
P.O. Box 38, Hwy. 65 West County Home Rd.
**Wentworth 27375-0038**

Rowan-Cabarrus Community College
Box 1595
**Salisbury 28145-1595**

Southeastern Community College
4564 Chadburn Hwy.
**Whiteville 28472**

Surry Community College
P.O. Box 304
**Dobson 27017-0304**

Vance-Granville Community College
State Rd. 1126, P.O. Box 917
**Henderson 27536**

Wake Technical Community College
9101 Fayetteville Rd.
**Raleigh 27603-5696**

Wayne Community College
3000 Wayne Memorial Dr.
**Goldsboro 27533-8002**

Wilkes Community College
Collegiate Dr.
**Wilkesboro 28697**

### NORTH DAKOTA

Bismarck State College
P.O. Box 5587
**Bismarck 58506-5587**

North Dakota State College of Science
800 North Sixth St.
**Wahpeton 58076**

### OHIO

Central Ohio Technical College
1179 University Dr.
**Newark 43055-1767**

Cincinnati State Technical and Community College
3520 Central Pkwy.
**Cincinnati 45223**

Clark State Community College
570 East Leffel Ln.
**Springfield 45505**

Columbus State Community College
550 East Spring St.
**Columbus 43216**

Cuyahoga Community College District
700 Carnegie Ave.
**Cleveland 44115-2878**

Devry Institute of Technology
1350 Alum Creek Dr.
**Columbus 43209-2764**

Edison State Community College
1973 Edison Dr.
**Piqua 45356**

ETI Technical College
2076 Youngstown Warren Rd.
**Niles 44446-4398**

ETI Technical College
1320 West Maple St. NW
**North Canton 44720**

ITT Technical Institute
North Meridian Rd.
**Youngstown 44509**

Lakeland Community College
7700 Clocktower Dr.
**Kirtland 44094-5198**

Lima Technical College
4240 Campus Dr.
**Lima 45804**

Lorain County Community College
1005 Abbe Rd. N
**Elyria 44035**

North Central Technical College
2441 Kenwood Cir., P.O. Box 698
**Mansfield 44901**

Northwest State Community College
22-600 South Rte. 34
**Archbold 43502-9542**

Owens Community College
30335 Oregon Rd., P.O. Box 10000
**Toledo 43699-1947**

Owens Community College, Findlay Campus
300 Davis St.
**Findlay 45840**

RETS Technical Center
116 Westpark Rd.
**Centerville 45459**

Shawnee State University
940 Second St.
**Portsmouth 45662**

Sinclair Community College
444 West Third St.
**Dayton 45402**

Stark State College of Technology
6200 Frank Ave. NW
**Canton 44720**

Terra State Community College
2830 Napoleon Rd.
**Fremont 43420**

Tri-County Vocational School
15675 St. Rte. 691
**Nelsonville 45764**

University of Akron, Main Campus
302 Buchtel Common
**Akron 44325-4702**

University of Cincinnati, Clermont College
College Dr.
**Batavia 45103**

University of Cincinnati, Main Campus
P.O. Box 210127
**Cincinnati 45221-0127**

University of Toledo
2801 West Bancroft
**Toledo 43606**

Wright State University, Lake Campus
7600 Rte. 703E
**Celina 45822**

Youngstown State University
One University Plz.
**Youngstown 44555**

### OKLAHOMA

Cameron University
2800 Gore Blvd.
**Lawton 73505**

Central Oklahoma Area Vocational Technical School
3 Court Cir.
**Drumright 74030**

Kiamichi AVTS SD #7, Poteau Campus
1509 South McKenna
**Poteau 74953**

Northeastern Oklahoma Agricultural and Mechanical College
200 I St. NE
**Miami 74354**

Oklahoma City Community College
7777 South May Ave.
**Oklahoma City 73159**

Rose State College
6420 South East 15th
**Midwest City 73110**

Tulsa Community College
6111 East Skelly Dr.
**Tulsa 74135**

### OREGON

Chemeketa Community College
4000 Lancaster Dr. NE
**Salem 97305**

ITT Technical Institute
6035 NE 78th Ct.
**Portland 97218**

Lane Community College
4000 East 30th Ave.
**Eugene 97405**

Linn-Benton Community College
6500 SW Pacific Blvd.
**Albany 97321**

Mount Hood Community College
26000 SE Stark St.
**Gresham 97030**

Oregon Institute of Technology
3201 Campus Dr.
**Klamath Falls 97601-8801**

Portland Community College
P.O. Box 19000
**Portland 97280-0990**

Rogue Community College
3345 Redwood Hwy.
**Grants Pass 97527**

### PENNSYLVANIA

Altoona Area Vocational Technical School
1500 4th Ave.
**Altoona 16602**

Butler County Community College
College Dr. Oak Hills
**Butler 16003-1203**

Community College of Allegheny County
800 Allegheny Ave.
**Pittsburgh 15233-1895**

Community College of Beaver County
One Campus Dr.
**Monaca 15061**

Community College of Philadelphia
1700 Spring Garden St.
**Philadelphia 19130**

Delaware County Community College
901 South Media Line Rd.
**Media 19063-1094**

Harrisburg Area Community College, Harrisburg Campus
One HACC Dr.
**Harrisburg 17110**

Johnson Technical Institute
3427 North Main Ave.
**Scranton 18508-1495**

Lincoln Technical Institute
5151 Tilghman St.
**Allentown 18104**

Luzerne County Community College
1333 South Prospect St.
**Nanticoke 18634**

Montgomery County Community College
340 Dekalb Pke.
**Blue Bell 19422**

New Castle School of Trades
Youngstown Rd. 1
**Pulaski 16143**

Northampton County Area Community College
3835 Green Pond Rd.
**Bethlehem 18020-7599**

Pennco Technical
3815 Otter St.
**Bristol 19007**

Pennsylvania College of Technology
One College Ave.
**Williamsport 17701**

Pennsylvania Institute of Technology
800 Manchester Ave.
**Media 19063**

Pennsylvania State University, Abington College
1600 Woodland Rd.
**Abington 19001**

Pennsylvania State University, Altoona College
3000 Ivyside Park
**Altoona 16601-3760**

Pennsylvania State University, Beaver Campus
Brodhead Rd.
**Monaca 15061**

Pennsylvania State University, Berks-Lehigh Valley Campus
Tulpehocken Rd., P.O. Box 7009
**Reading 19610-6009**

Pennsylvania State University, Erie Behrend College
Station Rd.
**Erie 16563**

Pennsylvania State University, Main Campus
201 Old Main
**University Park 16802**

Pennsylvania State University, New Kensington Campus
3550 Seventh St. Rd.
**New Kensington 15068**

Pennsylvania State University, Schuylkill-Capital College
200 University Dr.
**Schuylkill Haven 17972-2208**

Pennsylvania State University, Wilkes-Barre Campus
P.O. Box PSU, Old Rte. 115
**Lehman 18627**

Pennsylvania State University, Worthington-Scranton Campus
120 Ridge View Dr.
**Dunmore 18512**

Pennsylvania State University, York Campus
1031 Edgecomb Ave.
**York 17403**

Schuykill County Area Vocational Technical School
101 Technology Dr.
**Frackville 17931**

Thaddeus Stevens State School of Technology
750 East King St.
**Lancaster 17602**

Thompson Institute
5650 Derry St.
**Harrisburg 17111**

Westmoreland County Community College
**Youngwood 15697-1895**

## RHODE ISLAND

Community College of Rhode Island
400 East Ave.
**Warwick 02886-1807**

Johnson and Wales University
8 Abbott Park Place
**Providence 02903-3376**

New England Institute of Technology
2500 Post Rd.
**Warwick 02886**

## SOUTH CAROLINA

Aiken Technical College
P.O. Drawer 696
**Aiken 29802**

Central Carolina Technical College
506 North Guignard Dr.
**Sumter 29150**

Florence Darlington Technical College
P.O. Box 100548
**Florence 29501-0548**

Greenville Technical College
P.O. Box, 5616 Station B
**Greenville 29606-5616**

Horry-Georgetown Technical College
P.O. Box 1966
**Conway 29526**

Midlands Technical College
P.O. Box 2408
**Columbia 29202**

Nielsen Electronics Institute
1600 Meeting St.
**Charleston 29405**

Technical College of the Lowcountry
921 South Ribaut Rd.
**Beaufort 29902**

Trident Technical College
P.O. Box 118067
**Charleston 29423-8067**

York Technical College
452 South Anderson Rd.
**Rock Hill 29730**

## TENNESSEE

Cleveland State Community College
P.O. Box 3570
**Cleveland 37320-3570**

Dyersburg State Community College
1510 Lake Rd.
**Dyersburg 38024**

ITT Technical Institute
1645 Downtown West Blvd., Ste. 41
**Knoxville 37923**

ITT Technical Institute
441 Donelson Pike
**Nashville 37214**

Nashville State Technical Institute
120 White Bridge Rd.
**Nashville 37209**

Northeast State Technical Community College
P.O. Box 246
**Blountville 37617**

State Technical Institute at Memphis
5983 Macon Cove
**Memphis 38134**

## TEXAS

Angelina College
P.O. Box 1768
**Lufkin 75902-1768**

Austin Community College
5930 Middle Fiskville Rd.
**Austin 78752**

Central Texas College
P.O. Box 1800
**Killeen 76540-1800**

Cisco Junior College
Rte. 3, P.O. Box 3
**Cisco 76437**

Del Mar College
101 Baldwin
**Corpus Christi 78404-3897**

Devry Institute of Technology
4801 Regent Blvd.
**Irving 75063-2440**

Eastfield College
3737 Motley Dr.
**Mesquite 75150**

El Paso Community College
P.O. Box 20500
**El Paso 79998**

Grayson County College
6101 Grayson Dr.
**Denison 75020**

Hallmark Institute of Technology
8901 Wetmore Rd.
**San Antonio 78216**

Hill College
P.O. Box 619
**Hillsboro 76645**

Houston Community College System
22 Waugh Dr.
**Houston 77270-7849**

Interactive Learning Systems
8585 North Stemmons Fwy., Twin Towers
**Dallas 75247**

ITT Technical Institute
2201 Arlington Downs Rd.
**Arlington 76011**

ITT Technical Institute
1640 Eastgate Dr., Ste. 100
**Garland 75041**

Kilgore College
1100 Broadway
**Kilgore 75662-3299**

Lamar University, Beaumont
4400 MLK, P.O. Box 10001
**Beaumont 77710**

Lamar University, Orange
410 Front St.
**Orange 77630-5899**

Lee College
200 Lee Dr.
**Baytown 77520-4703**

Midland College
3600 North Garfield
**Midland 79705**

Mountain View College
4849 West Illinois
**Dallas 75211**

National Institute of Technology, Corinthian Schools, Inc.
3622 Fredericksburg Rd.
**San Antonio 78201**

North Harris Montgomery Community College District
250 North Sam Houston Pkwy. E, Ste. 300
**Houston 77060**

North Lake College
5001 North MacArthur Blvd.
**Irving 75038-3899**

Richland College
12800 Abrams Rd.
**Dallas 75243-2199**

San Antonio College
1300 San Pedro Ave.
**San Antonio 78284**

San Jacinto College, South Campus
13735 Beamer Rd.
**Houston 77089-6009**

South Plains College
1401 College Ave.
**Levelland 79336**

Southwest School of Electronics
5424 Hwy. 290 West, Ste. 200
**Austin 78735**

Tarrant County Junior College
1500 Houston St.
**Fort Worth 76102**

Texarkana College
2500 North Robison Rd.
**Texarkana 75599**

Texas State Technical College, Harlingen Campus
2424 Boxwood
**Harlingen 78550-3697**

Texas State Technical College, Waco Campus
3801 Campus Dr.
**Waco 76705**

Tyler Junior College
1327 South Baxter Ave.
**Tyler 75711**

Victoria College
2200 East Red River
**Victoria 77901**

Weatherford College
308 East Park Ave.
**Weatherford 76086**

Wharton County Junior College
911 Boling Hwy.
**Wharton 77488**

## UTAH

ITT Technical Institute
920 West Levoy Dr.
**Murray 84123**

Salt Lake Community College
P.O. Box 30808
**Salt Lake City 84130**

Utah Valley State College
800 West 1200 S
**Orem 84058**

## VERMONT

Champlain College
163 South Willard St.
**Burlington 05401**

## VIRGINIA

Commonwealth College, Hampton
1120 West Mercury Blvd.
**Hampton 23666**

Commonwealth College, Virginia Beach
301 Centre Pointe Dr.
**Virginia Beach 23462**

ITT Technical Institute
863 Glenrock Rd.
**Norfolk 23502**

Maryland Drafting Institute
8001 North Forbes Place
**Springfield 22151**

Tesst Technology Institute
1400 Duke St.
**Alexandria 22314**

Wise Skills Center
515 Hurricane Rd. N
**Wise 24293**

## WASHINGTON

Bellingham Technical College
3028 Lindbergh Ave.
**Bellingham 98225**

Centralia College
600 West Locust St.
**Centralia 98531**

Clark College
1800 East McLoughlin Blvd.
**Vancouver 98663**

Columbia Basin College
2600 North 20th Ave.
**Pasco 99301**

Edmonds Community College
20000 68th Ave. W
**Lynnwood 98036**

Green River Community College
12401 SE 320th St.
**Auburn 98092**

ITT Technical Institute
12720 Gateway Dr., Ste. 100
**Seattle 98168**

Olympic College
1600 Chester Ave.
**Bremerton 98337-1699**

Perry Technical Institute
2011 West Washington Ave.
**Yakima 98903**

Pierce College
9401 Farwest Dr. SW
**Lakewood 98498**

Seattle Community College, North Campus
9600 College Way N
**Seattle 98103**

South Puget Sound Community College
2011 Mottman Rd. SW
**Olympia 98512**

Spokane Community College
North 1810 Greene Ave.
**Spokane 99207**

## WEST VIRGINIA

Bluefield State College
219 Rock St.
**Bluefield 24701**

Cabell County Vocational Technical Center
1035 Norway Ave.
**Huntington 25705**

The College of West Virginia
500 South Kanawha St.
**Beckley 25801**

Fairmont State College
1201 Locust Ave.
**Fairmont 26554**

West Virginia Institute of Technology
**Montgomery 25136**

West Virginia State College
Rte. 25
**Institute 25112**

### WISCONSIN

Blackhawk Technical College
P.O. Box 5009
**Janesville 53547**

Chippewa Valley Technical College
620 West Clairemont Ave.
**Eau Claire 54701**

Fox Valley Technical College
1825 North Bluemound Dr.
**Appleton 54913-2277**

Gateway Technical College
3520 30th Ave.
**Kenosha 53144-1690**

Lakeshore Technical College
1290 North Ave.
**Cleveland 53015**

Mid-State Technical College
500 32nd St. N
**Wisconsin Rapids 54494**

Milwaukee Area Technical College
700 West State St.
**Milwaukee 53233-1443**

Moraine Park Technical College
235 North National Ave.
**Fond Du Lac 54936-1940**

Northcentral Technical College
1000 Campus Dr.
**Wausau 54401-1899**

Northeast Wisconsin Technical College
2740 West Mason St.
**Green Bay 54307-9042**

Southwest Wisconsin Technical College
1800 Bronson Blvd.
**Fennimore 53809**

Waukesha County Technical College
800 Main St.
**Pewaukee 53072**

Western Wisconsin Technical College
304 North Sixth St., P.O. Box 908
**La Crosse 54602-0908**

### WYOMING

Casper College
125 College Dr.
**Casper 82601**

Central Wyoming College
2660 Peck Ave.
**Riverton 82501**

## Electronic Technology

### ALABAMA

Community College of the Air Force
130 West Maxwell Blvd.
**Montgomery 36112-6613**

J F Drake State Technical College
3421 Meridian St. N
**Huntsville 35811**

John C Calhoun State Community College
Hwy. 31 N
**Decatur 35602**

### ALASKA

University of Alaska, Anchorage
3211 Providence Dr.
**Anchorage 99508**

### ARIZONA

Arizona Western College
P.O. Box 929
**Yuma 85366**

Central Arizona College
8470 North Overfield Rd.
**Coolidge 85228-9778**

Cochise College
4190 West Hwy. 80
**Douglas 85607-9724**

Devry Institute of Technology
2149 West Dunlap Ave.
**Phoenix 85021**

Gateway Community College
108 North 40th St.
**Phoenix 85034**

Glendale Community College
6000 West Olive Ave.
**Glendale 85302**

ITT Technical Institute
4837 East McDowell Rd.
**Phoenix 85008-4292**

ITT Technical Institute
1840 East Benson Hwy.
**Tucson 85714**

Mesa Community College
1833 West Southern Ave.
**Mesa 85202**

Pima Community College
2202 West Anklam Rd.
**Tucson 85709-0001**

### ARKANSAS

Arkansas State University, Beebe Branch
P.O. Drawer H
**Beebe 72012**

Arkansas Valley Technical Institute
P.O. Box 506, Hwy. 23 N
**Ozark 72949**

Black River Technical College
Hwy. 304, P.O. Box 468
**Pocahontas 72455**

Foothills Technical Institute
1800 East Moore St.
**Searcy 72143**

Garland County Community College
101 College Dr.
**Hot Springs 71913**

Mississippi County Community College
P.O. Box 1109
**Blytheville 72316-1109**

Northwest Technical Institute
709 South Old Missouri Rd.
**Springdale 72764**

Ouachita Technical College
One College Circle
**Malvern 72104**

Pulaski Technical College
3000 West Scenic Dr.
**North Little Rock 72118**

Quapaw Technical Institute
200 Mid America Blvd.
**Hot Springs 71913**

Southeast Arkansas Technical College
1900 Hazel
**Pine Bluff 71603**

Southern Arkansas University Technical
SAU Technical Station
**Camden 71701**

Westark Community College
P.O. Box 3649
**Fort Smith 72913**

### CALIFORNIA

Adelante Career Institute
14547 Titus
**Van Nuys 91402**

Butte College
3536 Butte Campus Dr.
**Oroville 95965**

California Human Development Corp. Center for Employment Training
2895 North Teepee St.
**Stockton 95205**

Center for Employment Training, Escondido
1131 Washington Ave. E
**Escondido 92025**

Center for Employment Training, Oxnard
730 South A St.
**Oxnard 93030**

Center for Employment Training, San Diego
3295 Market St.
**San Diego 92102**

Center for Employment Training, San Jose-Vine
701 Vine St.
**San Jose 95110**

Center for Employment Training, Santa Ana
120 West Fifth St.
**Santa Ana 92701**

Center for Employment Training, Watsonville
10 Blanca Ln.
**Watsonville 95076**

Cerro Coso Community College
3000 College Heights Blvd.
**Ridgecrest 93555-7777**

Chaffey Community College
5885 Haven Ave.
**Rancho Cucamonga 91737-3002**

City College of San Francisco
50 Phelan Ave.
**San Francisco 94112**

College of San Mateo
1700 West Hillsdale Blvd.
**San Mateo 94402**

College of the Sequoias
915 South Mooney Blvd.
**Visalia 93277**

Contra Costa College
2600 Mission Bell Dr.
**San Pablo 94806**

Cosumnes River College
8401 Center Pkwy.
**Sacramento 95823-5799**

De Anza College
21250 Stevens Creek Blvd.
**Cupertino 95014**

Diablo Valley College
321 Golf Club Rd.
**Pleasant Hill 94523**

East Los Angeles Skill Center
3921 Selig Pl.
**Los Angeles 90031**

El Camino College
16007 Crenshaw Blvd.
**Torrance 90506**

Foothill College
12345 El Monte Rd.
**Los Altos Hills 94022**

Foundation College
3478 Buskirk Ave., Ste. 100
**Pleasant Hill 94523**

Fullerton College
321 East Chapman Ave.
**Fullerton 92832-2095**

Goodwill Industries of Santa Cruz
350 Encinal St.
**Santa Cruz 95060**

Heald College School of Technology, Martinez
2860 Howe Rd.
**Martinez 94553**

ITT Technical Institute
2035 East 223rd
**Carson 90810**

ITT Technical Institute
630 East Brier, Ste. 150
**San Bernardino 92408-2800**

ITT Technical Institute
9680 Granite Ridge Dr.
**San Diego 92123**

Long Beach City College
4901 East Carson St.
**Long Beach 90808**

Los Angeles Trade Technical College
400 West Washington Blvd.
**Los Angeles 90015-4181**

Marin Regional Occupational Program
P.O. Box 4925
**San Rafael 94913**

Moorpark College
7075 Campus Rd.
**Moorpark 93021**

Mount San Antonio College
1100 North Grand
**Walnut 91789**

Orange Coast College
2701 Fairview Rd.
**Costa Mesa 92626**

Pacific Union College
1 Angwin Ave.
**Angwin 94508-9707**

Pasadena City College
1570 East Colorado Blvd.
**Pasadena 91106**

Rancho Santiago Community College
1530 West 17th St.
**Santa Ana 92706**

San Diego City College
1313 12th Ave.
**San Diego 92101**

San Diego Mesa College
7250 Mesa College Dr.
**San Diego 92111-4998**

San Joaquin Delta College
5151 Pacific Ave.
**Stockton 95207**

Santa Rosa Junior College
1501 Mendocino Ave.
**Santa Rosa 95401-4395**

Sawyer College, A Corinthian School
8475 Jackson Rd.
**Sacramento 95826**

School of Communications Electronics
184 Second St.
**San Francisco 94105**

Sierra College
5000 Rocklin Rd.
**Rocklin 95677**

Southwestern College
900 Otay Lakes Rd.
**Chula Vista 91910**

Travel and Trade Career Institute
3635 Atlantic Ave.
**Long Beach 90807**

Vallecitos CET, Inc.
597 C St.
**Hayward 94541**

Victor Valley College
18422 Bear Valley Rd.
**Victorville 92392-9699**

### COLORADO

Aims Community College
P.O. Box 69
**Greeley 80632**

Arapahoe Community College
2500 West College Dr.
**Littleton 80160-9002**

Colorado Technical University
4435 North Chestnut
**Colorado Springs 80907-3896**

Community College of Aurora
16000 East Centre Tech Pkwy.
**Aurora 80011-9036**

Community College of Denver
P.O. Box 173363
**Denver 80217**

Denver Institute of Technology
7350 North Broadway
**Denver 80221**

Denver Technical College
925 South Niagara St.
**Denver 80224**

Denver Technical College at Colorado Springs
225 South Union Blvd.
**Colorado Springs 80910**

Front Range Community College
3645 West 112th Ave.
**Westminster 80030**

ITT Technical Institute
2121 South Blackhawk St.
**Aurora 80014**

Mesa State College
P.O. Box 2647
**Grand Junction 81502**

Pikes Peak Community College
5675 South Academy Blvd.
**Colorado Springs 80906-5498**

Pueblo Community College
900 West Orman Ave.
**Pueblo 81004**

Red Rocks Community College
13300 West Sixth Ave.
**Lakewood 80228**

T H Pickens Technical Center
500 Airport Blvd.
**Aurora 80011**

Trinidad State Junior College
600 Prospect St.
**Trinidad 81082**

## CONNECTICUT

Porter and Chester Institute
138 Weymouth Rd.
**Enfield 06082**

Porter and Chester Institute
670 Lordship Blvd.
**Stratford 06497**

Porter and Chester Institute
320 Sylvan Lake Rd.
**Watertown 06779-1400**

Porter and Chester Institute
125 Silas Deane Hwy.
**Wethersfield 06109**

Ridley Lowell Business and Technical Institute
470 Bank St.
**New London 06320**

University of Hartford
200 Bloomfield Ave.
**West Hartford 06117**

## DELAWARE

Delaware Technical and Community College, Owens Campus
P.O. Box 610
**Georgetown 19947**

Delaware Technical and Community College, Stanton-Wilmington Campus
400 Stanton-Christiana Rd.
**Newark 19702**

Delaware Technical and Community College, Terry Campus
1832 North Dupont Pkwy.
**Dover 19901**

## DISTRICT OF COLUMBIA

University of the District of Columbia
4200 Connecticut Ave. NW
**Washington 20008**

## FLORIDA

ATI Career Training Center
2880 NW 62nd St.
**Fort Lauderdale 33309**

Brevard Community College
1519 Clearlake Rd.
**Cocoa 32922**

Central Florida Community College
3001 SW College Rd.
**Ocala 34474**

Chipola Junior College
3094 Indian Cir.
**Marianna 32446**

Edison Community College
8099 College Pkwy. SW
**Ft Myers 33906-6210**

Florida Technical College
1819 North Semoran Blvd.
**Orlando 32807**

Florida Technical College of Jacksonville, Inc.
8711 Lone Star Rd.
**Jacksonville 32211**

Gulf Coast Community College
5230 West Hwy. 98
**Panama City 32401**

Hillsborough Community College
P.O. Box 31127
**Tampa 33631-3127**

Indian River Community College
3209 Virginia Ave.
**Fort Pierce 34981**

ITT Technical Institute
4809 Memorial Hwy.
**Tampa 33634-7515**

Lively Technical Center
500 North Appleyard Dr.
**Tallahassee 32304**

Lindsey Hopkins Technical Education Center
750 NW 20th St.
**Miami 33127**

Manatee Community College
5840 26th St. W
**Bradenton 34207**

Miami-Dade Community College
300 NE Second Ave.
**Miami 33132**

Miami Lakes Technical Education Center
5780 NW 158th St.
**Miami Lakes 33169**

Okaloosa-Walton Community College
100 College Blvd.
**Niceville 32578**

Pensacola Junior College
1000 College Blvd.
**Pensacola 32504**

Saint Petersburg Junior College
8580 66 St. N
**Pinellas Park 34665**

Santa Fe Community College
3000 NW 83rd St.
**Gainesville 32606**

Seminole Community College
100 Weldon Blvd.
**Sanford 32773-6199**

Southern College
5600 Lake Underhill Rd.
**Orlando 32807**

Valencia Community College
P.O. Box 3028
**Orlando 32802**

Withlacoochee Technical Institute
1201 West Main St.
**Inverness 32650**

## GEORGIA

Bainbridge College
2500 East Shotwell St.
**Bainbridge 31717**

Chattahoochee Technical Institute
980 South Cobb Dr.
**Marietta 30060-3398**

Clayton College and State University
5900 Lee St., P.O. Box 285
**Morrow 30260**

Dalton College
213 North College Dr.
**Dalton 30720**

Devry Institute of Technology
250 North Arcadia
**Decatur 30030**

Floyd College
P.O. Box 1864
**Rome 30162-1864**

## HAWAII

Electronics Institute
1270 Queen Emma St., Rm. 108
**Honolulu 96813**

Honolulu Community College
874 Dillingham Blvd.
**Honolulu 96817**

## IDAHO

Eastern Idaho Technical College
1600 South 2500 E
**Idaho Falls 83404**

Idaho State University
741 South 7th Ave.
**Pocatello 83209**

ITT Technical Institute
12302 Explorer Dr.
**Boise 83713**

Ricks College
**Rexburg 83460-4107**

## ILLINOIS

Carl Sandburg College
2232 South Lake Storey Rd.
**Galesburg 61401**

College of Du Page
425 22nd St.
**Glen Ellyn 60137-6599**

College of Lake County
19351 West Washington St.
**Grayslake 60030-1198**

Devry Institute of Technology
1221 North Swift Rd.
**Addison 60101**

Devry Institute of Technology
3300 North Campbell Ave.
**Chicago 60618**

Illinois Central College
One College Dr.
**East Peoria 61635-0001**

Illinois Eastern Community Colleges, Olney Central College
305 North West St.
**Olney 62450**

ITT Technical Institute, Hoffman Estates
375 West Higgins Rd.
**Hoffman Estates 60195**

John A Logan College
700 Logan College Rd.
**Carterville 62918**

Joliet Junior College
1215 Houbolt Rd.
**Joliet 60431**

Kankakee Community College
P.O. Box 888
**Kankakee 60901**

Kaskaskia College
27210 College Rd.
**Centralia 62801**

Lincoln Land Community College
Shepherd Rd.
**Springfield 62194-9256**

McHenry County College
8900 U.S. Hwy. 14
**Crystal Lake 60012**

Moraine Valley Community College
10900 South 88th Ave.
**Palos Hills 60465-0937**

Oakton Community College
1600 East Golf Rd.
**Des Plaines 60016**

Rock Valley College
3301 North Mulford Rd.
**Rockford 61114**

Sauk Valley Community College
173 Rte. 2
**Dixon 61021**

South Suburban College
15800 South State St.
**South Holland 60473**

Southern Illinois University, Carbondale
Faner Hall 2179
**Carbondale 62901-4512**

Taylor Business Institute
200 North Michigan Ave., Ste. 301
**Chicago 60601**

Triton College
2000 Fifth Ave.
**River Grove 60171**

Waubonsee Community College
Rte. 47 at Harter Rd.
**Sugar Grove 60554-0901**

William Rainey Harper College
1200 West Algonquin Rd.
**Palatine 60067-7398**

Zarem Golde ORT Technical Institute
3050 West Touhy
**Chicago 60645**

## INDIANA

Indiana University, Purdue University at Fort Wayne
2101 Coliseum Blvd. E
**Fort Wayne 46805**

Indiana University, Purdue University at Indianapolis
355 North Lansing
**Indianapolis 46202**

ITT Technical Institute
4919 Coldwater Rd.
**Fort Wayne 46825**

ITT Technical Institute
9511 Angola Ct.
**Indianapolis 46268**

Ivy Tech State College, Central Indiana
One West 26th St.
**Indianapolis 46206-1763**

Ivy Tech State College, Columbus
4475 Central Ave.
**Columbus 47203**

Ivy Tech State College, East Central
4301 South Cowan Rd., P.O. Box 3100
**Muncie 47302**

Ivy Tech State College, Kokomo
1815 East Morgan St.
**Kokomo 46901**

Ivy Tech State College, Lafayette
3101 South Creasy Ln., P.O. Box 6299
**Lafayette 47903**

Ivy Tech State College, North Central
1534 West Sample St.
**South Bend 46619**

Ivy Tech State College, Northeast
3800 North Anthony Blvd.
**Fort Wayne 46805**

Ivy Tech State College, Northwest
1440 East 35th Ave.
**Gary 46409**

Ivy Tech State College, South Central
8204 Hwy. 311
**Sellersburg 47172**

Ivy Tech State College, Southeast
590 Ivy Tech Dr.
**Madison 47250**

Ivy Tech State College, Southwest
3501 First Ave.
**Evansville 47710**

Ivy Tech State College, Wabash Valley
7999 U.S. Hwy. 41
**Terre Haute 47802-4898**

Purdue University, Calumet Campus
2233 171st St.
**Hammond 46323**

Purdue University, Main Campus
1076 Freehafer Hall
**West Lafayette 47907-1076**

Purdue University, North Central Campus
1401 South U.S. Hwy. 421
**Westville 46391**

Vincennes University
1002 North First St.
**Vincennes 47591**

## IOWA

Des Moines Community College
2006 Ankeny Blvd.
**Ankeny 50021**

Eastern Iowa Community College District
306 West River Dr.
**Davenport 52801-1221**

Hamilton Technical College
1011 East 53rd St.
**Davenport 52807**

Hawkeye Community College
1501 East Orange Rd.
**Waterloo 50704**

Indian Hills Community College
525 Grandview
**Ottumwa 52501**

Iowa Central Community College
330 Ave. M
**Fort Dodge 50501**

Iowa Western Community College
2700 College Rd., P.O. Box 4C
**Council Bluffs 51502**

Kirkwood Community College
P.O. Box 2068
**Cedar Rapids 52406**

North Iowa Area Community College
500 College Dr.
**Mason City 50401**

Northeast Iowa Community College, Calmar
Hwy. 150 S, Box 400
**Calmar 52132-0400**

Northwest Iowa Technical College
603 West Park St.
**Sheldon 51201**

Western Iowa Technical Community College
4647 Stone Ave., P.O. Box 5199
**Sioux City 51102-0265**

## KANSAS

Hesston College
P.O. Box 3000
**Hesston 67062**

Kansas State University
Anderson Hall
**Manhattan 66506**

Pittsburg State University
1701 South Broadway
**Pittsburg 66762**

Topeka Technical College
1620 Northwest Gage
**Topeka 66618**

Washburn University of Topeka
1700 College Ave.
**Topeka 66621**

Wichita Technical Institute
942 South West St.
**Wichita 67213-1681**

## KENTUCKY

Institute of Electronic Technology
P.O. Box 8252
**Paducah 42001**

Kentucky Technical, Hazard Regional Technology Center
101 Vo-Tech Dr.
**Hazard 41701**

Kentucky Technical, Madisonville State Vocational Technical School
150 School Ave.
**Madisonville 42431**

Lexington Electronic Institute, Inc.
3340 Holwyn Rd.
**Lexington 40503**

Mayo Regional Technology Center
Third St.
**Paintsville 41240**

RETS Electronic Institute
300 High Rise Dr.
**Louisville 40213**

University of Louisville
2301 South Third St.
**Louisville 40292-0001**

## LOUISIANA

Delgado Community College
501 City Park Ave.
**New Orleans 70119**

Grantham College of Engineering
34641 Grantham College Rd.
**Slidell 70460**

McNeese State University
4100 Ryan St.
**Lake Charles 70609**

RETS Training Center
3321 Hessmer Ave.
**Metairie 70002**

## MAINE

Eastern Maine Technical College
354 Hogan Rd.
**Bangor 04401**

Kennebec Valley Technical College
92 Western Ave.
**Fairfield 04937-1367**

Northern Maine Technical College
33 Edgemont Dr.
**Presque Isle 04769**

Southern Maine Technical College
Fort Rd.
**South Portland 04106**

## MARYLAND

Anne Arundel Community College
101 College Pkwy.
**Arnold 21012**

Baltimore City Community College
2901 Liberty Heights Ave.
**Baltimore 21215**

Capitol College
11301 Springfield Rd.
**Laurel 20708**

Catonsville Community College
800 South Rolling Rd.
**Catonsville 21228**

Cecil Community College
1000 North East Rd.
**North East 21901-1999**

Essex Community College
7201 Rossville Blvd.
**Baltimore 21237**

Frederick Community College
7932 Opossumtown Pike
**Frederick 21702**

Harford Community College
401 Thomas Run Rd.
**Bel Air 21015**

Montgomery College of Rockville
51 Mannakee St.
**Rockville 20850**

Prince Georges Community College
301 Largo Rd.
**Largo 20774-2199**

The Radio Electronic Television Schools, Inc.
1520 South Caton Ave.
**Baltimore 21227-1063**

Tesst Technology Center
5122 Baltimore Ave.
**Hyattsville 20781**

## MASSACHUSETTS

Berkshire Community College
1350 West St.
**Pittsfield 01201-5786**

Bristol Community College
777 Elsbree St.
**Fall River 02720**

Bunker Hill Community College
250 New Rutherford Ave.
**Boston 02129**

Computer Learning Center of Boston
Five Middlesex Ave.
**Somerville 02145**

Franklin Institute of Boston
41 Berkeley St.
**Boston 02116**

ITT Technical Institute
1671 Worcester Rd.
**Framingham 01701-5404**

Massachusetts Bay Community College
50 Oakland St.
**Wellesley Hills 02181**

Massasoit Community College
One Massasoit Blvd.
**Brockton 02402**

Middlesex Community College
Springs Rd.
**Bedford 01730**

Mount Wachusett Community College
444 Green St.
**Gardner 01440**

Northeast Institute of Industrial Technology
41 Phillips St.
**Boston 02114**

Northeastern University
360 Huntington Ave.
**Boston 02115**

Northern Essex Community College
Elliott Way
**Haverhill 01830-2399**

Quinsigamond Community College
670 West Boylston St.
**Worcester 01606**

RETS Electronic School
965 Commonwealth Ave.
**Boston 02215**

Southeastern Technical Institute
250 Foundry St.
**South Easton 02375**

Springfield Technical Community College
One Armory Square
**Springfield 01105**

University of Massachusetts at Lowell
One University Ave.
**Lowell 01854**

Wentworth Institute of Technology
550 Huntington Ave.
**Boston 02115**

Worcester Technical Institute
251 Belmont St.
**Worcester 01605**

## MICHIGAN

Baker College of Flint
G1050 West Bristol Rd.
**Flint 48507**

Bay De Noc Community College
2001 North Lincoln Rd.
**Escanaba 49289**

Delta College
**University Center 48710**

Ferris State University
901 South State St.
**Big Rapids 49307**

Glen Oaks Community College
62249 Shimmel Rd.
**Centreville 49032**

Grand Rapids Community College
143 Bostwick Ave. NE
**Grand Rapids 49503-3295**

Great Lakes Junior College of Business
310 South Washington Ave.
**Saginaw 48607**

Heath Kit Company
455 Riverview Dr.
**Benton Harbor 49023**

Henry Ford Community College
5101 Evergreen Rd.
**Dearborn 48128**

ITT Technical Institute
1522 East Big Beaver Rd.
**Troy 48083**

Jackson Community College
2111 Emmons Rd.
**Jackson 49201-8399**

Kalamazoo Valley Community College
6767 West O Ave.
**Kalamazoo 49009**

Kellogg Community College
450 North Ave.
**Battle Creek 49017**

Lake Michigan College
2755 East Napier Ave.
**Benton Harbor 49022-8099**

Lake Superior State University
650 West Easterday Ave.
**Sault Sainte Marie 49783**

Lansing Community College
419 North Capitol Ave.
**Lansing 48901-7210**

Lawrence Technological University
21000 West Ten Mile Rd.
**Southfield 48075-1058**

Macomb Community College
14500 Twelve Mile Rd.
**Warren 48093-3896**

Michigan Technological University
1400 Townsend Dr.
**Houghton 49931-1295**

Monroe County Community College
1555 South Raisinville Rd.
**Monroe 48161**

Mott Community College
1401 East Court St.
**Flint 48503**

Muskegon Community College
221 South Quarterline Rd.
**Muskegon 49442**

Northwestern Michigan College
1701 East Front St.
**Traverse City 49684**

Oakland Community College
2480 Opdyke Rd.
**Bloomfield Hills 48304-2266**

Schoolcraft College
18600 Haggerty Rd.
**Livonia 48152**

Siena Heights College
1247 Siena Heights Dr.
**Adrian 49221**

Wayne County Community College
801 West Fort St.
**Detroit 48226**

## MINNESOTA

Brown Institute Ltd.
2225 East Lake St.
**Minneapolis 55407**

Hennepin Technical College
9000 Brooklyn Blvd.
**Brooklyn Park 55445**

NEI College of Technology
825 41st Ave. NE
**Columbia Heights 55421-9990**

Northwest Technical College, Moorhead
1900 28th Ave. S
**Moorhead 56560**

Red Wing/Winona Technical College, Winona Campus
1250 Homer Rd., P.O. Box 409
**Winona 55987**

Saint Cloud Technical College
1540 Northway Dr.
**Saint Cloud 56303**

Saint Paul Technical College
235 Marshall Ave.
**Saint Paul 55102**

## MISSISSIPPI

East Central Community College
**Decatur 39327**

East Mississippi Community College
P.O. Box 158
**Scooba 39358**

Hinds Community College, Raymond Campus
**Raymond 39154**

Itawamba Community College
602 West Hill St.
**Fulton 38843**

Jones County Junior College
900 South Courts St.
**Ellisville 39437**

Meridian Community College
910 Hwy. 19 N
**Meridian 39307**

Mississippi Gulf Coast Community College
Central Office, P.O. Box 67
**Perkinston 39573**

Northeast Mississippi Community College
Cunningham Blvd.
**Booneville 38829**

Pearl River Community College
Station A
**Poplarville 39470**

## MISSOURI

Devry Institute of Technology
11224 Holmes Rd.
**Kansas City 64131**

Drury College
900 North Benton Ave.
**Springfield 65802**

Electronics Institute
15329 Kensington Ave.
**Kansas City 64147**

ITT Technical Institute
13505 Lakefront Dr.
**Earth City 63045**

Jefferson College
1000 Viking Dr.
**Hillsboro 63050**

Linn Technical College
One Technology Dr.
**Linn 65051**

Longview Community College
500 Longview Rd.
**Lees Summit 64081**

Maple Woods Community College
2601 Northeast Barry Rd.
**Kansas City 64156**

Penn Valley Community College
3201 Southwest Trafficway
**Kansas City 64111**

Saint Louis Community College, Forest Park
5600 Oakland Ave.
**Saint Louis 63110**

Vatterott College
3925 Industrial Dr.
**Saint Ann 63074**

## MONTANA

May Technical College
1306 Central Ave.
**Billings 59103**

May Technical College, Great Falls
1807 Third St. NW
**Great Falls 59404**

Miles Community College
2715 Dickinson
**Miles City 59301**

## NEBRASKA

Metropolitan Community College Area
5300 North 30th St.
**Omaha 68111**

## NEVADA

Career College of Northern Nevada
1195A Corporate Blvd.
**Reno 89502**

Community College of Southern Nevada
3200 East Cheyenne Ave.
**Las Vegas 89030**

Western Nevada Community College
2201 West College Pkwy.
**Carson City 89703**

## NEW HAMPSHIRE

New Hampshire Community Technical College, Manchester/Stratham
1066 Front St.
**Manchester 03102**

New Hampshire Technical College at Nashua
505 Amherst St.
**Nashua 03061-2052**

New Hampshire Technical Institute
11 Institute Dr.
**Concord 03301**

## NEW JERSEY

Atlantic Community College
5100 Black Horse Pike
**Mays Landing 08330-2699**

Brookdale Community College
765 Newman Springs Rd.
**Lincroft 07738-1599**

Camden County College
P.O. Box 200
**Blackwood 08012**

County College of Morris
214 Center Grove Rd.
**Randolph 07869**

Devry Institute
630 U.S. Hwy. One
**North Brunswick 07095**

Essex County College
303 University Ave.
**Newark 07102**

Mercer County Community College
1200 Old Trenton Rd.
**Trenton 08690**

Metropolitan Technical Institute
11 Daniel Rd.
**Fairfield 07004**

Middlesex County College
155 Mill Rd.
**Edison 08818-3050**

Ocean County College
College Dr.
**Toms River 08753**

Pennco Technical
Erial Rd., P.O. Box 1427
**Blackwood 08012**

RETS Institute
103 Park Ave.
**Nutley 07110**

Star Technical Institute
1386 South Delsea Dr.
**Vineland 08360**

Thomas A Edison State College
101 West State St.
**Trenton 08608-1176**

Union County College
1033 Springfield Ave.
**Cranford 07016**

## NEW MEXICO

Albuquerque Technical-Vocational Institute
525 Buena Vista SE
**Albuquerque 87106**

Clovis Community College
417 Schepps Blvd.
**Clovis 88101**

Eastern New Mexico University, Roswell Campus
52 University Blvd.
**Roswell 88202**

ITT Technical Institute
5100 Masthead NE
**Albuquerque 87109**

Luna Vocational Technical Institute
P.O. Drawer K
**Las Vegas 87701**

Northern New Mexico Community College
1002 North Onate St.
**Espanola 87532**

## NEW YORK

Broome Community College
P.O. Box 1017
**Binghamton 13902**

Bryant and Stratton Business Institute, Buffalo
1028 Main St.
**Buffalo 1420[illegible]**

Bryant and Stratton Business Institute, Rochester
82 Saint Paul St.
**Rochester 14604**

Bryant and Stratton Business Institute, Syracuse
953 James St.
**Syracuse 13203-2502**

Cayuga County Community College
Franklin St.
**Auburn 13021**

Corning Community College
Spencer Hill
**Corning 14830**

CUNY Bronx Community College
West 181st St. & University Ave.
**Bronx 10453**

CUNY New York City Technical College
300 Jay St.
**Brooklyn 11201**

CUNY Queensborough Community College
56th Ave. & Springfield Blvd.
**New York 11364**

Dutchess Community College
53 Pendell Rd.
**Poughkeepsie 12601**

Erie Community College, North Campus
Main St. and Youngs Rd.
**Williamsville 14221**

Hudson Valley Community College
80 Vandenburgh Ave.
**Troy 12180**

Island Drafting and Technical Institute
128 Broadway Rte. 110
**Amityville 11701**

Jamestown Community College
525 Falconer St.
**Jamestown 14701**

Mohawk Valley Community College
1101 Sherman Dr.
**Utica 13501**

Monroe Community College
1000 East Henrietta Rd.
**Rochester 14623**

Nassau Community College
One Education Dr.
**Garden City 11530**

New York Institute of Technology, Old Westbury Campus
P.O. Box 8000
**Old Westbury 11568-8000**

Niagara County Community College
3111 Saunders Settlement Rd.
**Sanborn 14132**

Onondaga Community College
4941 Onongada Rd.
**Syracuse 13215**

Orange County Community College
115 South St.
**Middletown 10940**

Rochester Institute of Technology
One Lomb Memorial Dr.
**Rochester 14623-5603**

Rockland Community College
145 College Rd.
**Suffern 10901**

Schenectady County Community College
Washington Ave.
**Schenectady 12305**

Suburban Technical School
175 Fulton Ave.
**Hempstead 11550**

Suffolk County Community College, Ammerman Campus
533 College Rd.
**Selden 11784**

SUNY College of Technology & Agriculture at Morrisville
**Morrisville 13408**

SUNY College of Technology at Alfred
**Alfred 14802**

SUNY College of Technology at Canton
Cornell Dr.
**Canton 13617**

SUNY College of Technology at Delhi
**Delhi 13753**

SUNY College of Technology at Farmingdale
Melville Rd.
**Farmingdale 11735-1021**

SUNY Westchester Commmunity College
75 Grasslands Rd.
**Valhalla 10595**

Technical Career Institutes
320 West 31st St.
**New York 10001**

Tompkins-Cortland Community College
170 North St.
**Dryden 13053**

## NORTH CAROLINA

Asheville Buncombe Technical Community College
340 Victoria Rd.
**Asheville 28801**

Beaufort County Community College
P.O. Box 1069
**Washington 27889**

Blue Ridge Community College
College Dr.
**Flat Rock 28731-9624**

Brunswick Community College
P.O. Box 30
**Supply 28462**

Cape Fear Community College
411 North Front St.
**Wilmington 28401**

Catawba Valley Community College
2550 Hwy. 70 SE
**Hickory 28602-0699**

Central Carolina Community College
1105 Kelly Dr.
**Sanford 27330**

Central Piedmont Community College
P.O. Box 35009
**Charlotte 28235-5009**

Cleveland Community College
137 South Post Rd.
**Shelby 28152**

Craven Community College
800 College Ct.
**New Bern 28562**

Davidson County Community College
297 Davidson Community College Rd.
**Lexington 27292**

Durham Technical Community College
1637 Lawson St.
**Durham 27703**

Fayetteville Technical Community College
2201 Hull Rd.
**Fayetteville 28303-0236**

Forsyth Technical Community College
2100 Silas Creek Pkwy.
**Winston Salem 27103**

Guilford Technical Community College
P.O. Box 309
**Jamestown 27282**

Halifax Community College
P.O. Drawer 809
**Weldon 27890**

Haywood Community College
Freedlander Dr.
**Clyde 28721**

Isothermal Community College
P.O. Box 804
**Spindale 28160**

Johnston Community College
P.O. Box 2350
**Smithfield 27577-2350**

Mayland Community College
P.O. Box 547
**Spruce Pine 28777**

McDowell Technical Community College
Rte. 1, P.O. Box 170
**Marion 28752**

Mitchell Community College
500 West Broad
**Statesville 28677**

Robeson Community College
P.O. Box 1420
**Lumberton 28359**

Rowan-Cabarrus Community College
P.O. Box 1595
**Salisbury 28145-1595**

Southeastern Community College
4564 Chadburn Hwy.
**Whiteville 28472**

Surry Community College
P.O. Box 304
**Dobson 27017-0304**

Vance-Granville Community College
State Rd. 1126, P.O. Box 917
**Henderson 27536**

Wake Technical Community College
9101 Fayetteville Rd.
**Raleigh 27603-5696**

Wayne Community College
3000 Wayne Memorial Dr.
**Goldsboro 27533-8002**

Wilkes Community College
Collegiate Dr.
**Wilkesboro 28697**

## NORTH DAKOTA

North Dakota State College of Science
800 North Sixth St.
**Wahpeton 58076**

## OHIO

Central Ohio Technical College
1179 University Dr.
**Newark 43055-1767**

Cincinnati State Technical and Community College
3520 Central Pkwy.
**Cincinnati 45223**

Clark State Community College
570 East Leffel Ln.
**Springfield 45505**

Cleveland Institute of Electronics
1776 East 17th St.
**Cleveland 44114**

Columbus State Community College
550 East Spring St.
**Columbus 43216**

Cuyahoga Community College District
700 Carnegie Ave.
**Cleveland 44115-2878**

Devry Institute of Technology
1350 Alum Creek Dr.
**Columbus 43209-2764**

Edison State Community College
1973 Edison Dr.
**Piqua 45356**

ETI Technical College
2076 Youngstown Warren Rd.
**Niles 44446-4398**

Franklin University
201 South Grant Ave.
**Columbus 43215-5399**

ITT Technical Institute
3325 Stop Eight Rd.
**Dayton 45414**

ITT Technical Institute
1030 North Meridian Rd.
**Youngstown 44509**

Kent State University, Trumbull Regional Campus
4314 Mahoning Ave. NW
**Warren 44483**

Kent State University, Tuscaraws Regional Campus
University Dr. NE
**New Philadelphia 44663**

Lakeland Community College
7700 Clocktower Dr.
**Kirtland 44094-5198**

Lima Technical College
4240 Campus Dr.
**Lima 45804**

Lorain County Community College
1005 Abbe Rd. N
**Elyria 44035**

Muskingum Area Technical College
1555 Newark Rd.
**Zanesville 43701**

North Central Technical College
2441 Kenwood Circle, P.O. Box 698
**Mansfield 44901**

Northwest State Community College
22 600 South Rte. 34
**Archbold 43502-9542**

Owens Community College
39335 Oregon Rd.
**Toledo 43699-1947**

RETS Technical Center
116 Westpark Rd.
**Centerville 45459**

Sinclair Community College
444 West Third St.
**Dayton 45402**

Stark State College of Technology
6200 Frank Ave. NW
**Canton 44720**

Technology Education College
288 South Hamilton Rd.
**Columbus 43213**

Terra Technical College
2830 Napoleon Rd.
**Fremont 43420**

Total Technical Institute
6500 Pearl Rd.
**Parma Heights 44130**

Tri-County Vocational School
15675 State Rte. 691
**Nelsonville 45764**

University of Akron, Main Campus
302 Buchtel Common
**Akron 44325-4702**

University of Cincinnati, Clermont College
College Dr.
**Batavia 45103**

University of Cincinnati, Main Campus
P.O. Box 210127
**Cincinnati 45221-0127**

University of Toledo
2801 West Bancroft
**Toledo 43606**

Washington State Community College
710 Colegate Dr.
**Marietta 45750**

Wright State University, Lake Campus
7600 Rte. 703E
**Celina 45822**

Youngstown State University
One University Plaza
**Youngstown 44555**

## OKLAHOMA

Cameron University
2800 Gore Blvd.
**Lawton 73505**

Central Oklahoma Area Vocational Technical School
Three Court Circle
**Drumright 74030**

Eastern Oklahoma State College
1301 West Main St.
**Wilburton 74578**

Kiamichi AVTS SD #7, Poteau Campus
1509 South McKenna, P.O. Box 825
**Poteau 74953**

Northeastern Oklahoma Agricultural and Mechanical College
200 I St. NE
**Miami 74354**

Oklahoma City Community College
7777 South May Ave.
**Oklahoma City 73159**

Oklahoma State University, Okmulgee
1801 East Fourth St.
**Okmulgee 74447-3901**

Pontotoc Area Vocational Technical School
601 West 33rd
**Ada 74820**

Rose State College
6420 Southeast 15th
**Midwest City 73110**

## OREGON

Chemeketa Community College
4000 Lancaster Dr. NE
**Salem 97305**

ITT Technical Institute
6035 Northeast 78th Ct.
**Portland 97218**

Lane Community College
4000 East 30th Ave.
**Eugene 97405**

Linn-Benton Community College
6500 Southwest Pacific Blvd.
**Albany 97321**

Mount Hood Community College
26000 Southeast Stark St.
**Gresham 97030**

Oregon Institute of Technology
3201 Campus Dr.
**Klamath Falls 97601-8801**

Portland Community College
P.O. Box 19000
**Portland 97280-0990**

Rogue Community College
3345 Redwood Hwy.
**Grants Pass 97527**

## PENNSYLVANIA

Butler County Community College
College Dr. Oak Hills
**Butler 16003-1203**

Community College of Allegheny County, Pittsburgh
800 Allegheny Ave.
**Pittsburgh 15233-1895**

Community College of Beaver County
One Campus Dr.
**Monaca 15061**

Delaware County Community College
901 South Media Line Rd.
**Media 19063-1094**

Harrisburg Area Community College, Harrisburg Campus
One HACC Dr.
**Harrisburg 17110**

Lehigh Carbon Community College
4525 Education Park Dr.
**Schnecksville 18078-2598**

Lincoln Technical Institute
5151 Tilghman St.
**Allentown 18104**

Luzerne County Community College
1333 South Prospect St.
**Nanticoke 18634**

Montgomery County Community College
340 Dekalb Pike
**Blue Bell 19422**

New Castle School of Trades
Youngstown Rd., RD 1
**Pulaski 16143**

Northampton County Area Community College
3835 Green Pond Rd.
**Bethlehem 18020-7599**

Pennco Technical
3815 Otter St.
**Bristol 19007**

Pennsylvania College of Technology
One College Ave.
**Williamsport 17701**

Pennsylvania Institute of Technology
800 Manchester Ave.
**Media 19063**

Pennsylvania State University, Abington College
1600 Woodland Rd.
**Abington 19001**

Pennsylvania State University, Altoona Campus
3000 Ivyside Park
**Altoona 16601-3760**

Pennsylvania State University, Beaver Campus
Brodhead Rd.
**Monaca 15061**

Pennsylvania State University, Berks-Lehigh Valley Campus
Tulpehocken Rd., P.O. Box 7009
**Reading 19610-6009**

Pennsylvania State University, Erie Behrend College
Station Rd.
**Erie 16563**

Pennsylvania State University, Main Campus
201 Old Main
**University Park 16802**

Pennsylvania State University, New Kensington Campus
3550 Seventh St. Rd.
**New Kensington 15068**

Pennsylvania State University, Schuylkill Campus
200 University Dr.
**Schuylkill Haven 17972-2208**

Pennsylvania State University, Wilkes-Barre Campus
P.O. PSU Old Rte. 115
**Lehman 18627**

Pennsylvania State University, Worthington-Scranton Campus
120 Ridge View Dr.
**Dunmore 18512**

Pennsylvania State University, York Campus
1031 Edgecomb Ave.
**York 17403**

Reading Area Community College
P.O. Box 1706
**Reading 19603-1706**

Thaddeus Stevens State School of Technology
750 East King St.
**Lancaster 17602**

Thompson Institute
5650 Derry St.
**Harrisburg 17111**

Thompson Institute
3440 Market St.
**Philadelphia 19104**

Westmoreland County Community College
**Youngwood 15697-1895**

### RHODE ISLAND

Community College of Rhode Island
400 East Ave.
**Warwick 02886-1807**

Johnson and Wales University
8 Abbott Park Place
**Providence 02903-3376**

New England Institute of Technology
2500 Post Rd.
**Warwick 02886**

### SOUTH CAROLINA

Central Carolina Technical College
506 North Guignard Dr.
**Sumter 29150**

Florence-Darlington Technical College
P.O. Box 100548
**Florence 29501-0548**

Greenville Technical College
Station B, P.O. Box 5616
**Greenville 29606-5616**

Horry-Georgetown Technical College
P.O. Box 1966
**Conway 29526**

Midlands Technical College
P.O. Box 2408
**Columbia 29202**

Nielsen Electronics Institute
1600 Meeting St.
**Charleston 29405**

Piedmont Technical College
P.O. Drawer 1467
**Greenwood 29648**

Technical College of the Low Country
921 Ribaut Rd.
**Beaufort 29901**

Trident Technical College
P.O. Box 118067
**Charleston 29423-8067**

York Technical College
452 South Anderson Rd.
**Rock Hill 29730**

### TENNESSEE

Chattanooga State Technical Community College
4501 Amnicola Hwy.
**Chattanooga 37406**

ITT Technical Institute
10208 Technology Dr.
**Knoxville 37932**

ITT Technical Institute
441 Donelson Pike
**Nashville 37214**

Nashville State Technical Institute
120 White Bridge Rd.
**Nashville 37209**

Northeast State Technical Community College
P.O. Box 246
**Blountville 37617**

Pellissippi State Technical Community College
P.O. Box 22990
**Knoxville 37933-0990**

State Technical Institute at Memphis
5983 Macon Cove
**Memphis 38134**

### TEXAS

ATI Career Computer Training Center
2351 West Northwest Hwy., Ste. 1301
**Dallas 75220**

Austin Community College
5930 Middle Fiskville Rd.
**Austin 78752**

Central Texas College
P.O. Box 1800
**Killeen 76540-1800**

Cisco Junior College
Rte. 3, P.O. Box 3
**Cisco 76437**

Del Mar College
101 Baldwin
**Corpus Christi 78404-3897**

Devry Institute of Technology
4801 Regent Blvd.
**Irving 75063-2440**

Eastfield College
3737 Motley Dr.
**Mesquite 75150**

El Paso Community College
P.O. Box 20500
**El Paso 79998**

Grayson County College
6101 Grayson Dr.
**Denison 75020**

Hallmark Institute of Technology
8901 Wetmore Rd.
**San Antonio 78216**

Hill College
P.O. Box 619
**Hillsboro 76645**

Houston Community College System
22 Waugh Dr., P.O. Box 7849
**Houston 77270-7849**

Interactive Learning Systems
8585 North Stemmons Fwy., Twin Towers
**Dallas 75247**

ITT Technical Institute
2201 Arlington Downs Rd.
**Arlington 76011**

ITT Technical Institute
6330 Hwy. 290 E, Ste. 150
**Austin 78723**

ITT Technical Institute
1640 Eastgate Dr., Ste. 100
**Garland 75041**

ITT Technical Institute
4242 Piedras Dr. E
**San Antonio 78228**

Kilgore College
1100 Broadway
**Kilgore 75662-3299**

Lamar University, Beaumont
4400 MLK, P.O. Box 10001
**Beaumont 77710**

Lamar University, Orange
410 Front St.
**Orange 77630-5899**

Lee College
200 Lee Dr.
**Baytown 77520-4703**

Midland College
3600 North Garfield
**Midland 79705**

Mountain View College
4849 West Illinois
**Dallas 75211**

National Education Center, NIT Campus
3622 Fredericksburg Rd.
**San Antonio 78201**

National Institute of Technology, Corinthian Schools Inc.
10945 Estate Ln.
**Dallas 75238**

North Harris Montgomery Community College District
250 North Sam Houston Pkwy. E, Ste. 300
**Houston 77060**

North Lake College
5001 North MacArthur Blvd.
**Irving 75038-3899**

San Antonio College
1300 San Pedro Ave.
**San Antonio 78284**

San Jacinto College, South Campus
13735 Beamer Rd.
**Houston 77089-6009**

South Plains College
1401 College Ave.
**Levelland 79336**

Southwest School of Electronics
5424 Hwy. 290 W, Ste. 200
**Austin 78735**

Tarrant County Junior College
1500 Houston St.
**Fort Worth 76102**

Texarkana College
2500 North Robison Rd.
**Texarkana 75599**

Texas State Technical College, Waco Campus
3801 Campus Dr.
**Waco 76705**

Tyler Junior College
1327 South Baxter Ave.
**Tyler 75711**

Victoria College
2200 East Red River
**Victoria 77901**

Weatherford College
308 East Park Ave.
**Weatherford 76086**

Wharton County Junior College
911 Boling Hwy.
**Wharton 77488**

### UTAH

ITT Technical Institute
920 West Levoy Dr.
**Murray 84123**

Salt Lake Community College
P.O. Box 30808
**Salt Lake City 84130**

Utah Valley State College
800 West 1200 S
**Orem 84058**

### VERMONT

Champlain College
163 South Willard St.
**Burlington 05401**

Vermont Technical College
P.O. Box 500
**Randolph Center 05061**

### VIRGINIA

Blue Ridge Community College
P.O. Box 80
**Weyers Cave 24486**

Central Virginia Community College
3506 Wards Rd.
**Lynchburg 24502**

Commonwealth College
1120 West Mercury Blvd.
**Hampton 23666**

Commonwealth College
301 Centre Pointe Dr.
**Virginia Beach 23462**

Dabney S Lancaster Community College
P.O. Box 1000
**Clifton Forge 24422-1000**

Danville Community College
1008 South Main St.
**Danville 24541**

Germanna Community College
2130 Germanna Hwy.
**Locust Grove 22508**

ITT Technical Institute
863 Glenrock Rd.
**Norfolk 23502-3701**

J Sargeant Reynolds Community College
P.O. Box 85622
**Richmond 23285-5622**

John Tyler Community College
13101 Jefferson Davis Hwy.
**Chester 23831-5399**

Lord Fairfax Community College
173 Skirmisher Ln.
**Middletown 22645**

New River Community College
P.O. Drawer 1127
**Dublin 24084**

Northern Virginia Community College
4001 Wakefield Chapel Rd.
**Annandale 22003**

Patrick Henry Community College
P.O. Box 5311
**Martinsville 24115-5311**

Southside Virginia Community College
109 Campus Dr.
**Alberta 23821**

Southwest Virginia Community College
P.O. Box SVCC
**Richlands 24641**

Tesst Technology Institute
1400 Duke St.
**Alexandria 22314**

Thomas Nelson Community College
P.O. Box 9407
**Hampton 23670**

Tidewater Community College
121 College Pl.
**Norfolk 23510**

Tidewater Technical
616 Denbigh Blvd.
**Newport News 23608**

Tidewater Technical
2697 Dean Dr., Ste. 100
**Virginia Beach 23452**

Virginia Highlands Community College
P.O. Box 828
**Abingdon 24210-0828**

Virginia Western Community College
3095 Colonial Ave.
**Roanoke 24015**

Wise Skills Center
515 Hurricane Rd. N
**Wise 24293**

### WASHINGTON

Bellingham Technical College
3028 Lindbergh Ave.
**Bellingham 98225**

Centralia College
600 West Locust St.
**Centralia 98531**

Clark College
1800 East McLoughlin Blvd.
**Vancouver 98663-3598**

Columbia Basin College
2600 North 20th Ave.
**Pasco 99301**

Edmonds Community College
20000 68th Ave. W
**Lynnwood 98036**

Green River Community College
12401 Southeast 320th St.
**Auburn 98092**

ITT Technical Institute
12720 Gateway Dr., Ste. 100
**Seattle 98168**

Lake Washington Technical College
11605 132nd Ave. NE
**Kirkland 98034**

Olympic College
1600 Chester Ave.
**Bremerton 98310-1699**

Perry Technical Institute
2011 West Washington Ave.
**Yakima 98903**

Pierce College
9401 Farwest Dr. SW
**Lakewood 98498**

Seattle Community College, North Campus
9600 College Way N
**Seattle 98103**

South Puget Sound Community College
2011 Mottman Rd. SW
**Olympia 98512**

Spokane Community College
North 1810 Greene Ave.
**Spokane 99207**

### WEST VIRGINIA

Bluefield State College
219 Rock St.
**Bluefield 24701**

Cabell County Vocational Technical Center
1035 Norway Ave.
**Huntington 25705**

The College of West Virginia
500 South Kanawha St.
**Beckley 25801**

Fairmont State College
1201 Locust Ave.
**Fairmont 26554**

James Rumsey Technical Institute
Rte. 6, P.O. Box 268
**Martinsburg 25401**

National Institute of Technology, A Corinthian School
5514 Big Tyler Rd.
**Cross Lanes 25313**

West Virginia Institute of Technology
**Montgomery 25136**

West Virginia State College
Rte. 25
**Institute 25112**

### WISCONSIN

Blackhawk Technical College
P.O. Box 5009
**Janesville 53547**

Chippewa Valley Technical College
620 West Clairemont Ave.
**Eau Claire 54701**

Fox Valley Technical College at Appleton
1825 North Bluemound Dr.
**Appleton 54913-2277**

Gateway Technical College
3520 30th Ave.
**Kenosha 53144-1690**

Lakeshore Technical College
1290 North Ave.
**Cleveland 53015**

Madison Area Technical College System District Number Four
3550 Anderson St.
**Madison 53704**

Mid-State Technical College, Main Campus
500 32nd St. N
**Wisconsin Rapids 54494**

Milwaukee Area Technical College
700 West State St.
**Milwaukee 53233-1443**

Northcentral Technical College
1000 Campus Dr.
**Wausau 54401-1899**

Northeast Wisconsin Technical College
2740 West Mason St., P.O. Box 19042
**Green Bay 54307-9042**

Waukesha County Technical College
800 Main St.
**Pewaukee 53072**

### WYOMING

Casper College
125 College Dr.
**Casper 82601**

Central Wyoming College
2660 Peck Ave.
**Riverton 82501**

## Instrumentation Technology

### DELAWARE

Delaware Technical and Community College, Stanton-Wilmington Campus
400 Stanton-Christiana Rd.
**Newark 19702**

### IDAHO

Idaho State University
741 South Seventh Ave.
**Pocatello 83209**

### ILLINOIS

Black Hawk College, Quad-Cities
6600 34th Ave.
**Moline 61265**

Moraine Valley Community College
10900 South 88th Ave.
**Palos Hills 60465-0937**

### LOUISIANA

ITI Technical College
13944 Airline Hwy.
**Baton Rouge 70817**

McNeese State University
4100 Ryan St.
**Lake Charles 70609**

### MICHIGAN

Oakland Community College
2480 Opdyke Rd.
**Bloomfield Hills 48304-2266**

### MINNESOTA

Saint Cloud Technical College
1540 Northway Dr.
**Saint Cloud 56303**

### MISSISSIPPI

Pearl River Community College
Station A
**Poplarville 39470**

### MISSOURI

Ranken Technical College
4431 Finney Ave.
**Saint Louis 63113**

### NEW MEXICO

Albuquerque Technical-Vocational Institute
525 Buena Vista SE
**Albuquerque 87106**

### NEW YORK

Monroe Community College
1000 East Henrietta Rd.
**Rochester 14623**

### NORTH CAROLINA

Cape Fear Community College
411 North Front St.
**Wilmington 28401**

### OHIO

Shawnee State University
940 Second St.
**Portsmouth 45662**

### PENNSYLVANIA

Butler County Community College
College Dr. Oak Hills
**Butler 16003-1203**

### SOUTH CAROLINA

Orangeburg-Calhoun Technical College
3250 Saint Matthews Rd.
**Orangeburg 29118**

### TEXAS

Brazosport College
500 College Dr.
**Lake Jackson 77566**

Lamar University, Beaumont
4400 MLK, P.O. Box 10001
**Beaumont 77710**

Lee College
200 Lee Dr.
**Baytown 77520-4703**

San Jacinto College, Central Campus
8060 Spencer Hwy.
**Pasadena 77505**

Texas State Technical College, Harlingen Campus
2424 Boxwood
**Harlingen 78550-3697**

Texas State Technical College, Waco Campus
3801 Campus Dr.
**Waco 76705**

### WASHINGTON

Bellingham Technical College
3028 Lindbergh Ave.
**Bellingham 98225**

Perry Technical Institute
2011 West Washington Ave.
**Yakima 98903**

### WISCONSIN

Mid-State Technical College, Main Campus
500 32nd St. N
**Wisconsin Rapids 54494**

Northeast Wisconsin Technical College
2740 West Mason St., P.O. Box 19042
**Green Bay 54307-9042**

## Laboratory Technology

### DELAWARE

Delaware Technical and Community College, Stanton-Wilmington Campus
400 Stanton-Christiana Rd.
**Newark 19702**

### NEBRASKA

Central Community College Area
P.O. Box 4903
**Grand Island 68802**

### NEW YORK

Monroe Community College
1000 East Henrietta Rd.
**Rochester 14623**

## Mechanical and Engineering Technology

### ALABAMA

Alabama Aviation and Technical College
U.S. Hwy. 231
**Ozark 36360**

Community College of the Air Force
130 West Maxwell Blvd.
**Montgomery 36112-6613**

Jefferson State Community College
2601 Carson Rd.
**Birmingham 35215-3098**

### ARIZONA

Yavapai College
1100 East Sheldon St.
**Prescott 86301**

### CALIFORNIA

Antelope Valley College
3041 West Ave. K
**Lancaster 93536**

Citrus College
1000 West Foothill Blvd.
**Glendora 91741-1899**

City College of San Francisco
50 Phelan Ave.
**San Francisco 94112**

College of Alameda
555 Atlantic Ave.
**Alameda 94501**

College of San Mateo
1700 West Hillsdale Blvd.
**San Mateo 94402**

Ecologics Training Institute
4155 East La Palma Ave., Ste. 500
**Anaheim 92807**

ITT Technical Institute of West Covina
1530 West Cameron Ave.
**West Covina 91790**

Kushner Electroplating School
732 Glencoe Ct.
**Sunnyvale 94087**

Lassen Community College
Hwy. 139
**Susanville 96130**

Los Angeles Trade Technical College
400 West Washington Blvd.
**Los Angeles 90015-4181**

Los Angeles Valley College
5800 Fulton Ave.
**Van Nuys 91401**

Mission College
3000 Mission College Blvd.
**Santa Clara 95054-1897**

Orange Coast College
2701 Fairview Rd.
**Costa Mesa 92626**

San Joaquin Delta College
5151 Pacific Ave.
**Stockton 95207**

Solano County Community College District
4000 Suisun Valley Rd.
**Suisun 94585-3197**

Southwestern College
900 Otay Lakes Rd.
**Chula Vista 92010**

West Los Angeles College
4800 Freshman Dr.
**Culver 90230**

### COLORADO

Aims Community College
P.O. Box 69
**Greeley 80632**

Colorado School of Trades
1575 Hoyt St.
**Lakewood 80215**

Pikes Peak Community College
5675 South Academy Blvd.
**Colorado Springs 80906-5498**

Red Rocks Community College
13300 West Sixth Ave.
**Lakewood 80228**

Trinidad State Junior College
600 Prospect St.
**Trinidad 81082**

### CONNECTICUT

Porter and Chester Institute
138 Weymouth Rd.
**Enfield 06082**

Porter and Chester Institute
670 Lordship Blvd.
**Stratford 06497**

Porter and Chester Institute
320 Sylvan Lake Rd.
**Watertown 06779-1400**

Porter and Chester Institute
125 Silas Deane Hwy.
**Wethersfield 06109**

University of New Haven
300 Orange Ave.
**West Haven 06516**

### DELAWARE

Delaware Technical and Community College, Stanton-Wilmington Campus
400 Stanton-Christiana Rd.
**Newark 19702**

### GEORGIA

Augusta Technical Institute
3116 Deans Bridge Rd.
**Augusta 30906**

Clayton College and State University
5900 North Lee St.
**Morrow 30260**

Columbus Technical Institute
928 45th St.
**Columbus 31904-6572**

### HAWAII

Honolulu Community College
874 Dillingham Blvd.
**Honolulu 96817**

### ILLINOIS

Black Hawk College, Quad-Cities
6600 34th Ave.
**Moline 61265**

Carl Sandburg College
2232 South Lake Storey Rd.
**Galesburg 61401**

College of Du Page
425 22nd St.
**Glen Ellyn 60137-6599**

College of Lake County
19351 West Washington St.
**Grayslake 60030-1198**

Elgin Community College
1700 Spartan Dr.
**Elgin 60123**

Highland Community College
2998 West Pearl City Rd.
**Freeport 61032-9341**

Illinois Central College
One College Dr.
**East Peoria 61635-0001**

Illinois Valley Community College
815 North Orlando Smith Ave.
**Oglesby 61348-9692**

Kishwaukee College
21193 Malta Rd.
**Malta 60150**

Lake Land College
5001 Lake Land Blvd.
**Mattoon 61938**

Moraine Valley Community College
10900 South 88th Ave.
**Palos Hills 60465-0937**

Oakton Community College
1600 East Golf Rd.
**Des Plaines 60016**

Rock Valley College
3301 North Mulford Rd.
**Rockford 61114**

Sauk Valley Community College
173 Rte. 2
**Dixon 61021**

South Suburban College
15800 South State St.
**South Holland 60473**

Triton College
2000 Fifth Ave.
**River Grove 60171**

Waubonsee Community College
Rte. 47 at Harter Rd.
**Sugar Grove 60554-0901**

William Rainey Harper College
1200 West Algonquin Rd.
**Palatine 60067-7398**

### INDIANA

Ball State University
2000 University Ave.
**Muncie 47306**

Indiana University, Bloomington
Bryan Hall
**Bloomington 47405**

Indiana University, Purdue University at Fort Wayne
2101 Coliseum Blvd. E
**Fort Wayne 46805**

Indiana University, Purdue University at Indianapolis
355 North Lansing
**Indianapolis 46202**

ITT Technical Institute
4919 Coldwater Rd.
**Fort Wayne 46825**

Ivy State College, Northeast
3800 North Anthony Blvd.
**Fort Wayne 46805**

Purdue University, Calumet Campus
2233 171st St.
**Hammond 46323**

Purdue University, Main Campus
1076 Freehafer Hall
**West Lafayette 47907-1076**

Purdue University, North Central Campus
1401 U.S. Hwy. 421
**Westville 46391**

Vincennes University
1002 North First St.
**Vincennes 47591**

### IOWA

Hawkeye Community College
1501 East Orange Rd.
**Waterloo 50704**

Iowa Valley Community College District
P.O. Box 536
**Marshalltown 50158**

Kirkwood Community College
P.O. Box 2068
**Cedar Rapids 52406**

North Iowa Area Community College
500 College Dr.
**Mason City 50401**

Southeastern Community College
1015 South Gear Ave., P.O. Drawer F
**West Burlington 52655-0605**

### KANSAS

Hesston College
P.O. Box 3000
**Hesston 67062**

### KENTUCKY

Eastern Kentucky University
Lancaster Ave.
**Richmond 40475**

Louisville Technical Institute
3901 Atkinson Dr.
**Louisville 40218**

Morehead State University
University Blvd.
**Morehead 40351**

Murray State University
P.O. Box 9
**Murray 42071-0009**

Western Kentucky University
One Big Red Way
**Bowling Green 42101-3576**

### MAINE

Central Maine Technical College
1250 Turner St.
**Auburn 04210**

### MARYLAND

Anne Arundel Community College
101 College Pkwy.
**Arnold 21012**

Catonsville Community College
800 South Rolling Rd.
**Catonsville 21228**

Maryland Drafting Institute
2045 University Blvd.
**Langley Park 20783**

The Radio Electronic Television Schools, Inc.
1520 South Caton Ave.
**Baltimore 21227-1063**

### MASSACHUSETTS

Bristol Community College
777 Elsbree St.
**Fall River 02720**

Bunker Hill Community College
250 New Rutherford Ave.
**Boston 02129**

North Shore Community College
One Ferncroft Rd.
**Danvers 01923**

Northeast Institute of Industrial Technology
41 Phillips St.
**Boston 02114**

Northeastern University
360 Huntington Ave.
**Boston 02115**

Northern Essex Community College
Elliott Way
**Haverhill 01830-2399**

Smith & Wesson Academy
299 Page Blvd.
**Springfield 01104**

Springfield Technical Community College
One Armory Square
**Springfield 01105**

University of Massachusetts at Lowell
One University Ave.
**Lowell 01854**

Wentworth Institute of Technology
550 Huntington Ave.
**Boston 02115**

## MICHIGAN

Delta College
**University Center 48710**

Glen Oaks Community College
62249 Shimmel Rd.
**Centreville 49032**

Henry Ford Community College
5101 Evergreen Rd.
**Dearborn 48128**

ITT Technical Institute
4020 Sparks Dr. SE
**Grand Rapids 49546-6197**

Kalamazoo Valley Community College
6767 West O Ave.
**Kalamazoo 49009**

Lake Michigan College
2755 East Napier Ave.
**Benton Harbor 49022-8099**

Lake Superior State University
650 West Easterday Ave.
**Sault Sainte Marie 49783**

Lansing Community College
419 North Capitol Ave.
**Lansing 48901-7210**

Lawrence Institute of Technology
21000 West Ten Mile Rd.
**Southfield 48075-1058**

Macomb Community College
14500 Twelve Mile Rd.
**Warren 48093-3896**

Michigan Technological University
1400 Townsend Dr.
**Houghton 49931-1295**

Mid Michigan Community College
1375 South Clare Ave.
**Harrison 48625**

Mott Community College
1401 East Court St.
**Flint 48503**

Oakland Community College
2480 Opdyke Rd.
**Bloomfield Hills 48304-2266**

Schoolcraft College
18600 Haggerty Rd.
**Livonia 48152**

Washtenaw Community College
P.O. Drawer 1
**Ann Arbor 48016-1610**

## MINNESOTA

Alexandria Technical College
1601 Jefferson St.
**Alexandria 56308**

Hennepin Technical College
9000 Brooklyn Blvd.
**Brooklyn Park 55445**

Minnesota Multi-Housing Association
8030 Old Cedar Ave., Ste. 202
**Bloomington 55425**

Musicians Technical Training Center
304 Washington Ave. N
**Minneapolis 55401**

Normandale Community College
9700 France Ave. S
**Bloomington 55431**

## MISSOURI

Central Missouri State University
**Warrensburg 64093**

Jefferson College
1000 Viking Dr.
**Hillsboro 63050**

Mineral Area College
P.O. Box 1000
**Park Hills 63601-1000**

Saint Louis Community College, Forest Park
5600 Oakland Ave.
**Saint Louis 63110**

## NEW HAMPSHIRE

Keene State College
229 Main
**Keene 03431**

New Hampshire Technical Institute
11 Institute Dr.
**Concord 03301**

## NEW JERSEY

County College of Morris
214 Center Grove Rd.
**Randolph 07869**

Middlesex County College
155 Mill Rd.
**Edison 08818-3050**

Union County College
1033 Springfield Ave.
**Cranford 07016**

## NEW MEXICO

Albuquerque Technical-Vocational Institute
525 Buena Vista SE
**Albuquerque 87106**

New Mexico State University, Main Campus
P.O. Box 30001, Weddell Dr.
**Las Cruces 88003**

University of New Mexico, Los Alamos
4000 University Dr.
**Los Alamos 87544**

## NEW YORK

Adirondack Community College
Bay Rd.
**Queensbury 12804**

Broome Community College
P.O. Box 1017
**Binghamton 13902**

Corning Community College
Spencer Hill
**Corning 14830**

CUNY New York City Technical College
300 Jay St.
**Brooklyn 11201**

CUNY Queensborough Community College
56th Ave. & Springfield Blvd.
**New York 11364**

Erie Community College, North Campus
Main St. and Youngs Rd.
**Williamsville 14221**

Hudson Valley Community College
80 Vandenburgh Ave.
**Troy 12180**

Jamestown Community College
525 Falconer St.
**Jamestown 14701**

Monroe Community College
1000 East Henrietta Rd.
**Rochester 14623**

Niagara County Community College
3111 Saunders Settlement Rd.
**Sanborn 14132**

Onondaga Community College
4941 Onondaga Rd.
**Syracuse 13215**

Rochester Institute of Technology
One Lomb Memorial Dr.
**Rochester 14623-5603**

Suffolk County Community College, Ammerman Campus
533 College Rd.
**Selden 11784**

SUNY at Buffalo
Capen Hall
**Buffalo 14260**

SUNY College of Agriculture & Technology at Cobleskill
**Cobleskill 12043**

SUNY College of Technology & Agriculture at Morrisville
**Morrisville 13408**

SUNY College of Technology at Alfred
**Alfred 14802**

SUNY College of Technology at Canton
Cornell Dr.
**Canton 13617**

SUNY College of Technology at Farmingdale
Melville Rd.
**Farmingdale 11735-1021**

## NORTH CAROLINA

Alamance Community College
P.O. Box 8000
**Graham 27253**

Asheville Buncombe Technical Community College
340 Victoria Rd.
**Asheville 28801**

Blue Ridge Community College
College Dr.
**Flat Rock 28731-9624**

Cape Fear Community College
411 North Front St.
**Wilmington 28401**

Catawba Valley Community College
2550 Hwy. 70 SE
**Hickory 28602-0699**

Central Carolina Community College
1105 Kelly Dr.
**Sanford 27330**

Central Piedmont Community College
P.O. Box 35009
**Charlotte 28235-5009**

Chowan College
**Murfreesboro 27855**

College of the Albemarle
1208 North Road St.
**Elizabeth City 27906-2327**

Forsyth Technical Community College
2100 Silas Creek Pkwy.
**Winston Salem 27103**

Gaston College
201 Hwy. 321 S
**Dallas 28034**

Guilford Technical Community College
P.O. Box 309
**Jamestown 27282**

Isothermal Community College
P.O. Box 804
**Spindale 28160**

Montgomery Community College
P.O. Box 787
**Troy 27371**

Richmond Community College
P.O. Box 1189
**Hamlet 28345**

Rowan-Cabarrus Community College
P.O. Box 1595
**Salisbury 28145-1595**

Surry Community College
P.O. Box 304
**Dobson 27017-0304**

Wake Technical Community College
9101 Fayetteville Rd.
**Raleigh 27603-5696**

## OHIO

Cincinnati State Technical and Community College
3520 Central Pkwy.
**Cincinnati 45223**

Clark State Community College
570 East Leffel Ln.
**Springfield 45505**

Columbus State Community College
550 East Spring St.
**Columbus 43216**

Cuyahoga Community College District
700 Carnegie Ave.
**Cleveland 44115-2878**

Franklin University
201 South Grant Ave.
**Columbus 43215-5399**

Hocking Technical College
3301 Hocking Pkwy.
**Nelsonville 45764**

Lakeland Community College
7700 Clocktower Dr.
**Kirtland 44094-5198**

Lima Technical College
4240 Campus Dr.
**Lima 45804**

Lorain County Community College
1005 Abbe Rd. N
**Elyria 44035**

Miami University, Oxford Campus
500 High St.
**Oxford 45056**

Northwest State Community College
22-600 South Rte. 34
**Archbold 43502-9542**

Sinclair Community College
444 West Third St.
**Dayton 45402**

Stark State College of Technology
6200 Frank Ave. NW
**Canton 44720**

Terra State Community College
2830 Napoleon Rd.
**Fremont 43420**

University of Akron, Main Campus
302 Buchtel Common
**Akron 44325-4702**

University of Cincinnati, Main Campus
P.O. Box 210127
**Cincinnati 45221-0127**

University of Toledo
2801 West Bancroft
**Toledo 43606**

Youngstown State University
One University Plaza
**Youngstown 44555**

### OKLAHOMA

Murray State College
One Murray Campus
**Tishomingo 73460**

Rose State College
6420 Southeast 15th
**Midwest City 73110**

Tulsa Community College
6111 East Skelly Dr.
**Tulsa 74135**

### OREGON

Oregon Institute of Technology
3201 Campus Dr.
**Klamath Falls 97601-8801**

### PENNSYLVANIA

American Center for Technical Arts and Sciences
1616 Orthodox St.
**Philadelphia 19124**

Community College of Allegheny County
800 Allegheny Ave.
**Pittsburgh 15233-1895**

Community College of Beaver County
One Campus Dr.
**Monaca 15061**

Delaware County Community College
901 South Media Line Rd.
**Media 19063-1094**

Gannon University
109 West Sixth St.
**Erie 16541**

Harrisburg Area Community College, Harrisburg Campus
One HACC Dr.
**Harrisburg 17110**

ICS, Center for Degree Studies
925 Oak St.
**Scranton 18508**

Lincoln Technical Institute
5151 Tilghman St.
**Allentown 18104**

Luzerne County Community College
1333 South Prospect St.
**Nanticoke 18634**

Machine Shop Technologies Institute, Inc.
110 South Main St. West End
**Pittsburgh 15220**

Pennsylvania College of Technology
One College Ave.
**Williamsport 17701**

Pennsylvania Gunsmith School
812 Ohio River Blvd.
**Pittsburgh 15202**

Pennsylvania Institute of Technology
800 Manchester Ave.
**Media 19063**

Pennsylvania State University, Abington Campus
1600 Woodland Rd.
**Abington 19001**

Pennsylvania State University, Altoona Campus
3000 Ivyside Park
**Altoona 16601-3760**

Pennsylvania State University, Berks Campus
Tulpehocken Rd., P.O. Box 7009
**Reading 19610-6009**

Pennsylvania State University, Du Bois Campus
College Place
**Du Bois 15801**

Pennsylvania State University, Erie Behrend College
Station Rd.
**Erie 16563**

Pennsylvania State University, Hazleton Campus
Highacres
**Hazleton 18201**

Pennsylvania State University, McKeesport Campus
University Dr.
**McKeesport 15132-7698**

Pennsylvania State University, New Kensington Campus
3550 Seventh St. Rd.
**New Kensington 15068**

Pennsylvania State University, Wilkes-Barre Campus
P.O. PSU Old Rte. 115
**Lehman 18627**

Pennsylvania State University, York Campus
1031 Edgecomb Ave.
**York 17403**

Pittsburgh Institute of Aeronautics
Five Allegheny County Airport
**West Mifflin 15122**

Triangle Technical, Dubois
P.O. Box 551
**Dubois 15801**

### RHODE ISLAND

Community College of Rhode Island
400 East Ave.
**Warwick 02886-1807**

### SOUTH CAROLINA

Midlands Technical College
P.O. Box 2408
**Columbia 29202**

Spartanburg Technical College
Business I-85
**Spartanburg 29305**

Trident Technical College
P.O. Box 118067
**Charleston 29423-8067**

York Technical College
452 South Anderson Rd.
**Rock Hill 29730**

### TENNESSEE

Chattanooga State Technical Community College
4501 Amnicola Hwy.
**Chattanooga 37406**

Nashville State Technical Institute
120 White Bridge Rd.
**Nashville 37209**

Pellissippi State Technical Community College
P.O. Box 22990
**Knoxville 37933-0990**

State Technical Institute of Memphis
5983 Macon Cove
**Memphis 38134**

### TEXAS

Kilgore College
1100 Broadway
**Kilgore 75662-3299**

Lamar University, Beaumont
4400 MLK, P.O. Box 10001
**Beaumont 77710**

Richland College
12800 Abrams Rd.
**Dallas 75243-2199**

San Antonio College
1300 San Pedro Ave.
**San Antonio 78284**

San Jacinto College, Central Campus
8060 Spencer Hwy.
**Pasadena 77505**

Texas State Technical College, Waco Campus
3801 Campus Dr.
**Waco 76705**

### VERMONT

Vermont Technical College
P.O. Box 500
**Randolph Center 05061**

### VIRGINIA

Blue Ridge Community College
P.O. Box 80
**Weyers Cave 24486**

Central Virginia Community College
3506 Wards Rd.
**Lynchburg 24502**

Dabney S Lancaster Community College
P.O. Box 1000
**Clifton Forge 24422-1000**

Danville Community College
1008 South Main St.
**Danville 24541**

Eastern Shore Community College
29300 Lankford Hwy.
**Melfa 23410**

J Sargeant Reynolds Community College
P.O. Box 85622
**Richmond 23285-5622**

John Tyler Community College
13101 Jefferson Davis Hwy.
**Chester 23831-5399**

Lord Fairfax Community College
173 Skirmisher Ln.
**Middletown 22645**

Maryland Drafting Institute
8001 North Forbes Place
**Springfield 22151**

New River Community College
P.O. Drawer 1127
**Dublin 24084-1127**

Northern Virginia Community College
4001 Wakefield Chapel Rd.
**Annandale 22003**

Patrick Henry Community College
P.O. Box 5311
**Martinsville 24115-5311**

Rappahannock Community College Glenns Campus
12745 College Dr.
**Glenns 23149**

Southside Virginia Community College
109 Campus Dr.
**Alberta 23821**

Southwest Virginia Community College
P.O. Box SVCC
**Richlands 24641**

Thomas Nelson Community College
P.O. Box 9407
**Hampton 23670**

Tidewater Community College
121 College Pl.
**Norfolk 23510**

Virginia Highlands Community College
P.O. Box 828
**Abingdon 24210-0828**

Virginia Western Community College
3095 Colonial Ave.
**Roanoke 24015**

Wytheville Community College
1000 East Main St.
**Wytheville 24382**

### WASHINGTON

Bellingham Technical College
3028 Lindbergh Ave.
**Bellingham 98225**

Columbia Basin College
2600 North 20th Ave.
**Pasco 99301**

Lower Columbia College
P.O. Box 3010
**Longview 98632**

Peninsula College
1502 East Lauridsen Blvd.
**Port Angeles 98362**

Seattle Community College, South Campus
6000 16th Ave. SW
**Seattle 98106**

Spokane Community College
North 1810 Greene Ave.
**Spokane 99207**

### WEST VIRGINIA

Bluefield State College
219 Rock St.
**Bluefield 24701**

Marshall University
400 Hal Greer Blvd.
**Huntington 25755**

West Virginia Institute of Technology
**Montgomery 25136**

West Virginia University at Parkersburg
300 Campus Dr.
**Parkersburg 26101**

### WISCONSIN

Blackhawk Technical College
P.O. Box 5009
**Janesville 53547**

Fox Valley Technical College
1825 North Bluemound Dr.
**Appleton 54913-2277**

Gateway Technical College
3520 30th Ave.
**Kenosha 53144-1690**

ITT Technical Institute
6300 West Layton Ave.
**Greenfield 53220**

Lakeshore Technical College
1290 North Ave.
**Cleveland 53015**

Milwaukee Area Technical College
700 West State St.
**Milwaukee 53233-1443**

North Central Technical College
1000 Campus Dr.
**Wausau 54401-1899**

Northeast Wisconsin Technical College
2740 West Mason St., P.O. Box 19042
**Green Bay 54307-9042**

Waukesha County Technical College
800 Main St.
**Pewaukee 53072**

Western Wisconsin Technical College
304 North Sixth St., P.O. Box 908
**La Crosse 54602-0908**

### WYOMING

Sheridan College
3059 Coffeen Ave.
**Sheridan 82801**

## Metallurgy

### ALABAMA

Community College of the Air Force
130 West Maxwell Blvd.
**Montgomery 36112-6613**

### CALIFORNIA

Don Bosco Technical Institute
1151 San Gabriel Blvd.
**Rosemead 91770-4299**

### WISCONSIN

Milwaukee Area Technical College
700 West State St.
**Milwaukee 53233-1443**

## Natural Sciences

### ALABAMA

Community College of the Air Force
130 West Maxwell Blvd.
**Montgomery 36112-6613**

### ARIZONA

Arizona Western College
P.O. Box 929
**Yuma 85366**

### CALIFORNIA

Antelope Valley College
3041 West Ave. K
**Lancaster 93536**

Cerritos College
11110 Alondra Blvd.
**Norwalk 90650**

Chaffey Community College
5885 Haven Ave.
**Rancho Cucamonga 91737-3002**

City College of San Francisco
50 Phelan Ave.
**San Francisco 94112**

Coastline Community College
11460 Warner Ave.
**Fountain Valley 92708**

College of Marin
835 College Ave.
**Kentfield 94904**

College of Oceaneering
272 South Fries Ave., Los Angeles Harbor
**Wilmington 90744-6399**

College of San Mateo
1700 West Hillsdale Blvd.
**San Mateo 94402**

College of the Canyons
26455 Rockwell Canyon Rd.
**Santa Clarita 91355**

Contra Costa College
2600 Mission Bell Dr.
**San Pablo 94806**

Crafton Hills College
11711 Sand Canyon Rd.
**Yucaipa 92399-1799**

Cuesta College
P.O. Box 8106
**San Luis Obispo 93403-8106**

El Camino College
16007 Crenshaw Blvd.
**Torrance 90506**

Feather River Community College District
570 Golden Eagle Ave.
**Quincy 95971-6023**

Fresno City College
1101 East University Ave.
**Fresno 93741**

Fullerton College
321 East Chapman Ave.
**Fullerton 92632-2095**

Gemological Institute of America
5345 Armada Dr.
**Carlsbad 92008**

Glendale Community College
1500 North Verdugo Rd.
**Glendale 91208-2894**

Hartnell College
156 Homestead Ave.
**Salinas 93901**

Imperial Valley College
P.O. Box 158
**Imperial 92251-0158**

Lake Tahoe Community College
One College Dr.
**South Lake Tahoe 96150**

Laney College
900 Fallon St.
**Oakland 94607**

Las Positas College
3033 Collier Canyon Rd.
**Livermore 94550-7650**

Lassen College
Hwy. 139
**Susanville 96130**

Long Beach City College
4901 East Carson St.
**Long Beach 90808**

Los Angeles Valley College
5800 Fulton Ave.
**Van Nuys 91401**

Merced College
3600 M St.
**Merced 95348-2898**

Mira Costa College
One Barnard Dr.
**Oceanside 92056-3899**

Mission College
3000 Mission College Blvd.
**Santa Clara 95054-1897**

Modesto Junior College
435 College Ave.
**Modesto 95350-5800**

Mount San Antonio College
1100 North Grand
**Walnut 91789**

Mount San Jacinto College
1499 North State St.
**San Jacinto 92383**

Napa Valley College
2277 Napa Vallejo Hwy.
**Napa 94558**

Ohlone College
43600 Mission Blvd.
**Fremont 94539**

Palomar College
1140 West Mission
**San Marcos 92069-1487**

Pasadena City College
1570 East Colorada Blvd.
**Pasadena 91106**

Patten College
2433 Coolidge Ave.
**Oakland 94601**

Porterville College
100 East College Ave.
**Porterville 93257**

Rancho Santiago Community College District
1530 West 17th St.
**Santa Ana 92706**

San Diego City College
1313 12th Ave.
**San Diego 92101**

San Diego Mesa College
7250 Mesa College Dr.
**San Diego 92111-4998**

San Joaquin Delta College
5151 Pacific Ave.
**Stockton 95207**

Santa Barbara City College
721 Cliff Dr.
**Santa Barbara 93109-2394**

Santa Monica College
1900 Pico Blvd.
**Santa Monica 90405-1628**

Santa Rosa Junior College
1501 Mendocino Ave.
**Santa Rosa 95401-4395**

Sierra College
5000 Rocklin Rd.
**Rocklin 95677**

Solano County Community College District
4000 Suisun Valley Rd.
**Suisun 94585-3197**

Victor Valley College
18422 Bear Valley Rd.
**Victorville 92392-9699**

West Valley College
14000 Fruitvale Ave.
**Saratoga 95070**

Yuba College
2088 North Beale Rd.
**Marysville 95901**

### COLORADO

College of the Canons
Forge Road Industrial Park
**Canon City 81212**

Denver Institute of Technology
7350 North Broadway
**Denver 80221**

### CONNECTICUT

Connecticut Institute of Technology
Two Elizabeth St.
**West Haven 06516**

Manchester Community College
60 Bidwell St.
**Manchester 06040-1046**

Mitchell College
437 Pequot Ave.
**New London 06320**

### FLORIDA

Palm Beach Community College
4200 Congress Ave.
**Lake Worth 33461**

### GEORGIA

Athens Area Technical Institute
U.S. Hwy. 29 N
**Athens 30610-0399**

### IDAHO

North Idaho College
1000 West Garden Ave.
**Coeur D'Alene 83814**

Ricks College
**Rexburg 83460-4107**

### ILLINOIS

Belleville Area College
2500 Carlyle Rd.
**Belleville 62221**

Black Hawk Community College, East Campus
P.O. Box 489
**Kewanee 61443**

Carl Sandburg College
2232 South Lake Storey Rd.
**Galesburg 61401**

City College of Chicago, Chicago City-Wide College
226 West Jackson Blvd.
**Chicago 60606**

City College of Chicago, Olive-Harvey College
10001 South Woodlawn Ave.
**Chicago 60628**

City College of Chicago, Richard J Daley College
7500 South Pulaski Rd.
**Chicago 60652**

City College of Chicago, Truman College
1145 Wilson Ave.
**Chicago 60640**

City College of Chicago, Wright College
4300 North Narragansett
**Chicago 60634**

College of Du Page
425 22nd St.
**Glen Ellyn 60137-6599**

College of Lake County
19351 West Washington St.
**Grayslake 60030-1198**

Danville Area Community College
2000 East Main St.
**Danville 61832**

Elgin Community College
1700 Spartan Dr.
**Elgin 60123**

Highland Community College
2998 West Pearl City Rd.
**Freeport 61032-9341**

Illinois Eastern Community Colleges, Olney Central College
305 North West St.
**Olney 62450**

Illinois Valley Community College
815 North Orlando Smith Ave.
**Oglesby 61348-9692**

John A Logan College
700 Logan College Rd.
**Carterville 62918**

John Wood Community College
150 South 48th St.
**Quincy 62301-9147**

Joliet Junior College
1215 Houbolt Rd.
**Joliet 60431**

Kaskaskia College
27210 College Rd.
**Centralia 62801**

Kishwaukee College
21193 Malta Rd.
**Malta 60150**

Lake Land College
5001 Lake Land Blvd.
**Mattoon 61938**

Lewis and Clark Community College
5800 Godfrey Rd.
**Godfrey 62035**

Lincoln Land Community College
Shepherd Rd.
**Springfield 62194-9256**

McHenry County College
8900 U.S. Hwy. 14
**Crystal Lake 60012**

Moraine Valley Community College
10900 South 88th Ave.
**Palos Hills 60465-0937**

Morton College
3801 South Central Ave.
**Cicero 60804**

Oakton Community College
1600 East Golf Rd.
**Des Plaines 60016**

Parkland College
2400 West Bradley Ave.
**Champaign 61821**

Prairie State College
202 Halsted St.
**Chicago Heights 60411**

Rend Lake College
468 North Ken Graz Pkwy.
**Ina 62846**

Richland Community College
One College Park
**Decatur 62521**

Rock Valley College
3301 North Mulford Rd.
**Rockford 61114**

Sauk Valley Community College
173 Rte. 2
**Dixon 61021**

Shawnee Community College
8364 Shawnee College Rd.
**Ullin 62992**

South Suburban College
15800 South State St.
**South Holland 60473**

Southeastern Illinois College
3575 College Rd.
**Harrisburg 62946**

Spoon River College
23235 North Co. 22
**Canton 61520**

Triton College
2000 Fifth Ave.
**River Grove 60171**

Waubonsee Community College
Rte. 47 at Harter Rd.
**Sugar Grove 60554-0901**

William Rainey Harper College
1200 West Algonquin Rd.
**Palatine 60067-7398**

## INDIANA

Purdue University, Main Campus
1076 Freehafer Hall
**West Lafayette 47907-1076**

Vincennes University
1002 North First St.
**Vincennes 47591**

## KANSAS

Barton County Community College
245 Northeast 30th Rd.
**Great Bend 67530**

Colby Community College
1255 South Range
**Colby 67701**

Dodge City Community College
2501 North 14th Ave.
**Dodge City 67801**

Hutchinson Community College
1300 North Plum St.
**Hutchinson 67501**

Kansas City Kansas Community College
7250 State Ave.
**Kansas City 66112**

## KENTUCKY

Thomas More College
333 Thomas More Pkwy.
**Crestview Hills 41017-3428**

## LOUISIANA

Southern University Shreveport, Bossier City Campus
3050 Martin L King Dr.
**Shreveport 71107**

## MICHIGAN

Alpena Community College
666 Johnson St.
**Alpena 49707**

Delta College
**University Center 48710**

Ferris State University
901 South State St.
**Big Rapids 49307**

Grand Rapids Community College
143 Bostwick Ave. NE
**Grand Rapids 49503-3295**

Henry Ford Community College
5101 Evergreen Rd.
**Dearborn 48128**

Jackson Community College
2111 Emmons Rd.
**Jackson 49201-8399**

Kettering University
1700 West Third Ave.
**Flint 48504-4898**

Lake Michigan College
2755 East Napier Ave.
**Benton Harbor 49022-8099**

Lake Superior State University
650 West Easterday Ave.
**Sault Sainte Marie 49783**

Lansing Community College
419 North Capitol Ave.
**Lansing 48901-7210**

Mott Community College
1401 East Court St.
**Flint 48503**

North Central Michigan College
1515 Howard St.
**Petoskey 49770**

Oakland Community College
2480 Opdyke Rd.
**Bloomfield Hills 48304-2266**

Southwestern Michigan College
58900 Cherry Grove Rd.
**Dowagiac 49047-9793**

West Shore Community College
3000 North Stiles Rd.
**Scottville 49454**

## MINNESOTA

Alexandria Technical College
900 Brooklyn Blvd.
**Brooklyn Park 55445**

Hennepin Technical College
9000 Brooklyn Blvd.
**Brooklyn Park 55445**

## MISSISSIPPI

Mississippi Gulf Coast Community College
Central Office, P.O. Box 67
**Perkinston 39573**

## MISSOURI

Crowder College
601 Laclede
**Neosho 64850**

Drury College
900 North Benton Ave.
**Springfield 65802**

## NEBRASKA

Central Community College, Grand Island
P.O. Box 4903
**Grand Island 68802**

## NEW JERSEY

Essex County College
303 University Ave.
**Newark 07102**

Gloucester County College
Tanyard Rd.
**Sewell 08080**

Middlesex County College
155 Mill Rd.
**Edison 08818-3050**

Thomas A Edison State College
101 West State St.
**Trenton 08608-1176**

Union County College
1033 Springfield Ave.
**Cranford 07016**

## NEW MEXICO

Santa Fe Community College
6401 South Richards Ave.
**Santa Fe 87505**

## NEW YORK

CUNY Kingsborough Community College
2001 Oriental Blvd.
**Brooklyn 11235**

Mohawk Valley Community College, Utica Branch
1101 Sherman Dr.
**Utica 13501**

Niagara County Community College
3111 Saunders Settlement Rd.
**Sanborn 14132**

Rochester Institute of Technology
One Lomb Memorial Dr.
**Rochester 14623-5603**

SUNY College of Technology at Alfred
**Alfred 14802**

SUNY Empire State College
Two Union Ave.
**Saratoga Springs 12866**

## NORTH CAROLINA

Coastal Carolina Community College
444 Western Blvd.
**Jacksonville 28546-6877**

Guilford Technical Community College
P.O. Box 309
**Jamestown 27282**

Lees-McRae College
P.O. Box 128
**Banner Elk 28604**

Louisburg College
501 North Main St.
**Louisburg 27549**

## OHIO

Cincinnati State Technical and Community College
3520 Central Pkwy.
**Cincinnati 45223**

Lorain County Community College
1005 Abbe Rd. N
**Elyria 44035**

Miami University, Oxford Campus
500 High St.
**Oxford 45056**

## OKLAHOMA

Carl Albert State College
1507 South McKenna
**Poteau 74953-5208**

Connors State College
Rte. 1, P.O. Box 1000
**Warner 74469**

Northern Oklahoma College
Box 310 Tonkawa
**Tonkawa 74653**

Oklahoma City Community College
7777 South May Ave.
**Oklahoma City 73159**

Rogers University, Claremore
1701 West Will Rogers Blvd.
**Claremore 74017**

Rose State College
6420 Southeast 15th
**Midwest City 73110**

Saint Gregory's University
1900 West MacArthur
**Shawnee 74801**

Seminole State College
2701 Boren Blvd.
**Seminole 74868**

Tulsa Community College
6111 East Skelly Dr.
**Tulsa 74135**

Western Oklahoma State College
2801 North Main St.
**Altus 73521-1397**

## OREGON

Oregon Institute of Technology
3201 Campus Dr.
**Klamath Falls 97601-8801**

Treasure Valley Community College
650 College Blvd.
**Ontario 97914**

## PENNSYLVANIA

Community College of Allegheny County, Pittsburgh
800 Allegheny Ave.
**Pittsburgh 15233-1895**

Delaware County Community College
901 South Media Line Rd.
**Media 19063-1094**

Harrisburg Area Community College, Harrisburg Campus
One HACC Dr.
**Harrisburg 17110**

Montgomery County Community College
340 Dekalb Pike
**Blue Bell 19422**

Northampton County Area Community College
3835 Green Pond Rd.
**Bethlehem 18020-7599**

Pennsylvania State University, New Kensington Campus
3550 Seventh St. Rd.
**New Kensington 15068**

Pennsylvania State University, Wilkes-Barre Campus
P.O. PSU Old Rte. 115
**Lehman 18627**

Reading Area Community College
P.O. Box 1706
**Reading 19603-1706**

## RHODE ISLAND

Community College of Rhode Island
400 East Ave.
**Warwick 02886-1807**

## TEXAS

Austin Community College
5930 Middle Fiskville Rd.
**Austin 78752**

Collin County Community College, Central Park
2200 West University Dr.
**McKinney 75070**

Grayson County College
6101 Grayson Dr.
**Denison 75020**

Howard County Junior College District
1001 Birdwell Ln.
**Big Spring 79720**

Kilgore College
1100 Broadway
**Kilgore 75662-3299**

Midland College
3600 North Garfield
**Midland 79705**

North Harris Montgomery Community College District
250 North Sam Houston Pkwy. E, Ste. 300
**Houston 77060**

Panola College
1109 West Panola St.
**Carthage 75633**

Saint Philips College
1801 Martin Luther King Dr.
**San Antonio 78203**

San Jacinto College, Central Campus
8060 Spencer Hwy.
**Pasadena 77505**

San Jacinto College, North Campus
5800 Uvalde
**Houston 77049**

San Jacinto College, South Campus
13735 Beamer Rd.
**Houston 77089-6009**

Texarkana College
2500 North Robison Rd.
**Texarkana 75599**

Trinity Valley Community College
500 South Prairieville
**Athens 75751**

Tyler Junior College
1327 South Baxter Ave.
**Tyler 75711**

### UTAH

Dixie College
225 South 700 E
**Saint George 84770**

Salt Lake Community College
P.O. Box 30808
**Salt Lake City 84130**

### VIRGINIA

Northern Virginia Community College
4001 Wakefield Chapel Rd.
**Annandale 22003**

Piedmont Virginia Community College
501 College Dr.
**Charlottesville 22902**

Richard Bland College of William and Mary
11301 Johnson Rd.
**Petersburg 23805**

Thomas Nelson Community College
P.O. Box 9407
**Hampton 23670**

Tidewater Community College
121 College Pl.
**Norfolk 23510**

Virginia Western Community College
3095 Colonial Ave.
**Roanoke 24015**

### WASHINGTON

Bellingham Technical College
3028 Lindbergh Ave.
**Bellingham 98225**

### WISCONSIN

Fox Valley Technical College at Appleton
1825 North Bluemound Dr.
**Appleton 54913-2277**

Milwaukee Area Technical College
700 West State St.
**Milwaukee 53233-1443**

### WYOMING

Casper College
125 College Dr.
**Casper 82601**

Central Wyoming College
2660 Peck Ave.
**Riverton 82501**

Laramie County Community College
1400 East College Dr.
**Cheyenne 82007**

Northwest Community College
231 West Sixth St.
**Powell 82435**

Sheridan College
3059 Coffeen Ave.
**Sheridan 82801**

Western Wyoming Community College
2500 College Dr.
**Rock Springs 82902**

## Nuclear Technology

### FLORIDA

Central Florida Community College
3001 Southwest College Rd.
**Ocala 34474**

### GEORGIA

Georgia Military College, Kings Bay Center
Navy Campus Educational Center, P.O. Box 3109
**Kingsland 31548**

### IDAHO

Eastern Idaho Technical College
1600 South 2500 E
**Idaho Falls 83404**

### NEW YORK

Regents College, University of the State of New York
7 Columbia Cir.
**Albany 12203**

### SOUTH CAROLINA

Aiken Technical College
P.O. Drawer 696
**Aiken 29802**

### TEXAS

Texas State Technical College, Waco Campus
3801 Campus Dr.
**Waco 76705**

Wharton County Junior College
911 Boling Hwy.
**Wharton 77488**

### WASHINGTON

Columbia Basin College
2600 North 20th Ave.
**Pasco 99301**

### WISCONSIN

Lakeshore Technical College
1290 North Ave.
**Cleveland 53015**

# Index

All jobs mentioned in this volume are listed and cross-referenced in the index. Entries that appear in all capital letters have occupational profiles. For example, AEROSPACE ENGINEER, ANATOMIST, ASTRONOMER and so on are profiles in this volume. Entries that are not capitalized refer to jobs that do not have a separate profile but for which information is given.

Under some capitalized entries there is a section titled "Profile includes." This lists jobs that are mentioned in the profile. For example, in the case of PHOTONICS ENGINEER, jobs that are described in the profile are Crystal grower and Optical designer.

Some entries are followed by a job title in parentheses after the page number on which it can be found. This job title is the occupational profile in which the entry is discussed. For instance, the Agronomist entry is followed by the profile title (Botanist).